ELEMENTARY
CALCULUS

BY

F. BOWMAN, M.

HEAD OF THE DEPARTMENT OF MATHEMATIC
MANCHESTER, FORMERLY SCHOLAR OF

1724

LONGMANS

Longmans, Green and Co Ltd
48 GROSVENOR STREET, LONDON WI
RAILWAY CRESCENT, CROYDON, VICTORIA, AUSTRALIA
443 LOCKHART ROAD, HONG KONG
PRIVATE MAIL BAG 1036, IKEJA (LAGOS)
44 JALAN AMPANG, KUALA LUMPUR
ACCRA, AUCKLAND, IBADAN, KINGSTON (JAMAICA)
NAIROBI, SALISBURY (RHODESIA)

Longmans, Southern Africa (Pty) Ltd
THIBAULT HOUSE, THIBAULT SQUARE, CAPE TOWN

Longmans, Green and Co Inc
119 WEST 40TH STREET, NEW YORK 18

Longmans, Green and Co
137 BOND STREET, TORONTO 2

Orient Longmans Private Ltd
CALCUTTA, BOMBAY, MADRAS
DELHI, HYDERABAD, DACCA

First Published   .   .   . 1931
Second Edition, with chapter
on Differential Equations   . 1936
Twentieth Impression   .   . 1961

PRINTED IN GREAT BRITAIN AT
THE UNIVERSITY PRESS
ABERDEEN

PREFACE

THIS book has been written as a first course in the methods and applications of the Calculus. It is hoped that it may be found useful as a preparatory text-book for the more elementary examinations, and as an introduction to more advanced books.

For a satisfactory treatment of the important elementary applications of the Calculus to centres of gravity and moments of inertia, only the three simplest standard integrals (§ 84) are required. Accordingly, in the first part of the book one aim has been to reach these applications while the reader's knowledge of standard integrals is confined to the three simplest. Some space is then given to the logarithmic and exponential functions and to a more systematic study of integrals.

Implicit functions, parametric equations, and polar coordinates are discussed in separate chapters. The opening paragraphs of these chapters may be read at an earlier stage, if desired.

The examples are numerous; many have been constructed to give rational answers and so save needless arithmetic.

My thanks are due to Dr. W. N. Bailey, Messrs. W. S. Barratt, J. H. Hawkes, F. L. Heywood, J. P. Hindley, H. V. Lowry, Dr. L. S. Palmer, Dr. J. Prescott, and Mr. H. Tilsley, who have all helped me in one way or another; Mr. Tilsley has drawn the figures and checked many answers to the examples. For information as to errors that remain I shall be grateful.

F. BOWMAN

CONTENTS

CHAPTER I.

FUNCTIONS. LIMITS.

§ 1. Definitions.

A *constant* is a number or physical quantity whose value is fixed.

A *variable* is a number or physical quantity whose value changes.

An *independent variable* is one whose value does not depend upon the value of any other variable.

A *dependent variable* is one whose value depends upon one or more other variables.

A dependent variable is said to be a *function* of the variable (or variables) on which it depends. For example, the area of a circle is a *function* of its radius; the volume of a cylinder is a function of its height and of its radius; the period of vibration of a pendulum is a function of its length.

§ 2. Functional Notation.

—A function of x is often denoted by $f(x)$.

The value of the function $f(x)$ when $x = 2$ is denoted by $f(2)$, when $x = 0$ by $f(0)$, when $x = a$ by $f(a)$, when $x = a + b$ by $f(a + b)$, and so on.

A function of x may also be denoted by $\mathrm{F}(x)$, $\phi(x)$, . . .

Ex. 1. If $f(x) = 2x^2 - 3x + 1$, evaluate $f(2), f(1), f(-1)$. Also, express $f(2 + h)$ in ascending powers of h.

$$f(2) = 2.2^2 - 3.2 + 1 = 3,$$
$$f(1) = 2.1^2 - 3.1 + 1 = 0,$$
$$f(-1) = 2(-1)^2 - 3(-1) + 1 = 6.$$
$$f(2 + h) = 2(2 + h)^2 - 3(2 + h) + 1$$
$$= 2(4 + 4h + h^2) - 3(2 + h) + 1,$$
$$\therefore f(2 + h) = 3 + 5h + 2h^2.$$

Ex. 2. If $f(x) = x^3 - 7x$, solve the equation $f(x) = f(3)$.

Note first that one root of the given equation is known. For, if we put $x = 3$ in this equation we get $f(3) = f(3)$, which is true. Therefore $x = 3$ satisfies the equation.

Now, the equation is
$$x^3 - 7x = 3^3 - 7 \cdot 3 = 27 - 21 = 6,$$
or
$$x^3 - 7x - 6 = 0.$$

Since $x = 3$ satisfies this equation, $(x - 3)$ is a factor of the left-hand side, by the Factor Theorem in Algebra. Accordingly, factorising the left-hand side, we get

$$(x - 3)(x^2 + 3x + 2) = 0,$$
$$\therefore (x - 3)(x + 1)(x + 2) = 0,$$
$$\therefore x = 3, -1, \text{ or } -2.$$

Note that

(i) $x = a$ is always one solution of the equation $f(x) = f(a)$,

(ii) $(x - a)$ is one factor of $f(x) - f(a)$.

§ 3. Even Functions.

If $f(x)$ possesses the property that
$$f(-x) = f(x),$$
in words: the value of the function $f(x)$ remains the same when the variable x changes sign, then $f(x)$ is called an *even* function of x; because this property belongs, in particular, to the even powers of x.

The graph of an even function is symmetrical about the y-axis. (See e.g. Fig. 5.)

§ 4. Odd Functions.

If $f(x)$ possesses the property that
$$f(-x) = -f(x),$$
in words: the value of the function $f(x)$ changes only in sign when the variable x changes sign, then $f(x)$ is called an *odd* function of x; because this property belongs, in particular, to the odd powers of x.

The graph of an odd function is its own image in the origin O; that is to say, if P is any point on the graph, and if the line PO is produced to Q so that $OQ = PO$, then Q is also a point on the graph. (See e.g. Fig. 2.)

Ex. Prove that (i) $\cos x$ is an even function, (ii) $\sin x$ is an odd function.

(i) If $f(x) = \cos x$,
$$f(-x) = \cos(-x) = \cos x = f(x),$$
therefore $\cos x$ is an even function.

(ii) If $f(x) = \sin x$,
$$f(-x) = \sin(-x) = -\sin x = -f(x),$$
therefore $\sin x$ is an odd function.

Examples I.

1. If $f(x) = x^2 - 3x - 4$, evaluate $f(5)$, $f(4)$, $f(0)$, $f(-2)$.
2. If $f(x) = 2x^3 + x^2 - x + 6$, prove that $f(2) = 3f(1)$.
3. If $f(x) = 4x^2 + 3x - 2$, solve the equation $f(x) = 5$.

4. If $f(x) = 4x^3 - 7x$, solve the equation $f(x) = f(1)$.

5. If $f(x) = x^3 - 3x + 1$, express $f(2 + h)$ in ascending powers of h.

6. If $f(x) = x + x^{-1}$, prove that $\{f(x)\}^2 = 2 + f(x^2)$.

7. If $f(x) = \dfrac{x^3 - 3x^2 + 1}{x(1 - x)}$, prove that $f\left(\dfrac{1}{x}\right) = f(1 - x)$.

8. If $f(\theta) = \sin \theta$, and $F(\theta) = \cos \theta$, evaluate

$$f(0),\ f(\tfrac{1}{2}\pi),\ f(\pi),\ F(\tfrac{1}{4}\pi),\ F(\tfrac{2}{3}\pi),\ F(0) - F(\pi).$$

9. If $f(x) = 2^x$, evaluate $f(x)$ when $x = 1, 2, 3, 0, -1, -2, -3$.

10. If $f(x) = \tan x$, express $f(x + y)$ in terms of $f(x)$ and $f(y)$.

11. If $f(x) = \log x$, prove that $f(a^n) = n \log a$.

12. If $f(x) = \sin x \cos^3 x$, prove that $f(x + \pi) = f(x)$.

13. If $f(x) = 1 + \dfrac{x}{1!} + \dfrac{x^2}{2!} + \dfrac{x^3}{3!} + \dfrac{x^4}{4!} + \ldots$ to ∞, calculate the value of $f(1)$ to three decimal places.

14. Prove that the following are even functions of x :—

(i) $a + bx^2 + cx^4$, (ii) $x^2 - x^{-2}$, (iii) $\sec x$, (iv) $a^x + a^{-x}$.

15. Prove that the following are odd functions of x :—

(i) $ax + bx^3$, (ii) $x - x^{-1}$, (iii) $\tan x$, (iv) $a^x - a^{-x}$.

16. Draw any curve to represent the graph of a function for positive values of x. Then continue the graph for negative values of x, assuming (i) that the function is even, (ii) that the function is odd.

17. If $f(x) = ax + bx^2 + cx^3$, and if $f(1) = 2, f(2) = 2, f(3) = -6$, find the values of the constants a, b, c, and the value of $f(-2)$.

18. If $f(x) = \dfrac{cx + d}{ax + b}$, and if $f(2) = 5$, $f(-1) = \tfrac{1}{2}$, $f(\tfrac{1}{2}) = -4$, find the value of $f(4)$.

§ 5. Limits.

—A function of x may not have a value when $x = a$, but it may nevertheless *approach* a value when x approaches a; where a denotes some particular value of x.

For example, consider the function

$$y = \frac{x^2 - 4}{x - 2},$$

when $x = 2$, and when x approaches 2.

When $x = 2$,

$$y = \frac{2^2 - 4}{2 - 2} = \frac{0}{0},$$

which is meaningless, since we cannot divide by zero.

Nevertheless, y *approaches* a value when x approaches 2. For, when $x \neq 2$ we can divide by $(x - 2)$ and get

$$y = \frac{(x + 2)(x - 2)}{x - 2} = x + 2,$$

from which it follows that y approaches the value $2 + 2, = 4$, when x approaches 2, and in fact differs from 4 by as little as we please when x is sufficiently near to 2. Thus, when

$$
\begin{aligned}
x &= 2\cdot1, & y &= 4\cdot1, \\
x &= 2\cdot01, & y &= 4\cdot01, \\
x &= 2\cdot001, & y &= 4\cdot001,
\end{aligned}
$$

and so on, y approaching 4 as x approaches 2. In this case, we say that the value of y is *indeterminate* when $x = 2$, but that y approaches the *limit* 4 as x approaches 2.

Definition.   The form $\dfrac{0}{0}$ is *indeterminate*.

The value of a function of x may be indeterminate for some particular value of x.

Let y be a function whose value is indeterminate when $x = a$. Then, y may nevertheless *approach* a value, say m, when x approaches a ; and so that y differs from m by as little as we please when x is sufficiently near to a.   If this is the case, we say that y *approaches the limit* m *when* x *approaches* a, and write, for brevity,

$$y \to m, \text{ when } x \to a,$$
$$\text{or} \qquad \lim_{x \to a} (y) = m,$$

which we read : "the limit of y, when x approaches a, is m."

Ex. Find the limit of $\dfrac{x^3 - 3x^2}{x^2 - 9}$ when $x \to 3$.

Put $y = \dfrac{x^3 - 3x^2}{x^2 - 9}$. Then, when $x = 3$, $y = \dfrac{0}{0}$, which is indeterminate. But

$$y = \frac{x^2(x - 3)}{(x - 3)(x + 3)} = \frac{x^2}{x + 3}, \text{ when } x \neq 3,$$

$$\therefore \lim_{x \to 3} (y) = \frac{3^2}{3 + 3} = \frac{9}{6} = \frac{3}{2}.$$

Here $(x - 3)$ is called the *vanishing factor*.
Method.—Begin by cancelling out the vanishing factor.

Examples II.

In Exs. 1-16, find the limits of the given functions when x approaches the given values :—

1. $\dfrac{x^2 - 1}{x - 1}$, $(x \to 1)$.   2. $\dfrac{x^2 - 9}{x + 3}$, $(x \to -3)$.   3. $\dfrac{x^3 - 8}{x - 2}$, $(x \to 2)$.

4. $\dfrac{10x}{x^2 + 2x}$, $(x \to 0)$.   5. $\dfrac{x^3 + 1}{x^2 - 1}$, $(x \to -1)$.   6. $\dfrac{x^5 - x^4}{x^3 - x}$, $(x \to 1)$.

7. $\left(\dfrac{x^2-4}{x-2}\right)^2$, $(x\to 2)$.   8. $\dfrac{x^3-a^3}{x-a}$, $(x\to a)$.   9. $\dfrac{x^3-a^3}{x^2-a^2}$, $(x\to a)$.

10. $\dfrac{x^n-1}{x-1}$, $(x\to 1)$.   11. $\dfrac{x^n-a^n}{x-a}$, $(x\to a)$.   12. $\dfrac{x^n-a^n}{x^m-a^m}$, $(x\to a)$.

13. $\dfrac{x^2-2x-8}{x^2+6x+8}$, $(x\to -2)$.   14. $\dfrac{(x-1)^4-1+4x}{x^2}$, $(x\to 0)$.

15. $\dfrac{x^3-3x+2}{(x-1)^2}$, $(x\to 1)$.   16. $\dfrac{(x+4)^3-(x-8)^2}{x(x-3)}$, $(x\to 0)$.

17. Evaluate $\lim\limits_{h\to 0} \dfrac{f(2+h)-f(2)}{h}$, when $f(x)=\dfrac{1}{x}$.

18. Evaluate $\lim\limits_{h\to 0} \dfrac{f(x+h)-f(x)}{h}$, when $f(x)=\dfrac{1+x}{1-x}$.

§ 6. **Other Indeterminate Forms.**—There are other indeterminate forms besides $\dfrac{0}{0}$; for example, $\dfrac{\infty}{\infty}$ and $(\infty-\infty)$ are such forms.

Ex. Evaluate the limits

(i) $\lim\limits_{x\to\infty}\left(\dfrac{2x^2+5}{x^2+3x}\right)$,   (ii) $\lim\limits_{x\to 0}\left\{\left(2x+\dfrac{1}{x}\right)^2-\left(x-\dfrac{1}{x}\right)^2\right\}$.

(i) Put $y=\dfrac{2x^2+5}{x^2+3x}$. Then, when $x=\infty$, $y=\dfrac{\infty}{\infty}$, which is indeterminate. Nevertheless, y approaches a limit when $x\to\infty$. This becomes plain when we divide numerator and denominator by x^2, for we then get

$$y=\frac{2x^2+5}{x^2+3x}=\frac{2+\dfrac{5}{x^2}}{1+\dfrac{3}{x}},$$

$$\therefore \lim_{x\to\infty}(y)=\frac{2+0}{1+0}=2.$$

(ii) Put $y=\left\{\left(2x+\dfrac{1}{x}\right)^2-\left(x-\dfrac{1}{x}\right)^2\right\}$. Then, when $x=0$, $y=\infty-\infty$, which is indeterminate. But y approaches a limit when $x\to 0$. For, on simplifying, we get

$$y=3x^2+6,$$
$$\therefore \lim_{x\to 0}(y)=6.$$

§ 7. **Geometrical Limits.**

Tangent and chord.—Let A be a fixed point, and Q a variable point, on a smooth curve, and let AT be the tangent at A.

Now there is no chord AQ when Q coincides with A. But there is a definite chord AQ when Q does not coincide with A, however near Q may be to A (Fig. 1).

The limit of the position of the chord AQ, *when* Q → A, *is the tangent at* A.

In other words, when Q → A, the position of the chord AQ approaches the tangent AT, and differs from it by as little as we please when Q is near enough to A.

The ratio of the arc to the chord.—Another important geometrical limit is that, if A is a fixed point, and Q a variable point,

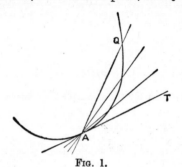

Fɪɢ. 1.

on a smooth curve, the limit of the ratio of the length of the *arc* AQ to that of the *chord* AQ is unity, when Q → A; that is,

$$\frac{\text{arc AQ}}{\text{chord AQ}} \to 1, \text{ when } Q \to A.$$

We shall assume that this is self-evident.

Examples III.

Find the limits of the given functions when x approaches the given values:

1. $\dfrac{2x-3}{x}$, $(x \to \infty)$.　　2. $\dfrac{x-6}{2x+3}$, $(x \to \infty)$.　　3. $\dfrac{3x}{x^2+1}$, $(x \to \infty)$.

4. $\dfrac{x^2+2}{(x+2)(x-3)}$, $(x \to \infty)$.　　　5. $\dfrac{3x^2-2x-6}{1-x^2}$, $(x \to \infty)$.

6. $\dfrac{x^2+x+1}{x+1} - \dfrac{2x^2+1}{2x+1}$, $(x \to \infty)$.

7. $\left(2x+\dfrac{1}{x}\right)^2 - \left(\dfrac{1}{x}-3x\right)^2$, $(x \to 0)$.

8. $\log(3x-1) - \log(x+8)$, $(x \to \infty)$.

§ 8. Approximations.—Two functions of x, say u and v, are said to be *approximately equal* when x is near enough to a, if their ratio u/v approaches the limit 1 when x approaches a. Thus,

$$u \doteqdot v \text{ when } x \text{ is near } a, \text{ if } \frac{u}{v} \to 1 \text{ when } x \to a.$$

(The sign $\doteqdot$ means "is approximately equal to.")

Note, as one consequence of this definition, that the value of a function can never be approximately equal to either zero or infinity.

Ex. Prove that $3x + 8x^2 \doteqdot 3x$, when x is small enough.
Proof.

$$\frac{3x + 8x^2}{3x} = 1 + \frac{8x}{3},$$

$$\therefore \frac{3x + 8x^2}{3x} \to 1 \text{ when } x \to 0.$$

Hence, by the definition just given, when x s near enough to 0, that is, when x is small enough,

$$3x + 8x^2 \doteqdot 3x.$$

Examples IV.

Prove the given approximations :—

1. (i) $2x + 3x^2 - x^3 \doteqdot 2x$, when x is small;
   (ii) $2x + 3x^2 - x^3 \doteqdot -x^3$, when x is large.

2. (i) $x(x-1)(2x+3) \doteqdot -3x$, when x is small;
   (ii) $x(x-1)(2x+3) \doteqdot 2x^3$, when x is large.

3. (i) $(x-3)^2(x-5) \doteqdot 4(x-5)$, when x is near 5;
   (ii) $(x-3)^2(x-5) \doteqdot -2(x-3)^2$, when x is near 3.

4. If $y = \frac{x-1}{x-3}$, (i) $y \doteqdot \frac{2}{x-3}$, when x is near 3;
   (ii) $y \doteqdot -\frac{1}{2}(x-1)$, when x is near 1.

5. If $y = \frac{2x + 3x^2}{x+1}$, (i) $y \doteqdot 2x$, when x is small;
   (ii) $y \doteqdot 3x$, when x is large.

6. If $y = \frac{1}{x^2} + \frac{1}{x^3}$, (i) $y \doteqdot \frac{1}{x^3}$, when x is small;
   (ii) $y \doteqdot \frac{1}{x^2}$, when x is large.

7. If $y = \frac{x^3 + 4x^2 + 1}{x}$, (i) $y \doteqdot \frac{1}{x}$, when x is small;
   (ii) $y \doteqdot x^2$, when x is large.

§ 9. Graphs.

If a variable y is a function of another variable x, the way in which y varies when x varies can be shown by means of a *graph*.

It is not always necessary to draw a graph to scale, but it is often helpful to sketch its essential features, by paying attention to the values of x for which $y = 0$, $y = \infty$, y is positive, how y behaves when x is small and when x is large; and so on.

A graph in which y is regarded as a function of x we shall call an (x, y) graph, naming the independent variable first.

§ 10. $y = $ a product of factors of the first degree in x.

Ex. Sketch the graphs of

(1) $y = x(x - 2)(x + 2)$;   (2) $y = (x + 1)(x - 3)^2$.

(1) See Fig. 2.   Before sketching the graph, we note that:

  (i) $y = 0$ when $x = 0, 2, -2$.
  (ii) y is positive when $x > 2$ and when $-2 < x < 0$.
  (iii) y is negative when $0 < x < 2$, and when $x < -2$.
  (iv) $y \doteqdot x^3$ when x is large.

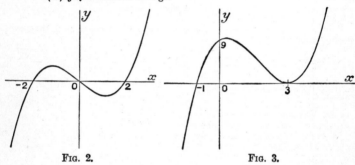

Fig. 2.   Fig. 3.

(2) See Fig. 3.   Before sketching the graph, we note that:

  (i) $y = 0$ when $x = -1, 3, 3$. The value 3 is put down twice here because the factor $(x - 3)$ occurs twice. The graph *touches* the x-axis where $x = 3$.
  (ii) y is positive when $x > -1$, negative when $x < -1$.
  (iii) $y \doteqdot x^3$ when x is large.

Examples V.

Sketch the graphs of the given functions :—

1. $y = x(1 - x)$.   **2.** $y = (x - 1)(x - 2)(x - 3)$.
3. (i) $y = x(x - 1{\cdot}9)(x - 2{\cdot}1)$;   (ii) $y = x(x - 2)^2$.
4. $y = (x - 2)^2(x + 1)$.   **5.** $y = x^2(x^2 - 1)$.
6. $y = x^2(x - 3)^2$.   **7.** $y = x^2(1 + x^2)$.
8. (i) $y = x(x - 1)(x - 2)(x - 3)$,
   (ii) $y = x(x - 1{\cdot}9)(x - 2)(x - 2{\cdot}1)$,
   (iii) $y = x(x - 2)^3$.
9. $y = (x + 1)^2(x - 1)^3$.   **10.** $y = x^3(2 - x)^3$.

§ 11. y = the reciprocal of a function of x.

Ex. Sketch the graphs of

$$(1)\ y = \frac{1}{(x+1)(2-x)}; \quad (2)\ y = \frac{1}{x^2+2}.$$

(1) Let $v = (x+1)(2-x)$. Then $y = \frac{1}{v}$. Thus y is the reciprocal of v.

For this reason, first sketch the (x, v) graph (dotted in Fig. 4); then *plot the reciprocals of its ordinates,* and so obtain the (x, y) graph (full-line curve in Fig. 4).

(2) Let $v = x^2 + 2$. Then $y = \frac{1}{v}$. Since y is the reciprocal of v, first sketch the (x, v) graph (dotted in Fig. 5), then plot the reciprocals of its ordinates, and so obtain the (x, y) graph (full-line curve in Fig. 5).

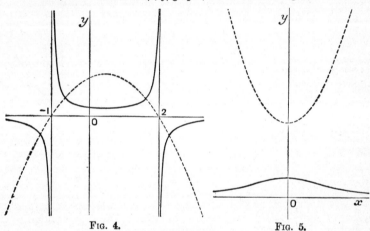

FIG. 4.   FIG. 5.

Examples VI.

Sketch the graphs of the given functions :—

1. $y = \frac{1}{x}.$

2. $y = \frac{1}{x-1}.$

3. $y = \frac{1}{3+2x}.$

4. $y = \frac{1}{x^2}.$

5. $y = \frac{1}{1-x^2}.$

6. $y = \frac{1}{x^2-x+1}.$

7. $y = \frac{1}{x(4-x)}.$

8. $y = \frac{1}{x(x^2-1)}.$

9. $y = \frac{1}{x^2(x-2)^2}.$

§ 12. y^2 = **a function of x.**—If $y^2 = u$, and u is a function of x, then

$$y = \pm\ \sqrt{u.}$$

For this reason, we can draw the (x, y) graph by first drawing the (x, u) graph and then *plotting the square-roots of its ordinates*.

Consider three particular cases first :

(1) $y^2 = x$.

Put $u = x$. Then the (x, u) graph is a straight line through the origin, and the (x, y) graph crosses the x-axis at right angles at the origin (Fig. 6).

We infer that, if $y^2 = u$, where u is any function of x, in general *the (x, y) graph crosses the x-axis at right angles at a point where the (x, u) graph cuts it*.

(2) $y^2 = x^2$.

Put $u = x^2$. Then the (x, u) graph *touches* the x-axis at the origin, and the (x, y) graph consists of the two straight lines $y = \pm x$, cutting each other at the origin (Fig. 7).

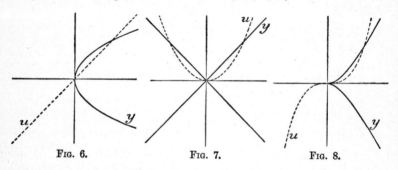

FIG. 6.   FIG. 7.   FIG. 8.

We infer that, if $y^2 = u$, where u is any function of x, in general the (x, y) graph has two branches, cutting each other, at a point where the (x, u) graph touches the x-axis.

A point of this kind on the (x, y) graph is called a *node*, or *double-point*. Hence, in general, *the (x, y) graph has a node at a point where the (x, u) graph touches the x-axis*.

(3) $y^2 = x^3$.

Put $u = x^3$. Then the (x, u) graph *touches and crosses* the x-axis at the origin, and the (x, y) has two branches that touch one another at the origin and have the x-axis for a common tangent there (Fig. 8). This kind of a point on a curve is called a *cusp*.

We infer that, if $y^2 = u$, where u is any function of x, *the (x, y) graph has a cusp at a point where the (x, u) graph touches and crosses the x-axis*.

Ex.   Sketch the graphs of

$$(1)\ y^2 = x^2(1 - x),\quad (2)\ y^2 = x^3(1 - x).$$

(1) Put $u = x^2(1 - x)$. Then $y = \pm \sqrt{u}$.

Hence, we first sketch the (x, u) graph (dotted in Fig. 9), then plot the square roots of its ordinates, and so obtain the (x, y) graph (full-line curve in Fig. 9).

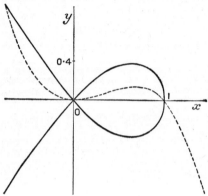

Fig. 9.

(i) There are two values of y, equal in magnitude but opposite in sign, for every *positive* value of u ; but *no real values of* y *wherever* u *is negative,* because the square-root of a negative number is unreal.

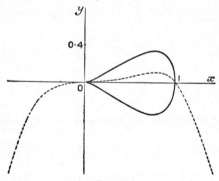

Fig. 10.

(ii) The (x, y) graph crosses the x-axis at right angles at the point $x = 1$, where the (x, u) graph cuts it.

(iii) The (x, y) graph has a node at the origin, where the (x, u) graph touches the x-axis.

(iv) The part of the (x, y) graph between $x = 0$ and $x = 1$ is called a *loop*.

(2) Put $u = x^3(1 - x)$. Then $y = \pm \sqrt{u}$.

In this case, u is positive only between $x = 0$ and $x = 1$, and the (x, y) graph consists of a single loop, with a cusp at $x = 0$ where the (x, u) graph is tangential to the x-axis and crosses it (Fig. 10).

Examples VII.

Sketch the given curves :—

1. $y^2 = x - 1$.
2. $y^2 = 1 - x$.
3. $y^2 = x^2 + 1$.
4. $y^2 = x^2 - 1$.
5. $y^2 = x(1 - x)$.
6. $y^2 = x(x - 3)^2$.
7. $y^2 = x^2(1 - x^2)$.
8. $y^2 = (x - 1)(x - 2)(x - 3)$.
9. $y^2 = x^3$.
10. $y^2 = (x - 2)^3$.
11. $y^2 = x(1 - x)^3$.
12. $y^2 = x^5$.
13. $y^2 = x^5(1 - x)$.
14. $y^2 = x^3(1 - x)^3$.
15. $y^2 = \dfrac{1}{x}$.
16. $y^2 = \dfrac{x - 1}{x}$.
17. $y^2 = \dfrac{x}{1 - x}$.
18. $y = \dfrac{1}{\sqrt{(1 - x^2)}}$.
19. $y = \dfrac{1}{\sqrt{(x^2 - x)}}$.
20. $y = \dfrac{1}{\sqrt{(x^2 + 1)}}$.

§ 13. Construction of Functions.

Ex. A cylinder of height $2x$ is inscribed in a sphere of radius 3. If V is the volume of the cylinder, express V in terms of x, and sketch the (x, V) graph.

Let $r =$ the radius of the cylinder. Then

$$V = 2\pi r^2 x.$$

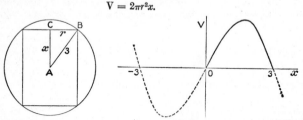

FIG. 11.   FIG. 12.

Let Fig. 11 be a section through the axis of the cylinder. Then, from the right-angled triangle ABC,

$$AC^2 + CB^2 = AB^2,$$
$$\therefore x^2 + r^2 = 3^2,$$
$$\therefore r^2 = 9 - x^2,$$
$$\therefore V = 2\pi x(9 - x^2).$$

This is the expression required. Since $2x$ is the height, x necessarily lies between 0 and 3. Accordingly, the (x, V) graph is indicated for values of x between 0 and 3 by the full-line curve in Fig. 12.

Examples VIII.

1. The volume of a tin box, with a square base and open at the top, is 4 cub. ft. If x ft. is the length of an edge of the base, and A sq. ft. is the total area of tin, express A in terms of x, and sketch the (x, A) graph.

2. From a cone of height 10, and base-radius 5, a smaller cone is cut by a plane, parallel to the base, at a distance x from the vertex. If y is the base-radius, z the base-area, and v the volume of the smaller cone, express y, z, and v in terms of x.

3. A point of light is a ft. above a horizontal table, and a horizontal plate of area A sq. ft. is beneath the light and x ft. above the table. If S is the area of the shadow of the plate on the table, express S in terms of a, A, and x.

4. AB, CD are two parallel lines cutting the line BD at right angles. Another line APQ cuts CD in P and BD in Q. If AB $= a$, BD $= b$, PD $= x$, DQ $= y$, express y in terms of a, b, and x.

5. ABCD is a trapezium ; AB, CD are the parallel sides, 4 ins. apart; P, Q are points in AD, BC, and PQ is parallel to AB at a distance x ins. from it. If AB $= 3$ ins., CD $= 5$ ins., and $z =$ area of the trapezium ABQP, express z in terms of x.

6. If local time in longitude θ degrees East is t hours ahead of Greenwich time, express t in terms of θ, and draw the (θ, t) graph from $\theta = 180°$ to $\theta = -180°$.

7. If r is the distance of the origin from the point (x, y) on the graph of $y = x + 2$, express r in terms of x.

8. The lengths of the sides of a triangle are $2x$, 6, and 8 ins. Express the area S in terms of x, and draw the (x, S) graph.

9. The slant side of a cone is 6 ins. long. If the height is x ins. and the volume V cub. ins., express V in terms of x, and sketch the (x, V) graph.

10. ABC is a triangle in which AB $= 6$, AC $= 8$, $\angle$ BAC $= \theta$. Express BC, and the area, in terms of θ, and find their greatest and least values.

11. ABC is a triangle in which AB $= 4$, $\angle$ ACB $= 30°$, $\angle$ ABC $= \theta$. Express AC, BC, and the area, in terms of θ.

12. ABC is a triangle in which AC $= 4$, $\angle$ ACB $= 30°$, $\angle$ ABC $= \theta$. Express AB, BC, and the area, in terms of θ.

13. A cone is of height h, base-radius r, slant side l, semi-vertical angle α, and volume V. Prove that

$$V = \tfrac{1}{3}\pi h^3 \tan^2 \alpha = \tfrac{1}{3}\pi r^3 \cot \alpha = \tfrac{1}{3}\pi l^3 \sin^2 \alpha \cos \alpha.$$

14. A cone of semi-vertical angle α and volume V is inscribed in a sphere of radius a. Prove that

$$V = \tfrac{8}{3}\pi a^3 \sin^2 \alpha \cos^4 \alpha.$$

CHAPTER II.

DIFFERENTIATION.

§ 14. Change in a Variable.—When the value of a variable changes continuously from a to b, the difference $(b - a)$ is called the *change* (or *increment*) in the variable.

In the Differential Calculus, a change in x is denoted by δx, a change in y by δy, a change in u by δu, a change in A by δA, and so on. Thus, if δx is the change in x when x changes from a to b, then

$$\delta x = b - a.$$

(i) Note that δx is found by subtracting the value at the beginning from the value at the end of the change, *whether the result is positive or negative.*

(ii) δx is positive or negative according as $b > a$ or $b < a$; that is, the change is positive or negative according as the variable has increased or decreased (algebraically).

§ 15. Change in a Function.—If y is a function of x, a change in x causes a change in y. We can calculate the change caused in y by a given change in x, as follows:—

Let $y = f(x)$, and let x change from a to b.

Let δy be the change caused in y. Then, if $y = y_1$ when $x = b$, and $y = y_0$ when $x = a$,

$$\delta y = y_1 - y_0.$$

But
$$y_1 = f(b),$$
$$y_0 = f(a),$$
$$\therefore y_1 - y_0 = f(b) - f(a),$$
$$\therefore \delta y = f(b) - f(a).$$

Ex. If $y = x^2$, find the change in y when x changes **from**

(i) 3 to 7, (ii) 3 to $(3 + \delta x)$.

In each case, let $y_0 = $ the value of y at the beginning of the change, $y_1 = $ the value of y at the end of the change.

(i)
$$y_1 = 7^2 = 49,$$
$$y_0 = 3^2 = 9,$$
$$\therefore y_1 - y_0 = 40,$$
$$\therefore \delta y = 40.$$

(ii) $$\begin{aligned} y_1 &= (3 + \delta x)^2 = 9 + 6\delta x + (\delta x)^2, \\ y_0 &= 3^2 = 9, \\ \therefore \ y_1 - y_0 &= 6\delta x + (\delta x)^2, \\ \therefore \ \delta y &= 6\delta x + (\delta x)^2. \end{aligned}$$

Note that here δy depends on δx (is a *function* of δx); also, that $\delta y = 0$ when $\delta x = 0$ (there is no change in y when there is none in x).

Examples IX.

In Exs. 1-4, find the change caused in y by the given changes in x :—

1. $y = 3x + 2$, when x changes from (i) 3 to 7, (ii) a to $(a + 4)$.
2. $y = 2x^2$, when x changes from (i) 1 to 3, (ii) 1 to $(1 + \delta x)$.
3. $y = x^3 - 4x + 3$, when x changes from 3 to $(3 + \delta x)$.
4. $y = 2^x + 2^{-x}$, when x changes from 0 to 2.
5. If $pv = 36$, find the change in v when p changes from 3 to 4.
6. If V cub. ins. is the volume of a cone, whose slant side is 5 ins. long, find the change in V when the height changes from 3 to 4 ins.

§ 16. **Differentiation.**—Let y be a function of x, and let the value of the function change from y to $(y + \delta y)$ while the variable changes from x to $(x + \delta x)$.

Consider the ratio of the change in y to the change in x, that is, the ratio of δy to δx, or

$$\frac{\delta y}{\delta x}.$$

When $\delta x = 0$, this ratio $= \dfrac{0}{0}$ (there is no change in y when there is none in x). Thus the ratio is indeterminate when $\delta x = 0$; but in general it approaches a limit when $\delta x \to 0$.

This limit is called the *differential coefficient of y with respect to x*. It is also called the *derived function*, or the *derivative*. It is usually denoted by $\dfrac{dy}{dx}$; thus

$$\frac{dy}{dx} = \lim_{\delta x \to 0} \left(\frac{\delta y}{\delta x} \right).$$

The process of finding this limit is called *differentiation*. Thus, *differentiation is the process of finding the limit of the ratio of δy to δx, when $\delta x \to 0$.*

Here the letters x and y typify the independent variable and the function respectively. Other letters may be used in other places.

§ 17. Ex. If $y = x^2$, find the differential coefficient of y with respect to x.

Let the value of the function change from y to $(y + \delta y)$ while the variable changes from x to $(x + \delta x)$. Then, at the end of the change,

$$y + \delta y = (x + \delta x)^2,$$
$$\therefore \ y + \delta y = x^2 + 2x\delta x + (\delta x)^2.$$

But, at the beginning of the change,

$$y = x^2.$$

By subtraction,

$$\delta y = 2x\delta x + (\delta x)^2,$$

$$\therefore \ \frac{\delta y}{\delta x} = 2x + \delta x,$$

$$\therefore \ \lim_{\delta x \to 0} \left(\frac{\delta y}{\delta x} \right) = 2x + 0 = 2x,$$

$$\therefore \ \frac{dy}{dx} = 2x.$$

§ 18. The derived function of $f(x)$ is denoted by $f'(x)$. It can be expressed in a formula as follows :—

Let $y = f(x)$, and let the function change from y to $(y + \delta y)$ while the variable changes from x to $(x + \delta x)$. Then

$$y + \delta y = f(x + \delta x), \quad y = f(x).$$

By subtraction,

$$\delta y = f(x + \delta x) - f(x),$$

$$\therefore \ \frac{\delta y}{\delta x} = \frac{f(x + \delta x) - f(x)}{\delta x},$$

$$\therefore \ f'(x) = \lim_{\delta x \to 0} \left\{ \frac{f(x + \delta x) - f(x)}{\delta x} \right\}.$$

§ 19. **Notation for the Differential Coefficient.**—The differential coefficient of y with respect to x is usually denoted by one of the four symbols

$$\frac{dy}{dx}, \quad y', \quad D_x y, \quad Dy.$$

The first and third of these symbols keep both the variables x and y in evidence. The second and fourth may be used when there is no need to draw attention to the independent variable.

Instead of $\frac{dy}{dx}$ we often write $\frac{d}{dx}(y)$, regarding $\frac{d}{dx}$ as a symbol denoting the operation of differentiation with respect to x. A similar notation is used for other variables; thus

$$\frac{d}{dx}(x^2) = 2x, \quad \frac{d}{du}(u^2) = 2u, \quad \frac{d}{dt}(t^2) = 2t.$$

§ 20. Differentiation from First Principles.—Although, by definition, differentiation is the process of finding a certain limit, we can construct rules that enable us to write down many differential coefficients by inspection. Accordingly, finding differential coefficients from the fundamental definition is called *differentiating from first principles*. The steps of the process of differentiating from first principles are set out in the rule below, and followed in the succeeding examples:—

Let y be a function of x, and let the function change from y to $(y + \delta y)$, while the variable changes from x to $(x + \delta x)$:—

Rule.—Write down the relation between $(y + \delta y)$ and $(x + \delta x)$, and the relation between y and x.

Subtract: this gives δy, expressed in terms of x and δx; simplify if necessary.

Divide both sides by δx: this gives $\frac{\delta y}{\delta x}$.

Find the limit of $\frac{\delta y}{\delta x}$ when $\delta x \to 0$: this gives $\frac{dy}{dx}$.

Ex. 1. Find $\frac{dy}{dx}$ from first principles, when (i) $y = \frac{1}{x}$, (ii) $y = \sqrt{x}$.

(i) $$y + \delta y = \frac{1}{x + \delta x}, \quad y = \frac{1}{x}.$$

By subtraction,

$$\delta y = \frac{1}{x + \delta x} - \frac{1}{x} = \frac{-\delta x}{(x + \delta x)x},$$

$$\therefore \frac{\delta y}{\delta x} = \frac{-1}{(x + \delta x)x},$$

$$\therefore \lim_{\delta x \to 0}\left(\frac{\delta y}{\delta x}\right) = \frac{-1}{(x + 0)x} = \frac{-1}{x^2},$$

$$\therefore \frac{dy}{dx} = -\frac{1}{x^2}.$$

(ii) $$y + \delta y = \sqrt{(x + \delta x)}, \quad y = \sqrt{x}.$$

By subtraction,

$$\delta y = \sqrt{(x + \delta x)} - \sqrt{x},$$

$$\therefore \frac{\delta y}{\delta x} = \frac{\sqrt{(x + \delta x)} - \sqrt{x}}{\delta x}.$$

In this case, to find the limit when $\delta x \to 0$, we multiply numerator and denominator by $\sqrt{(x + \delta x)} + \sqrt{x}$. This gives

$$\frac{\delta y}{\delta x} = \frac{(x + \delta x) - x}{\delta x \{\sqrt{(x + \delta x)} + \sqrt{x}\}} = \frac{1}{\sqrt{(x + \delta x)} + \sqrt{x}},$$

$$\therefore \lim_{\delta x \to 0} \left(\frac{\delta y}{\delta x} \right) = \frac{1}{\sqrt{(x + 0)} + \sqrt{x}} = \frac{1}{2\sqrt{x}},$$

$$\therefore \frac{dy}{dx} = \frac{1}{2\sqrt{x}}.$$

Ex. 2. Differentiate from first principles :—

$$\text{(i) } y = x^2 - 5x + 3, \quad \text{(ii) } y = \frac{1}{3x + 2}.$$

(i)
$$\begin{aligned} y + \delta y &= (x + \delta x)^2 - 5(x + \delta x) + 3 \\ &= x^2 + 2x\delta x + (\delta x)^2 - 5x - 5\delta x + 3, \\ y &= x^2 \qquad\qquad\qquad - 5x \qquad\quad + 3. \end{aligned}$$

By subtraction,

$$\delta y = 2x\delta x + (\delta x)^2 - 5\delta x,$$

$$\therefore \frac{\delta y}{\delta x} = 2x + \delta x - 5,$$

$$\therefore \lim_{\delta x \to 0} \left(\frac{\delta y}{\delta x} \right) = 2x + 0 - 5 = 2x - 5,$$

$$\therefore \frac{dy}{dx} = 2x - 5.$$

(ii)
$$y + \delta y = \frac{1}{3(x + \delta x) + 2}, \quad y = \frac{1}{3x + 2}.$$

By subtraction,

$$\delta y = \frac{1}{3(x + \delta x) + 2} - \frac{1}{3x + 2} = \frac{-3\delta x}{(3x + 3\delta x + 2)(3x + 2)},$$

$$\therefore \frac{\delta y}{\delta x} = \frac{-3}{(3x + 3\delta x + 2)(3x + 2)},$$

$$\therefore \lim_{\delta x \to 0} \left(\frac{\delta y}{\delta x} \right) = \frac{-3}{(3x + 0 + 2)(3x + 2)} = \frac{-3}{(3x + 2)^2},$$

$$\therefore \frac{dy}{dx} = \frac{-3}{(3x + 2)^2}.$$

Examples X.

Differentiate the given functions from first principles :—

1. $y = x^3$.
2. $y = 3x^2$.
3. $y = 3$.
4. $y = x$.
5. $y = 10x + 3$.
6. $y = -2x + 5$.
7. $y = 5x^2 - 7$.
8. $y = 3x^2 - x^3$.
9. $y = ax + b$.
10. $y = ax^2 + bx + c$.
11. $y = \dfrac{3}{x}$.
12. $y = \dfrac{1}{x^2}$.
13. $y = \dfrac{1}{x^3}$.
14. $y = \dfrac{1}{\sqrt{x}}$.

15. $y = \dfrac{1}{x+2}.$ **16.** $y = \dfrac{1}{4x-3}.$ **17.** $y = \dfrac{1}{ax+b}.$

18. $y = \dfrac{2x+3}{1-x}.$ **19.** $y = \sqrt{(3x-1)}.$ **20.** $y = \dfrac{1}{x^2+a^2}.$

§ 21. Differentiation by Rule.—We shall next prove some of the rules that enable us to write down differential coefficients by inspection. A list of the rules is given first, for the sake of reference. The proofs follow.

In these rules, x is the independent variable; y, u, v, w are functions of x; and a, c are constants.

$$y = x^n, \quad \frac{dy}{dx} = nx^{n-1}; \quad \text{or} \quad \frac{d}{dx}(x^n) = nx^{n-1}. \tag{1}$$

$$y = \frac{1}{x}, \quad \frac{dy}{dx} = -\frac{1}{x^2}; \quad \text{or} \quad \frac{d}{dx}\left(\frac{1}{x}\right) = -\frac{1}{x^2}. \tag{2}$$

$$y = \sqrt{x}, \quad \frac{dy}{dx} = \frac{1}{2\sqrt{x}}; \quad \text{or} \quad \frac{d}{dx}(\sqrt{x}) = \frac{1}{2\sqrt{x}}. \tag{3}$$

$$y = c, \quad \frac{dy}{dx} = 0; \quad \text{or} \quad \frac{d}{dx}(c) = 0. \tag{4}$$

$$y = ax, \quad \frac{dy}{dx} = a; \quad \text{or} \quad \frac{d}{dx}(ax) = a. \tag{5}$$

$$y = au, \quad \frac{dy}{dx} = a\frac{du}{dx}; \quad \text{or} \quad \frac{d}{dx}(au) = a\frac{du}{dx}. \tag{6}$$

$$y = u + v - w, \quad \frac{dy}{dx} = \frac{du}{dx} + \frac{dv}{dx} - \frac{dw}{dx}. \tag{7}$$

$$\frac{dy}{dx} = \frac{1}{\dfrac{dx}{dy}}. \tag{8}$$

Proof of (1).—We assume n to be a positive integer here, though the rule holds good for all values of n (see § 31). We have

$$y + \delta y = (x + \delta x)^n, \quad y = x^n.$$

By subtraction,

$$\delta y = (x + \delta x)^n - x^n.$$

Hence, by the Binomial Theorem,

$$\delta y = nx^{n-1}\delta x + \frac{n(n-1)}{2!}x^{n-2}(\delta x)^2 + \ldots + (\delta x)^n,$$

$$\therefore \frac{\delta y}{\delta x} = nx^{n-1} + \frac{n(n-1)}{2!}x^{n-2}\delta x + \ldots + (\delta x)^{n-1},$$

$$\therefore \lim_{\delta x \to 0} \left(\frac{\delta y}{\delta x} \right) = nx^{n-1} + 0 + 0 + \ldots + 0,$$

$$\therefore \frac{dy}{dx} = nx^{n-1}.$$

Ex. $\frac{d}{dx}(x^2) = 2x,$ $\frac{d}{dx}(x^3) = 3x^2,$ $\frac{d}{dx}(x^4) = 4x^3.$

Proofs of (2) *and* (3).—See Ex. 1, § 20.

Proof of (4).—Since a constant does not change,

$$y + \delta y = c, \qquad y = c.$$

By subtraction,

$$\delta y = 0,$$

$$\therefore \frac{\delta y}{\delta x} = 0,$$

$$\therefore \frac{dy}{dx} = 0.$$

Proof of (5).

$$y + \delta y = a(x + \delta x), \qquad y = ax.$$

By subtraction,

$$\delta y = a \delta x,$$

$$\therefore \frac{\delta y}{\delta x} = a,$$

$$\therefore \frac{dy}{dx} = a.$$

Ex. $\frac{d}{dx}(4x) = 4,$ $\frac{d}{dx}(x) = 1,$ $\frac{d}{dx}(-3x) = -3.$

Proof of (6).—Let δu be the change in u, and δy the change in y, caused by a change δx in x. Then, at the end of the change,

$$y + \delta y = a(u + \delta u).$$

But, at the beginning of the change,

$$y = au.$$

By subtraction,

$$\delta y = a \delta u,$$

$$\therefore \frac{\delta y}{\delta x} = a \frac{\delta u}{\delta x}.$$

Hence, when $\delta x \to 0$,

$$\frac{dy}{dx} = a\frac{du}{dx}.$$

Ex.   (i) $\dfrac{d}{dx}(5x^3) = 5\dfrac{d}{dx}(x^3)$.   (ii) $\dfrac{d}{dx}\left(\dfrac{3}{x}\right) = 3\dfrac{d}{dx}\left(\dfrac{1}{x}\right)$.

Proof of (7).—Let δu, δv, δw, δy be the changes in u, v, w, y, caused by a change δx in x. Then, at the end of the change,

$$y + \delta y = (u + \delta u) + (v + \delta v) - (w + \delta w).$$

But, at the beginning of the change,

$$y = u + v - w.$$

By subtraction,

$$\delta y = \delta u + \delta v - \delta w,$$

$$\therefore \frac{\delta y}{\delta x} = \frac{\delta u}{\delta x} + \frac{\delta v}{\delta x} - \frac{\delta w}{\delta x}.$$

Hence, when $\delta x \to 0$,

$$\frac{dy}{dx} = \frac{du}{dx} + \frac{dv}{dx} - \frac{dw}{dx}.$$

This is the *rule for differentiating a sum or difference of functions.*

Ex. Find $\dfrac{dy}{dx}$ when $y = 2x^3 - \dfrac{3}{x} + 4$.

$$\frac{dy}{dx} = \frac{d}{dx}(2x^3) - \frac{d}{dx}\left(\frac{3}{x}\right) + \frac{d}{dx}(4), \qquad \text{by (7)};$$

$$= 2\frac{d}{dx}(x^3) - 3\frac{d}{dx}\left(\frac{1}{x}\right) + 0, \qquad \text{by (6) and (4)};$$

$$= 6x^2 + \frac{3}{x^2}, \qquad \text{by (1) and (2).}$$

Proof of (8).—By a rule of fractions,

$$\frac{\delta y}{\delta x} = \frac{1}{\dfrac{\delta x}{\delta y}} \qquad\qquad\qquad \text{(i)}$$

Now δx and δy approach zero together, and when they do so,

$$\frac{\delta y}{\delta x} \to \frac{dy}{dx}, \quad \frac{\delta x}{\delta y} \to \frac{dx}{dy}.$$

Hence (i) becomes, in the limit,

$$\frac{dy}{dx} = \frac{1}{\dfrac{dx}{dy}}.$$

This rule is useful when it is easier to differentiate x with respect to y than y with respect to x.

Ex. If $x = y^3 - 2y - 1$, find dy/dx.
Differentiating x with respect to y, we get

$$\frac{dx}{dy} = 3y^2 - 2,$$
$$\therefore \frac{dy}{dx} = \frac{1}{3y^2 - 2}.$$

Here the differential coefficient is expressed in terms of y.

Examples XI.

In Exs. 1-16, find dy/dx, by rule :—

1. $y = x^4$.　　　2. $y = x^5$.　　　3. $y = 3x^2$.　　　4. $y = 5x$.

5. $y = -x$.　　　6. $y = \frac{1}{3}x^3$.　　　7. $y = 6\sqrt{x}$.　　　8. $y = 2x^2 - 5$.

9. $y = \dfrac{5}{x}$.　　　10. $y = \dfrac{1}{5x}$.　　　11. $y = x + \dfrac{1}{x}$.　　　12. $y = \dfrac{2}{x} - \sqrt{x}$.

13. $y = \dfrac{x^4}{4}$.　　　14. $y = \dfrac{x^n}{n}$.　　　15. $y = \dfrac{x^3 - 3}{x}$.　　　16. $y = \dfrac{x^n + 1}{x}$.

In Exs. 17-25, differentiate the given functions, by rule :—

17. $(x + 2)^2$.　　　18. $x^2 + x + 1$.　　　19. $2x^3 - 5x - 3$.

20. $ax^n + c$.　　　21. $ax(a - x)$.　　　22. $ax^n + bx^m + c$.

23. $\dfrac{ax + b}{x}$.　　　24. $\dfrac{ax^n(b + x)}{c}$.　　　25. $\dfrac{ax^2 + bx + c}{x}$.

In Exs. 26-31, find dy/dx in terms of y :—

26. $x = 3y - y^2$.　　　27. $y^2 + 1 = x$.　　　28. $y^3 = x$.

29. $x = y + \dfrac{1}{y}$.　　　30. $x = \dfrac{2y - 1}{y}$.　　　31. $x = \dfrac{y^3 - 3y + 1}{y}$.

32. Differentiate with respect to u :—

(i) $2u^3$,　(ii) $7\sqrt{u}$,　(iii) $a - u$,　(iv) $(2u + 5)^2$.

33. Differentiate with respect to v :—

(i) $\dfrac{1}{v}$,　(ii) $\dfrac{2v^2 + 3}{v}$,　(iii) $4 - \dfrac{5}{2v} - 2\sqrt{v}$.

34. If $y = ax^n$, where a is a constant, prove that $\dfrac{dy}{dx} = \dfrac{ny}{x}$.

35. If $pv = c$, where c is a constant, prove that $\dfrac{dp}{dv} = -\dfrac{p}{v}$.

CHAPTER III.

GRADIENTS.

§ 22. Gradient of a Straight Line.—If a straight line is drawn in the plane of two rectangular axes Ox, Oy, the change in y per unit change in x along the line is called the *gradient* of the line with respect to the x-axis.

Let m be the gradient of a line with respect to the x-axis, and let ψ be the angle it makes with the positive direction of the x-axis. We shall prove that

$$m = \tan \psi.$$

Proof.—Let AB be the line, P and Q two points on it. Draw PK parallel to Ox, and QK parallel to Oy (Figs. 13, 14).

Then, from P to Q, the change in y is KQ, and the change in x is PK. Hence, the change in y per unit change in x is KQ/PK,

$$\therefore \quad m = \frac{\text{KQ}}{\text{PK}} = \tan \angle \text{KPQ} = \tan \psi.$$

It is assumed that the same scales are used for x and y.

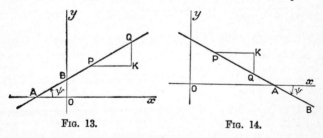

Fig. 13.   Fig. 14.

(i) In Fig. 13 the change in y is positive when the change in x is positive; the gradient of the line AB is therefore positive. The angle ψ is the positive acute angle xAB.

(ii) In Fig. 14 the change in y is negative when the change in x is positive; the gradient of the line AB is therefore negative. For the angle ψ, we may use either the negative acute angle xAB, or the positive obtuse angle xAQ

§ 23. The Gradient of a Graph.—The gradient of a graph at a point on it is defined to be *the gradient of the tangent at that point.*

We shall prove that, if y is a function of x, *the gradient of its graph at any point is equal to the value of the derived function for the value of x at that point.*

Proof.—Let m be the gradient of the graph at the point P (Fig. 15), and let PT be the tangent at P, making an angle ψ with the axis of x. Then, by definition,

$$m = \tan \psi. \qquad \text{(i)}$$

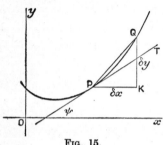

FIG. 15.

Let Q be any other point on the graph. Draw PK parallel to Ox, and QK parallel to Oy. Let (x, y) be the co-ordinates of P, and $(x + \delta x, y + \delta y)$ those of Q. Then KQ = δy, PK = δx,

$$\therefore \tan \text{KPQ} = \frac{\text{KQ}}{\text{PK}} = \frac{\delta y}{\delta x}. \qquad \text{(ii)}$$

Now, when Q → P along the curve, the position of the chord PQ approaches the tangent PT (§ 7), and hence ∠KPQ → ∠KPT. Also $\delta x \to 0$; hence, in the limit, (ii) becomes

$$\tan \text{KPT} = \lim_{\delta x \to 0} \left(\frac{\delta y}{\delta x} \right) = \frac{dy}{dx}. \qquad \text{(iii)}$$

But ∠KPT = ψ. Hence, by (i) and (iii),

$$m = \tan \psi = \frac{dy}{dx}. \qquad \text{(iv)}$$

Here m and ψ are *variables*; they depend upon the position of the point P. In § 22 they were constants, independent of the position of P.

Ex. Find the gradient of the graph of $y = x(7 - x)$, and the angle ψ, at the point where $x = 3$.

The gradient at any point of the graph is given by

$$m = \frac{dy}{dx} = 7 - 2x.$$

Hence, at the point where $x = 3$,

$$m = 7 - 2.3 = 1.$$

It follows that, at the same point, $\tan \psi = 1$,

$$\therefore \psi = 45°.$$

Examples XII.

1. Draw the graph of $y = x(4 - x)$ from $x = -1$ to $x = 5$. Also draw the tangents to the graph at the points where $x = 0, 1, 2, 3, 4$. Measure the gradients of the tangents and find their correct values by differentiation.

In Exs. 2-11, find the gradients of the graphs of the given functions at the points where x (or y) has the given value :—

2. $y = 3x^2$; $x = 2$.   **3.** $y = (2 - x)(1 + x)$; $x = 1$.

4. $y = \sqrt{x}$; $x = 1$.   **5.** $y = 3x - x^3$; $x = 0$.

6. $y = \dfrac{6}{x}$; $x = 2$.   **7.** $y = x + \dfrac{1}{x}$; $x = 1$.

8. $y^2 = x$; $y = 2$.   **9.** $x = 3y + 2y^{-1}$; $y = \frac{2}{3}$.

10. $x = y^2 - 2y$; $y = 1$.   **11.** $x = (y - 2)(y^2 - 1)$; $y = -1$.

In Exs. 12-15, find the co-ordinates of the points where the gradient is zero :—

12. $y = x^2 - 6x + 12$.   **13.** $y = \frac{1}{3}x^3 - \frac{1}{2}x^2 - 6x$.

14. $y = 4x + x^{-1} - 3$.   **15.** $y = x^5 - 5x^3 - 20x$.

In Exs. 16-20, find the range of values of x for which the gradient is (i) positive, (ii) negative :—

16. $y = x^2 - 6x$.   **17.** $y = x^3 - 12x$.   **18.** $y = x + x^{-1}$.

19. $y = x^3 - 6x^2 + 9x + 1$.   **20.** $y \equiv 4 + 12x + 3x^2 - 2x^3$.

21. If $y = 6x + 3x^2 + x^3$, show that the gradient is positive at every point.

22. If $y = ax + bx^2 + cx^3$, find the condition that the gradient should have the same sign at every point.

23. If $y = 6x - 10x^2 + 3x^3$, find the co-ordinates of the points on the graph where the gradient is equal to 2.

24. If $y = (1 - x)(x^2 + 2)$, find the angle at which the graph crosses the axis of y. Sketch the graph.

25. If $y = (x - 1)(x - 2)(x - 3)$, find the angles at which the graph crosses the co-ordinate axes. Sketch the graph.

26. If $y = 2x^2 - 7x + 10$, find the co-ordinates of the points where the tangent to the graph makes with the axis of x an angle of (i) $45°$, (ii) $-45°$.

27. If $y = x^2 - 2x + 3$, find the value of x at the point where the tangent to the graph makes $60°$ with the x-axis.

28. If y is a function of x, and a a constant, prove the following results graphically :—

     (i) $\dfrac{d}{dx}(a) = 0$,   (ii) $\dfrac{d}{dx}(y + a) = \dfrac{dy}{dx}$,   (iii) $\dfrac{d}{dx}(ay) = a\dfrac{dy}{dx}$.

§ 24. Angle of Intersection of Two Graphs.

If two curves intersect at a point P, their angle of intersection is defined to be *the angle between their tangents* at P.

Let two graphs intersect at a point P (Fig. 16). Let a be their angle of intersection, and m_1 and m_2 their gradients at **P.** We shall prove that

$$\tan a = \frac{m_1 - m_2}{1 + m_1 m_2}.$$

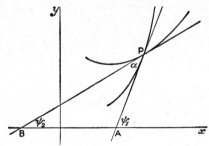

Fig. 16.

Proof.—Let PA, PB be the tangents to the two graphs at P, making angles ψ_1, ψ_2 respectively with the x-axis. Then

$$a = \angle \text{APB} = \angle x\text{AP} - \angle x\text{BP} = \psi_1 - \psi_2,$$

$$\therefore \tan a = \tan (\psi_1 - \psi_2) = \frac{\tan \psi_1 - \tan \psi_2}{1 + \tan \psi_1 \tan \psi_2} = \frac{m_1 - m_2}{1 + m_1 m_2},$$

since $\tan \psi_1 = m_1$ and $\tan \psi_2 = m_2$.

Method.—Find the co-ordinates of the points of intersection.

At each point of intersection find the gradients m_1 and m_2 of the two graphs.

Find the angles of intersection by substituting the values of m_1 and m_2 in the formula just proved.

Ex. Find the angles of intersection of the graphs of

$$y = x^3, \ y = x^2.$$

The values of x and y that satisfy the two equations

$$y = x^3, \ y = x^2,$$

are found to be $(0, 0)$ and $(1, 1)$. These are the co-ordinates of the points of intersection.

The gradients of the two graphs are given respectively by

$$m_1 = \frac{d}{dx}(x^3) = 3x^2, \quad m_2 = \frac{d}{dx}(x^2) = 2x.$$

Therefore, at the point $(0, 0)$,

$$m_1 = 0, \ m_2 = 0,$$
$$\therefore \tan a = 0, \ \therefore a = 0.$$

Hence, the two graphs *touch* one another at this point (the origin).
At the point (1, 1),

$$m_1 = 3, \quad m_2 = 2,$$

$$\therefore \tan \alpha = \frac{3 - 2}{1 + 3.2} = \frac{1}{7}, \quad \therefore \alpha = 8° 8'.$$

Hence the angle of intersection at the point (1, 1) is 8° 8'.

Examples XIII.

Find the angles of intersection of the given pairs of curves :—

1. $y = x^3$, $y = x$.	**2.** $y = 2x$, $y = x + x^3$.	**3.** $3y = x$, $y = x(x^2 - 3)$.
4. $x = 2$, $xy = 4$.	**5.** $y = x^2$, $xy = 1$.	**6.** $2y = x - 4$. $y = (x + 3)(x - 1)$.
7. $y = x^2$, $y^2 = x$.	**8.** $y^2 = 8x$, $x^2 = 27y$.	**9.** $x = 2y - y^2$, $2y = x + 4x^2$.
10. $y = mx$, $y = ax^2$.	**11.** $xy = c^2$, $y^2 = 8cx$.	**12.** $y^2 = 4a(a - x)$, $y^2 = 4b(b + x)$.

§ 25. The Normal to a Curve at a Point on it.—The *normal* to a curve, at any point P, is the line drawn through P perpendicular to the tangent at P.

In Fig. 17, let PT be the tangent, and PG the normal, at the point P. Then

$$\text{grad. of normal} = \tan x\text{GP} = -\tan \text{TGP}.$$

But, since TPG is a right-angled triangle,

$$\tan \text{TGP} = \cot \text{GTP} = \cot \psi = \frac{1}{\tan \psi} = \frac{1}{\dfrac{dy}{dx}} = \frac{dx}{dy},$$

$$\therefore \text{grad. of normal} = -\cot \psi = -\frac{dx}{dy}.$$

Thus, the gradient of the normal is *the reciprocal of the gradient of the tangent with the sign changed.*

§ 26. Equations of Tangent and Normal.—Let (x_A, y_A) be the co-ordinates of a point A on a graph.

Let $\left(\dfrac{dy}{dx}\right)_A$ = the value of $\dfrac{dy}{dx}$ at the point A

= the gradient of the tangent at A.

Now it is known from Co-ordinate Geometry that the equation

of the straight line that goes through the point (a, b) and has a gradient m is

$$y - b = m(x - a).$$

Consequently, the equation of the tangent at A is

$$y - y_A = \left(\frac{dy}{dx}\right)_A (x - x_A). \tag{1}$$

The equation of the normal at A is

$$y - y_A = -\left(\frac{dx}{dy}\right)_A (x - x_A). \tag{2}$$

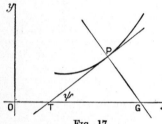

Fig. 17.

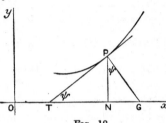

Fig. 18.

Ex. Find the equations of the tangent and normal to the graph of $y = 5x - x^2$ at the point where $x = 1$.

Let A be the point where $x = 1$. Then $x_A = 1$, $y_A = 4$.

Also, $\qquad \frac{dy}{dx} = 5 - 2x$, $\therefore \left(\frac{dy}{dx}\right)_A = 3.$

Hence the equation of the tangent at A is

$$y - 4 = 3(x - 1),$$

that is, $\qquad\qquad y = 3x + 1.$

The equation of the normal at A is

$$y - 4 = -\frac{1}{3}(x - 1),$$

that is, $\qquad\qquad x + 3y = 13.$

Examples XIV.

In Exs. 1-8, find the equations of the tangent and normal at the points where x has the given values :—

1. $y = x^2$; $x = 1$.
2. $y = x(4 - x)$; $x = 2$.
3. $y = x^3$; $x = \frac{1}{2}$.
4. $y = 3x^2 - 8x + 5$; $x = 3$.
5. $xy = 1$; $x = 1$.
6. $y = a + bx + cx^2$; $x = 0$.
7. $xy = c^2$; $x = c$.
8. $4ay = 4a^2 + x^2$; $x = 3a$.

9. Find the angle of intersection of the tangents to the curve $y = x - x^{-1}$ at the points where $x = -1$, $x = 3$.

10. Prove that the tangent to the curve $b^2y = x^2(a - x)$, at the point where $x = \frac{1}{2}a$, passes through the origin.

11. Find the co-ordinates of the points of intersection of the straight line $4x - 2y = 3$ with the parabola $y^2 = 4x$, and the equations of the tangents to the parabola at these points.

12. Prove that the graphs of $y = 2x - 3$ and $y = 10x - 2x^2 - 11$ touch one another, and find the equation of their common normal.

13. Prove that the parabolas $y = x^2 - 1$ and $y = 8x - x^2 - 9$ touch one another, and find the equations of their common tangent and common normal.

14. Prove that the graph of $y = 4 - x^2$ passes through the point (1, 3). If the normal at this point cuts the curve again in P, find the equation of the tangent at P.

15. The tangent to the curve $y = x(4 - x)^2$ at the point (3, 3) meets the curve again at P. If the tangent at P meets the curve again at Q, find the equation of the tangent at Q.

§ 27. Subnormal and Subtangent.

In Fig. 18 let PT be the tangent, PG the normal, and PN the ordinate, at P.

Then TN is called the *subtangent*, and NG the *subnormal*, at P. It is plain that

$$\text{subnormal} = \text{NG} = \text{NP} \tan \psi = y\frac{dy}{dx},$$

$$\text{subtangent} = \text{TN} = \text{NP} \cot \psi = y\frac{dx}{dy}.$$

Note.—In examples it is better to work from a rough graph than to use these formulæ.

Examples XV.

In Exs. 1-6, find the lengths of the subnormal and subtangent at the points where x has the given values :—

1. $y = 3x^2$; $x = 2$.   **2.** $y = x(5 - x)$; $x = 4$.

3. $y = \sqrt{x}$; $x = 9$.   **4.** $y = \sqrt{x} + x^{-1}$; $x = 4$.

5. $y = 12x^{-1}$; $x = 3$.   **6.** $y = 4 + 2x - x^3$; $x = 0$.

7. If P is the point where $x = 3$ on the curve $3y = 16x - 2x^2$, and if the tangent and normal at P cut the x-axis in T and G respectively, find the lengths of PT and PG.

8. The tangent to the curve $y = 5 - 2x^2$, at the point where $x = 1$, cuts the co-ordinate axes in A and B. Find the area of the triangle OAB.

9. The tangent to the curve $y = \dfrac{9}{x} + \dfrac{x}{4}$, at the point where $x = 3$, cuts the co-ordinate axes in A and B. Find the length of AB.

10. The tangent to the curve $xy = c^2$ at any point P cuts the co-ordinate axes in A and B. Prove that the point P bisects AB, and that the area of the triangle OAB is constant.

11. In the parabola $y^2 = 4ax$, prove that the subnormal at any point (x, y) is constant, and that the subtangent $= 2x$.

12. At any point (x, y) on the rectangular hyperbola $xy = c^2$, prove that the subtangent $= x$, and that the subnormal varies as $1/x^3$.

CHAPTER IV.

DIFFERENTIATION (*continued*).

§ 28. Function of a Function.

Ex. If $y = \sqrt{u}$, and $u = x^2 + 1$, then y is a function of u, and u is a function of x. Thus, y is a function of a function of x. In other words, y is a function of x through u.

We shall prove that, if y is a function of u, and u a function of x, then

$$\frac{dy}{dx} = \frac{dy}{du}\frac{du}{dx}.$$

Proof.—Let δu be the change in u, and δy the change in y, caused by a change δx in x. Then, by a rule of fractions,

$$\frac{\delta y}{\delta x} = \frac{\delta y}{\delta u} \times \frac{\delta u}{\delta x} \tag{i}$$

Now δx, δu, and δy approach zero together, and then

$$\frac{\delta y}{\delta x} \to \frac{dy}{dx}, \quad \frac{\delta y}{\delta u} \to \frac{dy}{du}, \quad \frac{\delta u}{\delta x} \to \frac{du}{dx};$$

hence (i) becomes, in the limit,

$$\frac{dy}{dx} = \frac{dy}{du}\frac{du}{dx}. \tag{1}$$

We could prove in a similar way that, if y is a function of v, v a function of u, and u a function of x, then

$$\frac{dy}{dx} = \frac{dy}{dv}\frac{dv}{du}\frac{du}{dx}. \tag{2}$$

Ex. 1. If $y = \sqrt{u}$, and $u = x^2 + 1$, find dy/dx.

$$y = \sqrt{u}, \qquad u = x^2 + 1,$$
$$\therefore \frac{dy}{du} = \frac{1}{2\sqrt{u}}, \quad \frac{du}{dx} = 2x,$$
$$\therefore \frac{dy}{dx} = \frac{dy}{du}\frac{du}{dx} = \frac{1}{2\sqrt{u}} \cdot 2x = \frac{x}{\sqrt{u}}$$
$$\therefore \frac{dy}{dx} = \frac{x}{\sqrt{(x^2 + 1)}}.$$

Ex. 2. If $y = (2x^2 - 3x + 5)^4$, find dy/dx.
Put $u = 2x^2 - 3x + 5$. Then

$$y = u^4, \qquad u = 2x^2 - 3x + 5,$$
$$\therefore \frac{dy}{du} = 4u^3, \quad \frac{du}{dx} = 4x - 3,$$
$$\therefore \frac{dy}{dx} = \frac{dy}{du}\frac{du}{dx} = 4u^3(4x - 3),$$
$$\therefore \frac{dy}{dx} = 4(2x^2 - 3x + 5)^3(4x - 3).$$

Ex. 3. If $y = \dfrac{1}{2 - 3x}$, find $\dfrac{dy}{dx}$.
Put $v = 2 - 3x$. Then

$$y = \frac{1}{v}, \qquad v = 2 - 3x,$$
$$\therefore \frac{dy}{dv} = -\frac{1}{v^2}, \quad \frac{dv}{dx} = -3,$$
$$\therefore \frac{dy}{dx} = \frac{dy}{dv}\frac{dv}{dx} = -\frac{1}{v^2}(-3) = \frac{3}{v^2}.$$
$$\therefore \frac{dy}{dx} = \frac{3}{(2 - 3x)^2}.$$

Let $y = f(u)$, where u is a function of x. Then, in place of (1) we can write

$$\frac{d}{dx}f(u) = f'(u)\frac{du}{dx}. \tag{3}$$

In particular,

$$\frac{d}{dx}(\sqrt{u}) = \frac{1}{2\sqrt{u}}\frac{du}{dx}, \tag{4}$$

$$\frac{d}{dx}\left(\frac{1}{v}\right) = -\frac{1}{v^2}\frac{dv}{dx}. \tag{5}$$

Examples XVI:

In Exs. 1-4, find dy/dx and express it in terms of x :—

1. $y = u^5$, $u = x^3 - 3x$.　　　　2. $y = u^n$, $u = ax^2 + bx + c$.
3. $y = \sqrt{u}$, $u = 4x + 5$.　　　　4. $y = \sqrt{v}$, $v = u^2 + 1$, $u = x^{-1}$.

In Exs. 5-21, differentiate the given functions :—

5. $(3x - 2)^3$.　　　　6. $(2 - x)^5$.　　　　7. $(x^3 - 3x^2 + 1)^4$.
8. $\sqrt{(4x - 1)}$.　　　　9. $\sqrt{(ax + b)}$.　　　　10. $\sqrt{(1 - 2x + 3x^2)}$.
11. $(ax + b)^n$.　　　　12. $\sqrt{(ax^2 + c)}$.　　　　13. $\sqrt{(ax^2 + bx + c)}$.
14. $\dfrac{1}{1 - x}$.　　　　15. $\dfrac{1}{2x - 3}$.　　　　16. $\dfrac{1}{ax^2 + bx + c}$.

17. $\dfrac{1}{x^3 - a^3}.$ 18. $\dfrac{1}{1 + \sqrt{x}}.$ 19. $\left(x + \dfrac{1}{x}\right)^n.$

20. $\{x - \sqrt{(1 - x^2)}\}^2.$ 21. $\sqrt{\{a^2 + (c - x)^2\}}.$

§ 29. **The Product Rule.**—If u and v are two functions of x, the differential coefficient of their product uv is given by

$$\frac{d}{dx}(uv) = u\frac{dv}{dx} + v\frac{du}{dx}. \tag{6}$$

Proof.—Put $y = uv$. Let δu, δv, δy be the changes in u, v, y caused by a change δx in x. Then, at the end of the change,

$$y + \delta y = (u + \delta u)(v + \delta v),$$
$$\therefore y + \delta y = uv + u\delta v + v\delta u + \delta u \delta v.$$

But, at the beginning of the change,

$$y = uv.$$

By subtraction,

$$\delta y = u\delta v + v\delta u + \delta u \delta v,$$

$$\therefore \frac{\delta y}{\delta x} = u\frac{\delta v}{\delta x} + v\frac{\delta u}{\delta x} + \delta u \cdot \frac{\delta v}{\delta x},$$

$$\therefore \lim_{\delta x \to 0}\left(\frac{\delta y}{\delta x}\right) = u\frac{dv}{dx} + v\frac{du}{dx} + 0 \cdot \frac{dv}{dx},$$

$$\therefore \frac{dy}{dx} = u\frac{dv}{dx} + v\frac{du}{dx}.$$

Similarly we could prove that, if u, v, w are functions of x,

$$\frac{d}{dx}(uvw) = vw\frac{du}{dx} + wu\frac{dv}{dx} + uv\frac{dw}{dx}.$$

Rule.—To differentiate a product, multiply the derivative of each factor by the other factors and add the results.

§ 30. **The Quotient Rule.**—If u and v are two functions of x, the differential coefficient of their quotient is given by

$$\frac{d}{dx}\left(\frac{u}{v}\right) = \frac{v\dfrac{du}{dx} - u\dfrac{dv}{dx}}{v^2}. \tag{7}$$

2

Proof.—Put $y = \dfrac{u}{v}$. Then $y + \delta y = \dfrac{u + \delta u}{v + \delta v}$, and by subtraction,

$$\delta y = \frac{u + \delta u}{v + \delta v} - \frac{u}{v} = \frac{v\delta u - u\delta v}{(v + \delta v)v},$$

$$\therefore \frac{\delta y}{\delta x} = \frac{v\dfrac{\delta u}{\delta x} - u\dfrac{\delta v}{\delta x}}{(v + \delta v)v}$$

Hence, when $\delta x \to 0$,

$$\frac{dy}{dx} = \frac{v\dfrac{du}{dx} - u\dfrac{dv}{dx}}{(v + 0)v} = \frac{v\dfrac{du}{dx} - u\dfrac{dv}{dx}}{v^2}$$

Ex. 1. If $y = (2x - 1)\sqrt{(3x + 2)}$, find dy/dx.

Put $\quad u = 2x - 1, \quad v = \sqrt{(3x + 2)}.$

Then $\quad \dfrac{du}{dx} = 2, \quad \dfrac{dv}{dx} = \dfrac{3}{2\sqrt{(3x + 2)}}.$

Hence, by the product rule,

$$\frac{dy}{dx} = \frac{3(2x - 1)}{2\sqrt{(3x + 2)}} + 2\sqrt{(3x + 2)},$$

$$\therefore \frac{dy}{dx} = \frac{18x + 5}{2\sqrt{(3x + 2)}}.$$

Ex. 2. If $y = \dfrac{4 - 3x}{x^2 + 2}$, find $\dfrac{dy}{dx}$.

Put $\quad u = 4 - 3x, \quad v = x^2 + 2.$

Then $\quad \dfrac{du}{dx} = -3, \quad \dfrac{dv}{dx} = 2x.$

Hence, by the quotient rule,

$$\frac{dy}{dx} = \frac{-3(x^2 + 2) - 2x(4 - 3x)}{(x^2 + 2)^2},$$

$$\therefore \frac{dy}{dx} = \frac{3x^2 - 8x - 6}{(x^2 + 2)^2}.$$

Examples XVII.

Differentiate the given functions with respect to x :—

1. $x^2(2x - 1)^4.$
2. $x(3x - 2)^3.$
3. $(2x - 1)^2(3x+1)^3.$
4. $(3 - 2x)\sqrt{x}.$
5. $x\sqrt{(x + 1)}.$
6. $(2 + x^2)\sqrt{(3-2x)}.$
7. $x^2\sqrt{(x + 1)}.$
8. $x^2\sqrt{(a^2 - x^2)}.$
9. $(2x+3)\sqrt{(x^2+4)}.$
10. $x^n(1 + x)^n.$
11. $x(1 - x)^2(x + 2)^3.$
12. $\dfrac{x}{1 - x}.$
13. $\dfrac{3x + 1}{3x - 1}.$
14. $\dfrac{1 + x^2}{1 - x^2}.$

15. $\dfrac{(x+1)^2}{x-1}$.

16. $\dfrac{2x^2+3}{1-2x}$.

17. $\dfrac{x^2+x+1}{x^2-x+1}$.

18. $\dfrac{x}{\sqrt{(1-x)}}$.

19. $\dfrac{\sqrt{(a^2-x^2)}}{x}$.

20. $\dfrac{\sqrt{a}+\sqrt{x}}{\sqrt{a}-\sqrt{x}}$.

21. $\left(\dfrac{2x-3}{3x+2}\right)^2$.

22. $\left(\dfrac{1+2x}{1-2x}\right)^{\frac{1}{2}}$.

23. $\left(\dfrac{ax+b}{cx+d}\right)^n$.

§ 31. Differentiation of x^n.—We shall now prove the rule for differentiating x^n when n is fractional or negative. The rule is the same as when n is a positive integer (§ 21), viz. :—

$$y = x^n, \ \frac{dy}{dx} = nx^{n-1}; \quad \text{or} \ \frac{d}{dx}(x^n) = nx^{n-1}.$$

Proof.—(1) Let $n = p/q$, where p and q are positive integers. Then

$$y = x^{\frac{p}{q}}, \tag{i}$$
$$\therefore y^q = x^p. \tag{ii}$$

Differentiating both sides of this equation with respect to x, we get, since p and q are positive integers,

$$qy^{q-1}\frac{dy}{dx} = px^{p-1},$$

$$\therefore \frac{dy}{dx} = \frac{px^{p-1}}{qy^{q-1}} = \frac{p}{q}\frac{x^{-1}}{y^{-1}}\frac{x^p}{y^q} = \frac{p}{q}\frac{y}{x}, \text{ by (ii)},$$

$$\therefore \frac{dy}{dx} = \frac{p}{q}x^{\frac{p}{q}-1}, \text{ by (i)}.$$

This proves the rule when n is a positive fraction.

(2) Let n be a negative integer or a negative fraction. Put $n = -m$. Then m is a positive integer or fraction, and

$$y = x^{-m} = \frac{1}{x^m}.$$

Putting $v = x^m$ in (5), § 28, we get, since m is positive,

$$\frac{dy}{dx} = -\frac{1}{x^{2m}}(mx^{m-1}) = -mx^{-m-1}.$$

This proves the rule when n is negative, and so for all values of n.

Corollary.—If u is a function of x,

$$\frac{d}{dx}(u^n) = nu^{n-1}\frac{du}{dx}. \tag{8}$$

Ex. 1. (i) $\dfrac{d}{dx}\left(\dfrac{1}{x^3}\right) = \dfrac{d}{dx}(x^{-3}) = -3x^{-4} = -\dfrac{3}{x^4}.$

(ii) $\dfrac{d}{dx}\left(\dfrac{1}{\sqrt{x}}\right) = \dfrac{d}{dx}(x^{-\frac{1}{2}}) = -\tfrac{1}{2}x^{-\frac{3}{2}}.$

Ex. 2. If $y = (x^2 + 1)^{-\frac{3}{2}}$, find dy/dx.
By the corollary, putting $u = x^2 + 1$,

$$\frac{dy}{dx} = -\frac{3}{2}(x^2 + 1)^{-\frac{5}{2}} \cdot 2x = -3x(x^2 + 1)^{-\frac{5}{2}}.$$

Ex. 3. If $y = \dfrac{x^2}{\sqrt{(1 + x^2)}}$, find $\dfrac{dy}{dx}$.

Here y, as given, is a quotient, but we shall express it as a product and use the product rule. It is often convenient to treat a quotient in this way. We write

$$y = x^2(1 + x^2)^{-\frac{1}{2}}.$$

Put $\qquad u = x^2, \qquad v = (1 + x^2)^{-\frac{1}{2}},$

$$\therefore \frac{du}{dx} = 2x, \quad \frac{dv}{dx} = -\frac{1}{2}(1 + x^2)^{-\frac{3}{2}} \cdot 2x = -x(1 + x^2)^{-\frac{3}{2}}.$$

Hence, by the product rule,

$$\frac{dy}{dx} = 2x(1 + x^2)^{-\frac{1}{2}} - x^3(1 + x^2)^{-\frac{3}{2}}.$$

$$= x(1 + x^2)^{-\frac{3}{2}}\{2(1 + x^2) - x^2\}$$

$$\therefore \frac{dy}{dx} = \frac{x(2 + x^2)}{(1 + x^2)^{3/2}}.$$

Examples XVIII.

In Exs. 1-28, differentiate the given functions :—

1. $x^{\frac{1}{2}}$, $x^{\frac{3}{2}}$, $3x^{\frac{4}{3}}$, $2\sqrt{x^5}$.

2. x^{-1}, $2x^{-2}$, $\frac{1}{3}x^{-3}$, x^{-n}.

3. $\dfrac{1}{x^2}$, $\dfrac{1}{x^3}$, $\dfrac{1}{x^4}$, $\dfrac{1}{x^n}$.

4. $\dfrac{3}{x^3}$, $\dfrac{1}{4x^4}$, $\dfrac{1}{\sqrt[3]{x}}$, $\left(\dfrac{2}{x}\right)^{\frac{1}{2}}$.

5. $x^2 + x^{-2}$.

6. $2(x^{\frac{1}{2}} + x^{\frac{3}{2}})$.

7. $(x^{\frac{1}{2}} + x^{-\frac{1}{2}})^2$.

8. $\dfrac{x^2}{4} - \dfrac{4}{x^5}$.

9. $\dfrac{2x - 3}{\sqrt{x}}$.

10. $\dfrac{2x^4 - 3x^2 - 5}{x^3}$.

11. $(x^2 - 2)^{-\frac{1}{2}}$.

12. $(3 - 2x)^{-2}$.

13. $\sqrt[3]{(3x^2 - 6x)}$.

14. $(1 - 2x)^{\frac{3}{2}}$.

15. $x^{\frac{1}{2}}(x + 2)^{\frac{1}{2}}$.

16. $\sqrt[5]{(x^5 - 5x^3)}$.

17. $\dfrac{1}{(2x - 3)^2}$.

18. $\dfrac{1}{(ax + b)^n}$.

19. $\dfrac{1}{3(2 - 3x)^3}$.

20. $\dfrac{1}{\sqrt{(1 - x^2)}}$.

21. $\dfrac{1}{\sqrt{(ax + b)}}$.

22. $\dfrac{1}{\sqrt{(x^2 + x + 1)}}$.

23. $\dfrac{x^2}{(x + 1)^2}$.

24. $\left(1 + \dfrac{1}{x^3}\right)^{\frac{3}{2}}$.

25. $\dfrac{1}{\sqrt{(2ax - x^2)}}$.

26. $\dfrac{x^3}{(3x+1)^2}.$ **27.** $\dfrac{x}{\sqrt{(a^2-x^2)}}.$ **28.** $\dfrac{x^2}{(1-x^2)^{\frac{3}{2}}}.$

29. If $y = \{x + \sqrt{(1+x^2)}\}^n$, prove that $\dfrac{dy}{dx} = \dfrac{ny}{\sqrt{(1+x^2)}}.$

30. If $pv^{1\cdot4} = C$, a constant, prove that $\dfrac{dp}{dv} = -\dfrac{1\cdot4p}{v}.$

31. If $pv^n = a$, and $v = bt^{\frac{1}{1-n}}$, express $\dfrac{dp}{dt}$ in terms of t, a, b, n; where a, b, n are constants.

32. If $y = \dfrac{x+a}{1-ax}$, prove that $\dfrac{dy}{dx} = \dfrac{1+y^2}{1+x^2}.$

33. Find the equations of the tangent and normal to the curve $y^3 = x^3$ at the point $(4, 8)$. If they intersect the x-axis in T, G respectively, prove that $TG = 26\frac{2}{3}$.

34. Find the length intercepted on the x-axis between the normals to the curves $xy = 12$, $x^2y = 36$, at their point of intersection.

35. Find the three angles of intersection of the curves whose equations are $2y = x^2$, $y(x-1) = x$.

36. Find the equations of the tangent and normal to the curve

$$y(4a^2 + x^2) = 8a^3$$

at the point where $x = 2a$.

§ **32. Successive Differentiation.**—A differential coefficient has itself a differential coefficient. We denote

$$\frac{d}{dx}\left(\frac{dy}{dx}\right) \text{ by } \frac{d^2y}{dx^2}, \quad \frac{d}{dx}\left(\frac{d^2y}{dx^2}\right) \text{ by } \frac{d^3y}{dx^3}, \cdots$$

These are called the second differential coefficient, third differential coefficient, . . . of y with respect to x.

They are also called the second derived function, third derived function, . . . and so on.

The successive derived functions of y are sometimes denoted by $y', y'', y''' \cdots$ (read "y-dash," "y-two-dash," . . .).

The successive derived functions of $f(x)$ are denoted by $f'(x)$, $f''(x), f'''(x), \cdots$

Ex. If
$$y = x^2 - 3x - 7,$$

$$y' = \frac{dy}{dx} = 2x - 3,$$

$$y'' = \frac{d^2y}{dx^2} = 2,$$

$$y''' = \frac{d^3y}{dx^3} = 0.$$

§ 33. **Derived Graphs.**—Let y be a function of x.   Then, on the graph of the function,

$$\text{the ordinate} = y, \quad \text{the gradient} = \frac{dy}{dx}.$$

The *graph of the derived function* is called *the derived graph.* The *derived graph* is therefore one in which values of the differential coefficient are plotted as ordinates.   Consequently, on the derived graph,

$$\text{the ordinate} = \frac{dy}{dx}, \quad \text{the gradient} = \frac{d^2y}{dx^2}.$$

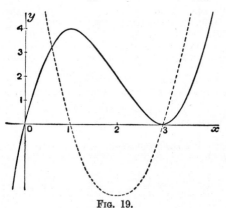

FIG. 19.

The graph of the *second derived function* is called the *second derived graph.*   The second derived graph is therefore one in which values of the second differential coefficient are plotted as ordinates.

Ex. Draw the graph, and the derived graph, of the function

$$y = x(x - 3)^2.$$

The graph of this function is the full-line curve in Fig. 19.
The derived function is found to be

$$\frac{dy}{dx} = 3(x - 1)(x - 3),$$

and its graph, the derived graph, is shown dotted in Fig. 19.
Note, in particular, that the values of x where the derived graph crosses the x-axis are the values of x where the gradient of the original graph is zero.

Examples XIX.

In Exs. 1-9, find dy/dx and d^2y/dx^2 :—

1. $y = x^3$.   **2.** $y = x^2 - 3x$.   **3.** $y = x^3 - 2x^2 + 1$.

4. $y = \sqrt{x}$.   **5.** $y = \sqrt{(3x - 1)}$.   **6.** $y = \sqrt{(x^2 + a^2)}$.

7. $y = \dfrac{1}{x}$.   **8.** $y = \dfrac{1}{2x - 5}$.   **9.** $y = \dfrac{1}{x^2 - 1}$.

In Exs. 10-15, draw the graph of the given function, and the derived graph, in one diagram :—

10. $y = x^2$.   **11.** $y = x^2 + x$.   **12.** $y = x(4 - x)$.

13. $y = x^3$.   **14.** $y = 3x - x^3$.   **15.** $y = 3x + x^3$.

In Exs. 16-19, draw the graph of the given function, the derived graph, and the second derived graph, in one diagram :—

16. $y = x^2 + 1$.   **17.** $y = 2x^3 + 3x^2 - 12x$.

18. $y = 3x - x^2$.   **19.** $y = \frac{1}{3}x^3 - 2x^2 + 5x$.

20. If $y = ax^3 + bx^2$, prove that $x^2\dfrac{d^2y}{dx^2} - 4x\dfrac{dy}{dx} + 6y = 0$.

21. If $y = ax + \dfrac{b}{x}$, prove that $x^2\dfrac{d^2y}{dx^2} + x\dfrac{dy}{dx} - y = 0$.

22. If $y = ax + b\sqrt{x} + \dfrac{c}{x}$, prove that

$$2x^3\dfrac{d^3y}{dx^3} + 5x^2\dfrac{d^2y}{dx^2} - x\dfrac{dy}{dx} + y = 0.$$

23. If $ay^2 + by + c = x$, prove that $\dfrac{d^2y}{dx^2} = -2a\left(\dfrac{dy}{dx}\right)^3$.

24. Prove that $\dfrac{d^2y}{dx^2} = -\dfrac{\dfrac{d^2x}{dy^2}}{\left(\dfrac{dx}{dy}\right)^3}$.

In Exs. 25-27, prove the given results :—

25. $\dfrac{d^3}{dx^3}\left(\dfrac{a^3}{x^3 - a^3}\right) = -\dfrac{6a^3(10x^6 + 16a^3x^3 + a^6)}{(x^3 - a^3)^4}$.

26. $\dfrac{d^n}{dx^n}\left(\dfrac{1}{x}\right) = \dfrac{(-1)^n n!}{x^{n+1}}$; $\dfrac{d^n}{dx^n}\left(\dfrac{1}{ax + b}\right) = \dfrac{(-1)^n n! \, a^n}{(ax + b)^{n+1}}$.

27. $\dfrac{d^n}{dx^n}\left(\dfrac{1}{x^2 - 1}\right) = \dfrac{(-1)^n n!}{2}\left\{\dfrac{1}{(x - 1)^{n+1}} - \dfrac{1}{(x + 1)^{n+1}}\right\}$.

CHAPTER V.

MAXIMA AND MINIMA.

§ 34. Maximum and Minimum Values of a Function.—A *maximum point* on an (x, y) graph is a point where the value of y exceeds all neighbouring values of y on the graph (e.g. the point A, Fig. 20). At such a point y is said to have a *maximum value*.

A *minimum point* is a point where the value of y is less than all neighbouring values of y (e.g. the point B). At such a point we say that y has a *minimum value*.

(Plainly a maximum value of a function is not always its greatest value, nor a minimum value its least.)

Confining ourselves to cases where the graph is a smooth curve at maximum or minimum points, we note that, at points on the graph near A, the gradient is positive to the left of A, zero at A, and negative to the right of A. At points near B, the gradient is negative to the left of B, zero at B, and positive to the right of B.

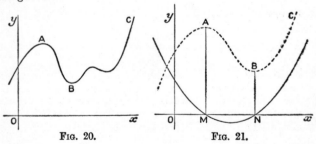

FIG. 20.   FIG. 21.

§ 35. Determination of Maximum and Minimum Values.—Let y be a function of x. We shall prove that y has a maximum value when $x = a$ if

$$\frac{dy}{dx} = 0, \text{ and } \frac{d^2y}{dx^2} \text{ is negative, when } x = a;$$

but y has a minimum value when $x = a$ if

$$\frac{dy}{dx} = 0, \text{ and } \frac{d^2y}{dx^2} \text{ is positive, when } x = a.$$

Proof.—Let the full-line curve in Fig. 21 be the graph of the *derived* function (§ 33). Let M be a point where this derived graph crosses the x-axis with a negative gradient. Let $x = a$ at M, and let A be the point on the original graph where $x = a$.

Now, at M, the ordinate of the derived graph is zero, and its gradient is negative ; therefore

$$\frac{dy}{dx} = 0, \text{ and } \frac{d^2y}{dx^2} \text{ is negative, when } x = a.$$

Also, on the derived graph near M, the *ordinate* is positive to the left of M, zero at M, and negative to the right of M. Hence, on the original graph near A, the *gradient* is positive to the left of A, zero at A, and negative to the right of A. It follows that A is a maximum point on the original graph.

Thus, y has a maximum value when $x = a$ if

$$\frac{dy}{dx} = 0, \text{ and } \frac{d^2y}{dx^2} \text{ is negative, when } x = a.$$

The first part of the theorem is now proved. We could prove the second part in a similar way, showing that to the point N, where the derived graph crosses the x-axis with a positive gradient, corresponds a minimum point B on the original graph. Hence the rule :—

First Rule for maximum and minimum values of y :—

Find $\frac{dy}{dx}$ and $\frac{d^2y}{dx^2}$. Solve the equation $\frac{dy}{dx} = 0$, and consider its roots. These are the values of x where the gradient is zero.

For each of these values of x, calculate the corresponding value of y, and examine the sign of d^2y/dx^2. If the sign is $+$, the corresponding value of y is a maximum; if the sign is $-$, the corresponding value of y is a minimum.

Ex. Find the maximum and minimum values of y when

$$y = x^3 - 6x^2 + 9x + 1. \tag{i}$$

Here $$\frac{dy}{dx} = 3x^2 - 12x + 9, \tag{ii}$$

$$\frac{d^2y}{dx^2} = 6x - 12. \tag{iii}$$

From (ii), $dy/dx = 0$ when

$$3(x^2 - 4x + 3) = 0,$$
$$\therefore\ 3(x - 1)(x - 3) = 0,$$
$$\therefore\ x = 1 \text{ or } 3.$$

Putting $x = 1$ in (i) and (iii), we get

$$y = 5;\ \frac{d^2y}{dx^2} = -6, \text{ which is negative.}$$

Putting $x = 3$ in (i) and (iii), we get

$$y = 1;\ \frac{d^2y}{dx^2} = +6, \text{ which is positive.}$$

Hence
$$y_{max} = 5, \text{ when } x = 1,$$
$$y_{min} = 1, \text{ when } x = 3,$$

where y_{max} and y_{min} denote maximum and minimum values of **y**.

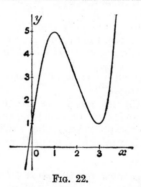

Fig. 22.

§ 36. Application to Sketching Graphs.

—In sketching **a** graph it is often helpful (1) to find the co-ordinates of the maximum and minimum points; (2) to examine the *sign of the gradient* for various values of x.

Ex. Sketch the graph of the function

$$y = x^3 - 6x^2 + 9x + 1.$$

This is the same function as in the last example.

We found the co-ordinates of the maximum and minimum points to be (1, 5), a maximum point, and (3, 1), a minimum point.

Also, from (ii) above, we have

$$\frac{dy}{dx} = 3(x - 1)(x - 3).$$

Now the factors $(x - 1)$, $(x - 3)$ are both positive when $x > 3$. Hence the gradient is positive when $x > 3$.

Both factors are negative when $x < 1$. Hence the gradient is positive when $x < 1$.

The factor $(x - 1)$ is positive, but $(x - 3)$ is negative, when x is between 1 and 3. Hence the gradient is negative when $1 < x < 3$. The graph is shown in Fig. 22.

*Examples XX.

In Exs. 1-15, find the maximum and (or) minimum values of the given functions and the corresponding values of x :—

1. $4x - x^2$. 2. $x^2 + x + 1$. 3. $x^2 - 3x + 1$.
4. $3x - x^3$. 5. $x^2(3 - x)$. 6. $(x + 3)(7 - x)$.
7. $\dfrac{1}{x} - \dfrac{1}{x^2}$. 8. $x^2 + \dfrac{16}{x}$. 9. $x + \dfrac{4}{x + 2}$.
10. $2x^3 - 15x^2 + 36x - 20$. 11. $(x - 2)(x - 5)^2$.
12. $\frac{1}{3}x^3 - \frac{1}{2}x^2 - 6x + \frac{1}{2}$. 13. $(9 - x)(15 + x^2)$.
14. $3x^4 - 4x^3 - 12x^2 + 2$. 15. $x(x + 1)(x - 2)$.

In Exs. 16-24, find the co-ordinates of the maximum and (or) minimum points, and sketch the graphs of the given functions :—

16. $2x^3 + 3x^2 - 12x$. 17. $20 + 3x - 4x^2 - x^3$.
18. $2x^3 - 3x^2 - 6$. 19. $x^3 - 3x^2 + 6x + 2$.
20. $(x - a)^2(b - x)$. 21. $x^4 - 4x^3 - 2x^2 + 12x + 3$.
22. $x + \dfrac{1}{x}$. 23. $\dfrac{1}{x^2} - \dfrac{2}{x^3}$. 24. $x + \dfrac{4}{x^2}$.

25. Prove that $x\sqrt{(4x - x^2)}$ has a maximum value when $x = 3$.
26. Prove that $x^2\sqrt{(9 - x^2)}$ has a maximum value when $x = \sqrt{6}$.
27. If $y = ax^4 + bx^3 + x^2$, and if $y = 0$ and $d^2y/dx^2 = 0$ when $x = 1$, find a and b. Sketch the (x, y) graph and find its greatest positive gradient between $x = 0$ and $x = 1$.
28. If $f(x)$ is a function of x, and if $f'(a) = 0$, show that
   (i) $f(a)$ is a maximum value of $f(x)$ if $f''(a) < 0$,
   (ii) $f(a)$ is a minimum value of $f(x)$ if $f''(a) > 0$.
29. Draw the graph of $y = x^3 - 3x + 1$ carefully to scale, and hence write down approximations to the roots of the equation

$$x^3 - 3x + 1 = 0.$$

30. Draw the graph of $y = x^3 - x + 1$ carefully to scale, and hence approximate to the real root of the equation

$$x^3 - x + 1 = 0.$$

§ 37. **Stationary Points and Turning Points.**—A *stationary point* on a graph is any point where the gradient is zero. A *turning point* is a maximum or minimum point. A stationary point is not necessarily a turning point; e.g. on the graph of $y = x^3$ the origin is a stationary, but not a turning, point.

*Exs. XXII may be worked after Exs. XX, if desired.

The rule of § 35 fails to decide the *kind* of stationary point in case $d^2y/dx^2 = 0$. The following rule applies to this exceptional case, and, in fact, to *all* cases :—

Second Rule for maximum and minimum values of y :—

Find $\dfrac{dy}{dx}$. Solve the equation $\dfrac{dy}{dx} = 0$, and consider its roots. Let a be one of its roots. Then y has a stationary value when $x = a$.

To decide the *kind* of stationary point, examine the *sign* of dy/dx when x is slightly less than a, and when x is slightly greater than a.

If the sign changes from $+$ to $-$, the point is a maximum point ; if the sign changes from $-$ to $+$ the point is a minimum point ; if the sign does not change, the point is neither a maximum nor a minimum point, but a point of inflexion (see § 70).

Ex. Given that $\dfrac{dy}{dx} = (x-1)(x-2)^2$, describe the shape of the (x, y) graph near the points where $x = 1$ and $x = 2$.

(Here we use the sign $<$ to mean " slightly less than," and the sign $<$ to mean " slightly greater than.")

Firstly, consider values of x near $x = 1$.

When $\qquad x < 1$, sign of gradient $= (-)(-)^2 = -$,

$\qquad\qquad x > 1$, sign of gradient $= (+)(-)^2 = +$;

hence, $x = 1$ gives a minimum point.

Secondly, consider values of x near $x = 2$.

When $\qquad x < 2$, sign of gradient $= (+)(-)^2 = +$,

$\qquad\qquad x > 2$, sign of gradient $= (+)(+)^2 = +$;

hence, $x = 2$ gives neither a maximum nor a minimum point, but a point where the graph is similar in shape to the graph of $y = x^3$ near the origin.

Examples XXI.

In Exs. 1-10, find the co-ordinates of the stationary points on the graphs of the given functions. State which of them are maximum or minimum points, and sketch the graphs :—

1. $y = x^3$. 2. $y = (x-2)^3$. 3. $y = 2 + 4x^3 + 3x^4$.
4. $y = x^4$. 5. $y = 2 - x^5$. 6. $y = x(4-x)^3$.
7. $y = x^3 - 3x^2 + 3x$. 8. $y = 2x^5 - 5x^4 + 20$.
9. $y = (x-4)^2(x+1)^3$. 10. $y = x^6 - 3x^4 + 3x^2 + 2$.

11. If $dy/dx = x^3(x^2-1)(x-1)$, prove that y has a minimum value when $x = 0$, and a maximum value when $x = -1$.

12. If $dy/dx = x^2(x-1)(x-2)^2(x-3)^3$, describe the shape of the (x, y) graph near the points where $x = 0$, $x = 1$, $x = 2$, $x = 3$.

§ 38. Applications.—Before giving practical examples of maxima and minima, we may notice the following points :—

(1) Maximum and minimum values of a *continuous* function occur alternately.

This is plain from the graph of a continuous function.

(2) If a function has only one turning value, it may be obvious from the nature of the problem whether it is a maximum or a minimum value.

(3) If $y = av$, where a is a positive constant, the values of x for which v has maximum (or minimum) values are the same as those for which y has maximum (or minimum) values. Consequently, to find these values of x, we may differentiate v instead of y.

(4) If $y = 1/v$, then y has a maximum value when v has a minimum value, and vice versa.

(5) If $y = \sqrt{u}$, then y has stationary values when u has *positive* stationary values.

(6) If y is a function of u, and u a function of x, since $\dfrac{dy}{dx} = \dfrac{dy}{du}\dfrac{du}{dx}$ it follows that $dy/dx = 0$ when either $dy/du = 0$ or $du/dx = 0$. Hence both these equations must be examined in finding maximum and minimum values of y as a function of x.

Examples XXII.

(In this set of Examples, the function that has to be differentiated is given. In the next two sets it has to be constructed.)

1. Assume that, when a stone is thrown upwards with a speed of 60 miles an hour, its height, h feet, after t seconds, is given by $h = 88t - 16t^2$. How high does it rise ?

2. If $h = ut - \frac{1}{2}gt^2$, where u and g are positive constants, find the maximum value of h.

3. Assume that the turning effect of a ship's rudder is proportional to $x(1 - x^2)$, where $x = \cos\theta$, and θ = the angle of inclination of the rudder to the fore and aft line. For what value of θ is the turning effect greatest ?

4. The length of time, T years, for which a comet remains within the earth's orbit is given by

$$\text{T} = (2x + 1)\sqrt{(2 - 2x)} \div 3\pi,$$

where x is a certain variable. Find the maximum value of T.

5. The power output of a wireless valve is proportional to $z/(z + \text{R})^2$, where z is a variable impedance, and R the valve resistance. Show that the power output is a maximum when $z = \text{R}$.

6. The amplification of a wireless valve in a certain circuit is proportional to $x/(x^2 + a)$, where x is a variable, and a a constant. Prove that the amplification is greatest when $x = \sqrt{a}$.

7. The efficiency E of a screw is given by

$$\text{E} = \frac{t(1 - \mu t)}{\mu + t},$$

where t = the tangent of the angle of pitch, and μ = the coefficient of friction (constant). For what value of t is E a maximum ?

§ 39. In the next two sets of examples it is necessary first to construct the function that has to be differentiated.

Method.—Let y be a variable whose maximum or minimum value is to be found.

Choose a suitable independent variable.

Express y as a function of this variable.

Find the turning values of y in the usual way.

Note.—A judicious choice of the independent variable may make the rest of the work lighter.

Ex. Find the maximum volume of a cone whose slant side has a constant length a.

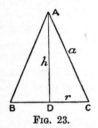

Fig. 23.

Let h be the height, r the base radius, and V the volume of the cone. Then

$$V = \tfrac{1}{3}\pi r^2 h.$$

From the right-angled triangle ADC, $r^2 = a^2 - h^2$,

$$\therefore \ V = \tfrac{1}{3}\pi h(a^2 - h^2), \tag{i}$$

$$\therefore \ \frac{dV}{dh} = \tfrac{1}{3}\pi(a^2 - 3h^2), \quad \frac{d^2V}{dh^2} = -2\pi h.$$

It follows that $dV/dh = 0$ when $3h^2 = a^2$, and therefore when $h = a/\sqrt{3}$ since h must be positive.

Putting $h = a/\sqrt{3}$ in (i), we find

$$V_{max} = \frac{2\pi a^3}{9\sqrt{3}},$$

this being a maximum value, since d^2V/dh^2 is negative.

In this problem h has been taken as the independent variable. Had r been so taken, the differentiation would not have been as easy.

Examples XXIII.

1. Find the maximum area of a rectangular piece of ground that can be enclosed by 100 yds. of fencing.

2. If the sum of two variable numbers is constant, prove that their product is a maximum when they are equal.

3. Find the minimum value of the sum of a positive number and its reciprocal.

4. If the product of two positive variable numbers is constant, prove that their sum is a minimum when they are equal.

5. An oblong sheet of cardboard is 2 ft. long by 9 ins. wide. Equal squares are cut out at the corners and the flaps are turned up to form an open box. Find its maximum volume.

6. If $z = xy$, and $2x + 3y = 12$, find the maximum value of z.

7. If $z = 4x + 3y$, and $xy = 3$, and x and y are positive, find the minimum value of z.

8. A Post Office regulation is that the sum of the length and girth of a parcel must not exceed 6 ft. What is the volume of the largest parcel, with square ends, that can be sent by post ?   Could a larger parcel be sent if its ends were circular ?

9. A lever, weighing 3 lbs. per foot, turns about one end A.   A vertical force is applied at the other end to raise a weight of 1 cwt. attached at a point 2 ft. from A.   For what length of lever will the least force be required ?

10. If the cost of a voyage, £C per hour, is given by

$$C = 16 + \frac{v^3}{1000},$$

where v is the speed of the ship in knots, what is the most economical speed for a given voyage ?

11. A tin box, with a square base and open at the top, is made to hold 4 cub. ft.   Find the least possible area of sheet tin that could be used in its construction.

12. A wireless mast tapers uniformly from the ground to the top, where its diameter is D.   When a horizontal pull is applied at the top, the greatest stress in a cross-section x ft. from the top varies as x/y^3, where y is the diameter of the section.   Prove that the tendency to break is greatest where $y = 1\frac{1}{2}$D.

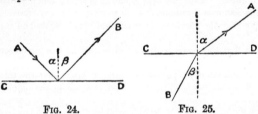

Fig. 24.   Fig. 25.

13. If two centres of heat are 10 ft. apart, and one is eight times as hot as the other, where will be the coolest point between them ?   [The intensity of heat varies inversely as the square of the distance from the centre of heat.]

14. A ship steaming due north at 16 m.p.h. sights another ship, right ahead, 2 miles off, steaming due east at 12 m.p.h.   What will be the shortest distance between them if they keep on their courses ?

15. Find the greatest breadth, parallel to the y-axis, of the loop of the curve $y^2 = x^2(3 - x)$.

16. If r is the distance from the origin to the point (x, y) on the straight line $3x + 4y = 5$, express r^2 in terms of x, and deduce the minimum value of r.

17. Find the shortest distance from the origin to a point on the curve $xy^2 = 1 - x$.

18. A lamp L is x ft. above the centre C of a circular table of diameter 5 ft.   Find x when the illumination of the table at a point A, 6 ins. from the edge, is a maximum.   [The intensity of illumination at A is proportional to $\cos \theta / \mathrm{AL}^2$, where $\theta = \angle$CLA.]

19. Fig. 24 represents a ray of light leaving the point A and reaching the point B, after reflection at the surface CD. Prove that $\alpha = \beta$, assuming that light travels along the path that makes the time a minimum.

20. Fig. 25 represents a ray of light leaving the point B beneath the water surface CD, and reaching the point A in air. If the speed of light is ι in air, and v in water, prove that

$$\frac{\sin \alpha}{\sin \beta} = \frac{u}{v}$$

on the same assumption as in the last example.

Examples XXIV.

1. A rectangle is inscribed in a triangle, two of the corners of the rectangle lying in the base of the triangle. Prove that the maximum area of the rectangle is half that of the triangle.

2. A given length of wire is bent into the shape of the boundary of a sector of a circle. When the area enclosed is a maximum, prove that the angle of the sector is 2 radians.

3. Prove that the rectangle of maximum area inscribed in a circle is a square.

4. Prove that the isosceles triangle of minimum area circumscribed to a circle is equilateral.

5. If the volume of a cylinder is constant, prove that the total area of its surface is a minimum when the height is equal to the diameter of the base.

6. Find the volume of the largest cylinder that can be cut from a solid sphere of radius a.

7. Find the volume of the largest cone that can be inscribed in a sphere of radius a.

8. Find the minimum volume of a cone circumscribed to a sphere of radius a.

9. A sector is cut out of a circular piece of canvas, and the bounding radii of the part that remains are drawn together to form a conical tent. What must be the angle of the sector cut out, if the tent has maximum volume ?

10. A straight line passes through the point (2, 3) and cuts the coordinate axes in A and B. Find the minimum area of the triangle AOB.

11. F is a fixed point in the angle bounded by two lines AB, AC. A line through F cuts AB, AC in P, Q respectively. Prove that the area of the triangle APQ is a minimum when F bisects PQ.

12. PQ and MN are two chords of the parabola $y^2 = 4ax$, both parallel to the axis of y; and PS, QR are the perpendiculars from P, Q on MN. If MN is fixed, find the maximum area of the rectangle PQRS.

§ 40. Maximum and Minimum Values of a Quotient.

Let $\qquad y = \dfrac{u}{v}, \qquad z = v\dfrac{du}{dx} - u\dfrac{dv}{dx}.$

Then, by the quotient rule, $\quad \dfrac{dy}{dx} = \dfrac{z}{v^2}$ $\qquad\qquad$ (i)

Hence, except when z and v vanish together, i.e. when z and v have a common factor, it follows that $dy/dx = 0$ when $z = 0$, and the sign of dy/dx is always the same as the sign of z (since v^2, being a square, is necessarily positive).

Hence, z *can replace* dy/dx *in the rule of* § 37.

Again, differentiating (i) by the product rule, we get

$$\frac{d^2y}{dx^2} = \frac{1}{v^2}\frac{dz}{dx} + z\left(-\frac{2}{v^3}\frac{dv}{dx}\right),$$

and hence, when $z = 0$,

$$\frac{d^2y}{dx^2} = \frac{1}{v^2}\frac{dz}{dx}. \qquad\qquad (ii)$$

From (i) and (ii), since v^2 is necessarily positive, $dy/dx = 0$ when $z = 0$ (except when z and v vanish together), and the sign of d^2y/dx^2 is the same as that of dz/dx.

Hence, z *and* $\dfrac{dz}{dx}$ *can replace* $\dfrac{dy}{dx}$ *and* $\dfrac{d^2y}{dx^2}$ *in* § 35.

Ex. Find the maximum and minimum values of y when

$$y = \frac{x}{x^2 - 3x + 4}. \qquad\qquad (i)$$

Put $\qquad\qquad u = x, \qquad v = x^2 - 3x + 4,$

$$\therefore \frac{du}{dx} = 1, \quad \frac{dv}{dx} = 2x - 3,$$

$$\therefore z = v\frac{du}{dx} - u\frac{dv}{dx} = (x^2 - 3x + 4) - x(2x - 3),$$

$$\therefore z = 4 - x^2, \qquad\qquad (ii)$$

$$\therefore \frac{dz}{dx} = -2x. \qquad\qquad (iii)$$

From (ii), $z = 0$ when $x = 2$ or -2.

Putting $x = 2$ in (i) and (iii), we get

$$y = 1; \frac{dz}{dx} = -4, \text{ which is negative.}$$

Putting $x = -2$ in (i) and (iii), we get

$$y = -\frac{1}{7}; \frac{dz}{dx} = +4, \text{ which is positive.}$$

Hence $\qquad\qquad y_{max} = 1$, when $x = 2$,

$\qquad\qquad\qquad y_{min} = -\frac{1}{7}$, when $x = -2$.

§ 41. Graph of a Quotient.—For the purpose of sketching the graph of $y = u/v$, where u and v are functions of x, note the following points :—

(1) $y = 0$ when $u = 0$. Therefore, solve the equation $u = 0$. If the roots are real, they are the values of x where the graph crosses the x-axis. If this equation has no real roots, the graph does not cross the x-axis anywhere.

(2) $y = \infty$ when $v = 0$. Therefore, solve the equation $v = 0$. If the roots are real, they are the values of x where the graph has vertical asymptotes. If this equation has no real roots, there are no vertical asymptotes.

(3) Examine the value of y when $x \to \infty$.

(4) Find the co-ordinates of the stationary points (if any).

(5) Examine the sign of the gradient for various values of x. This is the same as the sign of z [see (i), § 40].

(6) Find the value of y when $x = 0$. This is the value of y where the graph crosses the y-axis.

(7) Find the value of x where the graph crosses the horizontal asymptote (if there is one).

(8) If the general shape of the curve is still in doubt, calculate the co-ordinates of a few points on it.

Ex. 1. Draw the graph of

$$y = \frac{x^2 - 2x + 3}{x^2 + 2x - 3}. \tag{i}$$

Put $\qquad u = x^2 - 2x + 3, \qquad v = x^2 + 2x - 3.$
Then we find

$$z = v\frac{du}{dx} - u\frac{dv}{dx} = 4x(x - 3), \tag{ii}$$

$$\therefore \frac{dz}{dx} = 4(2x - 3). \tag{iii}$$

The equation $u = 0$ is

$$x^2 - 2x + 3 = 0,$$

which has no real roots, so the graph does not cut the x-axis.
The equation $v = 0$ is

$$x^2 + 2x - 3 = 0,$$
$$\therefore x = 1 \text{ or } - 3 ;$$

these are the values of x where the graph has vertical asymptotes.

From (i), we find $y \to 1$ when $x \to \infty$ (see § 6). Hence $y = 1$ is a horizontal asymptote.

From (i), (ii), and (iii), we find (see § 40) that the co-ordinates of the stationary points are :—

$$x = 0, y = -1, \text{ a maximum point;}$$
$$x = 3, y = \tfrac{1}{2}, \text{ a minimum point.}$$

From (ii), the gradient is positive when $x > 3$, positive when $x < 0$, negative when $0 < x < 3$.

The value of y when $x = 0$ is -1.

The value of x where the graph crosses the horizontal asymptote $y = 1$ is given by

$$1 = \frac{x^2 - 2x + 3}{x^2 + 2x - 3},$$

which gives $x = \frac{3}{2}$.

The graph can now be sketched (Fig. 26).

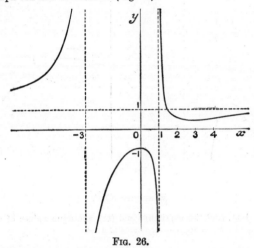

Fig. 26.

Ex. 2. Draw the curves

$$(1)\ \ y = \frac{x^2(1 - x)}{1 + x}, \qquad (2)\ \ y^2 = \frac{x^2(1 - x)}{1 + x}.$$

(1) Put $\qquad u = x^2(1 - x), \qquad v = 1 + x.$

Then we find

$$z = v\frac{du}{dx} - u\frac{dv}{dx} = -2x(x^2 + x - 1). \qquad \text{(i)}$$

The equation $u = 0$ is

$$x^2(1 - x) = 0,$$
$$\therefore\ x = 0,\ 0,\ 1.$$

Hence, the curve touches the x-axis at $x = 0$, and cuts it at $x = 1$.

The equation $v = 0$ is

$$1 + x = 0,$$
$$\therefore\ x = -1.$$

Hence there is one vertical asymptote, $x = -1$.

When $x \to \infty,\ y \doteq -x^2.$

From (i), y has turning values when $x = 0$, $x = \frac{1}{2}(-1 \pm \sqrt{5})$.
The graph is shown by the full-line curve in Fig. 27.

(2) The second graph is the dotted curve in the same figure. It can be sketched by plotting the square roots of the positive ordinates of the first graph (see § 12).

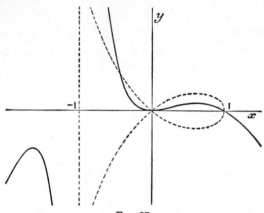

Fig. 27.

Examples XXV.

In Exs. 1-11, find the maximum and (or) minimum values of the given functions, and the corresponding values of x :—

1. $\dfrac{4x - 3}{x^2 + 1}$.

2. $\dfrac{3}{x^2 - x + 1}$.

3. $\dfrac{x^2}{x^2 - 2x + 3}$.

4. $\dfrac{(x + 1)^2}{x - 1}$.

5. $\dfrac{x^2 + x + 1}{x + 1}$.

6. $\dfrac{2x - a - b}{x^2 - ab}$.

7. $\dfrac{36}{x(3 - x)(x - 8)}$.

8. $\dfrac{2x^3 + 2x^2 - 5x + 3}{2x^2 + 3}$.

9. $\dfrac{x^3 + x}{x^4 + 1}$.

10. $\dfrac{x^3 - x}{(x^2 + 1)^2}$.

11. $\dfrac{x^3 + x^2 + x}{x^4 - x^2 + 1}$.

[*Hint.*—In Exs. 9, 10, 11, first divide numerator and denominator by x^2; then make the substitution that suggests itself.]

In Exs. 12-17, draw the graphs of the given functions :—

12. $\dfrac{1 - x^2}{1 + x^2}$.

13. $\dfrac{2x}{1 + x^2}$.

14. $\dfrac{x^2 + x + 1}{x^2 - x + 1}$.

15. $\dfrac{3x - 5}{x^2 - 1}$.

16. $\dfrac{4x^2}{(x + 2)^2}$.

17. $\dfrac{2x^2 - 3x - 3}{x^2 - 3x + 2}$.

18. If $y = \dfrac{4x}{x+1} + \dfrac{x}{x-1}$, prove that the value of y cannot lie between $\frac{1}{2}$ and $4\frac{1}{2}$ for any value of x.

19. If $y = \dfrac{2x^2 + 3x + 6}{x^2 + 2x + 4}$, prove that no two values of y can differ by more than $\frac{2}{3}$, and find the minimum value of y.

20. Draw the curves (i) $y = \dfrac{x^2(x+1)}{x-1}$, (ii) $y^2 = \dfrac{x^2(x+1)}{x-1}$.

21. Draw the curves (i) $y = \dfrac{x^3}{x+1}$, (ii) $y^2 = \dfrac{x^3}{x+1}$.

22. Draw the curves (i) $y = \dfrac{x^3}{x-1}$, (ii) $y^2 = \dfrac{x^3}{x^2-1}$.

23. Draw the curves (i) $y = \dfrac{x^2}{x^2+1}$, (ii) $y^2 = \dfrac{x^2}{x^2+1}$.

24. Draw the general shape of the curve $\dfrac{a^2}{x^2} - \dfrac{b^2}{y^2} + 1 = 0$.

CHAPTER VI.

TRIGONOMETRIC FUNCTIONS.

§ 42. Periodic Functions.—If $f(x)$ possesses the property that
$$f(x + T) = f(x),$$
in words : the value of the function $f(x)$ remains the same whenever the constant T is added to the value of the variable x, then $f(x)$ is called a *periodic* function, with period T.

Trigonometric functions are periodic functions.

In the Calculus angles are usually measured in radians.

Ex. Since
$$\sin (x + 2\pi) = \sin x, \qquad \cos (x + 2\pi) = \cos x,$$
the functions $\sin x$ and $\cos x$ have the period 2π. This is the smallest period of $\sin x$ and $\cos x$.

Since
$$\tan (x + \pi) = \tan x,$$
the function $\tan x$ has the period π. This is its smallest period.

Note that the period of $\tan x$ is half that of $\sin x$ and $\cos x$.

§ 43. Graphs of Periodic Functions.—If $f(x)$ is a periodic function, with period T, the graph of $f(x)$ can be drawn for all values of x when the part from $x = 0$ to $x = T$ has been drawn.

For the parts from $x = T$ to $x = 2T$, from $x = 2T$ to $x = 3T$, from $x = 3T$ to $x = 4T$, . . . are repetitions of the part from $x = 0$ to $x = T$.

The graphs of
$$y = \sin x, \qquad y = \cos x, \qquad y = \tan x,$$
are shown in Figs. 28, 29, 30, respectively.

Note that $\cos x$ is an *even* function, while $\sin x$ and $\tan x$ are *odd* functions (§§ 3, 4).

The functions cosec x, sec x, cot x, are defined by
$$\operatorname{cosec} x = \frac{1}{\sin x}, \quad \sec x = \frac{1}{\cos x}, \quad \cot x = \frac{1}{\tan x}.$$

We could, therefore, sketch the graphs of cosec x, sec x, and

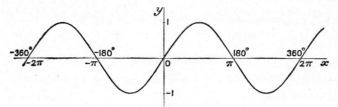

Fɪɢ. 28.—$y = \sin x.$

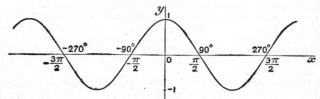

Fɪɢ. 29.—$y = \cos x.$

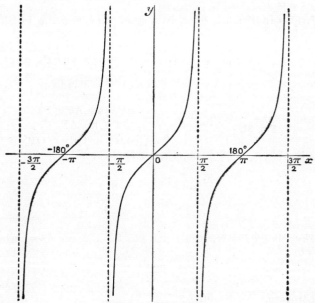

Fɪɢ. 30.—$y = \tan x.$

cot x, by plotting the reciprocals of the ordinates of the graphs of sin x, cos x, tan x, respectively (see § 11).

Examples XXVI.

Find the smallest periods of the given functions, and sketch their graphs:—

1. $y = \sin 2x$.
2. $y = \sin 3x$.
3. $y = \sin(ax + b)$.
4. $y = \sin \frac{1}{2}x$.
5. $y = \tan 2x$.
6. $y = \tan(ax + b)$.
7. $y = \operatorname{cosec} x$.
8. $y = \sec x$.
9. $y = \cot x$.
10. $y = \sin^2 x$. [Square the ordinates on the graph of sin x.]
11. $y = \sin^3 x$. [Cube the ordinates on the graph of sin x.]
12. $y = \cos^2 x$.
13. $y = 1 + \cos^3 x$.
14. $y = \tan^2 x$.
15. $y = \dfrac{\sin x}{\sin x - \cos x}$.
16. $y = \dfrac{\sin x - \cos x}{\sin x + \cos x}$.

§ 44. A trigonometric limit.

—We shall prove that
$$\lim_{\theta \to 0}\left(\frac{\sin \theta}{\theta}\right) = 1,$$
where θ is measured in radians.

Proof.—In Fig. 31, let A be a fixed point, and P a variable point, on the circumference of a circle, centre O. Draw PN perpendicular to OA, and PT perpendicular to OP.

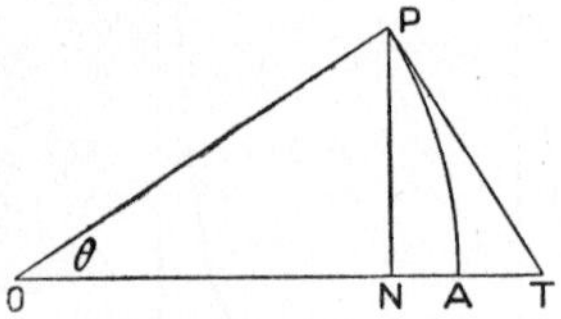

Let $\angle$AOP $= \theta$ radians. Then, if $\theta < \frac{1}{2}\pi$,
$$NP < \text{arc AP} < PT,$$
$$\therefore \frac{NP}{OP} < \frac{\text{arc AP}}{OP} < \frac{PT}{OP},$$

Fig. 31.

that is,
$$\sin \theta < \theta < \tan \theta,$$
$$\therefore \frac{1}{\sin \theta} > \frac{1}{\theta} > \frac{\cos \theta}{\sin \theta},$$
$$\therefore 1 > \frac{\sin \theta}{\theta} > \cos \theta.$$

Thus sin θ/θ lies between 1 and cos θ. But cos $\theta \to 1$ when $\theta \to 0$,
$$\therefore \lim_{\theta \to 0}\left(\frac{\sin \theta}{\theta}\right) = 1. \tag{1}$$

Corollary. $$\lim_{\theta \to 0}\left(\frac{1 - \cos \theta}{\theta^2}\right) = \tfrac{1}{2}. \tag{2}$$

For, by trigonometry,

$$\frac{1 - \cos \theta}{\theta^2} = \frac{2 \sin^2 \frac{1}{2}\theta}{\theta^2} = \frac{1}{2}\left(\frac{\sin \frac{1}{2}\theta}{\frac{1}{2}\theta}\right)^2,$$

$$\therefore \lim_{\theta \to 0}\left(\frac{1 - \cos \theta}{\theta^2}\right) = \frac{1}{2} \cdot 1^2 = \frac{1}{2}, \text{ by (1)}.$$

Examples XXVII.

In Exs. 1-8, find the limits of the given functions when the variable approaches the given values :—

1. $\dfrac{\sin 3\theta}{\theta}$, $(\theta \to 0)$.   **2.** $\dfrac{\tan \theta}{\theta}$, $(\theta \to 0)$.   **3.** $\dfrac{\sin ax}{\sin bx}$, $(x \to 0)$.

4. $\dfrac{\sin nx}{x}$, $(x \to 0)$.   **5.** $\dfrac{\sin^{-1}x}{x}$, $(x \to 0)$.   **6.** $x \sin \dfrac{\pi}{x}$, $(x \to \infty)$.

7. $\dfrac{\sin 2\theta}{\sin \theta}$, $(\theta \to \pi)$.   **8.** $\dfrac{\cos \theta}{\frac{1}{2}\pi - \theta}$, $(\theta \to \frac{1}{2}\pi)$.   **9** $\dfrac{1 - \cos 4\theta}{\theta^2}$, $(\theta \to 0)$.

In Exs. 10-17 prove the given approximations (see § 8), θ being a small angle in radians :—

10. $\tan \theta \doteqdot \theta$.   **11.** $\sin n\theta \doteqdot n\theta$.   **12.** $\cos (\frac{1}{2}\pi - \theta) \doteqdot \theta$.
13. $\cos \theta \doteqdot 1 - \frac{1}{2}\theta^2$.   **14.** $\sin \theta \doteqdot \tan \theta$.   **15.** $\cot (\frac{1}{2}\pi - \theta) \doteqdot \theta$.
16. $\sin 3\theta - \sin \theta \doteqdot 2\theta$.   **17.** $\cos 3\theta - \cos \theta \doteqdot -4\theta^2$.

§ 45. Differentiation of Trigonometric Functions.—Let x be an angle measured in radians.

We shall prove the first four of the following results, leaving the last two to the reader :—

$$y = \sin x, \qquad \frac{dy}{dx} = \cos x. \tag{1}$$

$$y = \cos x, \qquad \frac{dy}{dx} = -\sin x. \tag{2}$$

$$y = \tan x, \qquad \frac{dy}{dx} = \frac{1}{\cos^2 x} = \sec^2 x. \tag{3}$$

$$y = \sec x, \qquad \frac{dy}{dx} = \frac{\sin x}{\cos^2 x} = \sec x \tan x. \tag{4}$$

$$y = \cot x, \qquad \frac{dy}{dx} = \frac{-1}{\sin^2 x} = -\operatorname{cosec}^2 x. \tag{5}$$

$$y = \operatorname{cosec} x, \qquad \frac{dy}{dx} = \frac{-\cos x}{\sin^2 x} = -\operatorname{cosec} x \cot x. \tag{6}$$

Proof of (1).—Following the steps of the process for differentiating from first principles (§ 20), we have

$$y + \delta y = \sin (x + \delta x), \quad y = \sin x.$$

By subtraction,

$$\delta y = \sin (x + \delta x) - \sin x$$
$$= 2 \cos (x + \tfrac{1}{2}\delta x) \sin (\tfrac{1}{2}\delta x), \text{ by Trigonometry,}$$
$$\therefore \frac{\delta y}{\delta x} = \cos (x + \tfrac{1}{2}\delta x) \frac{2 \sin (\tfrac{1}{2}\delta x)}{\delta x}$$
$$= \cos (x + \tfrac{1}{2}\delta x) \frac{\sin (\tfrac{1}{2}\delta x)}{\tfrac{1}{2}\delta x}$$
$$\therefore \lim_{\delta x \to 0} \left(\frac{\delta y}{\delta x} \right) = \cos (x + 0) \times 1, \text{ by (1), § 44,}$$
$$\therefore \frac{dy}{dx} = \cos x.$$

Proof of (2) :—

$$y + \delta y = \cos (x + \delta x), \quad y = \cos x.$$

By subtraction,

$$\delta y = \cos (x + \delta x) - \cos x$$
$$= - 2 \sin (x + \tfrac{1}{2}\delta x) \sin (\tfrac{1}{2}\delta x), \text{ by Trigonometry,}$$
$$\therefore \frac{\delta y}{\delta x} = - \sin (x + \tfrac{1}{2}\delta x) \frac{\sin (\tfrac{1}{2}\delta x)}{\tfrac{1}{2}\delta x}$$
$$\therefore \lim_{\delta x \to 0} \left(\frac{\delta y}{\delta x} \right) = - \sin (x + 0) \times 1, \text{ by (1), § 44,}$$
$$\therefore \frac{dy}{dx} = - \sin x.$$

Proof of (3).—By the quotient rule,

$$\frac{d}{dx} \left(\frac{\sin x}{\cos x} \right) = \frac{\cos x (\cos x) - \sin x (- \sin x)}{\cos^2 x} = \frac{\cos^2 x + \sin^2 x}{\cos^2 x},$$
$$\therefore \frac{d}{dx} (\tan x) = \frac{1}{\cos^2 x} = \sec^2 x.$$

Proof of (4).—By (5), § 28,

$$\frac{d}{dx} \left(\frac{1}{\cos x} \right) = \frac{- 1}{\cos^2 x} (- \sin x) = \frac{\sin x}{\cos^2 x},$$
$$\therefore \frac{d}{dx} (\sec x) = \frac{\sin x}{\cos^2 x} = \sec x \tan x.$$

Examples XXVIII.

In Exs. 1-6, find dy/dx from first principles :—

1. $y = \tan x.$ **2.** $y = \sec x.$ **3.** $y = \operatorname{cosec} x.$
4. $y = \sin ax.$ **5.** $y = \sin^2 x.$ **6.** $y = \cot (ax + b).$

7. Draw carefully the graph of $y = \sin (\pi x)$ from $x = 0$ to $x = 1$, using the same scale for x and y. Measure the gradient at the point where $x = \frac{1}{3}$. What should the result be ?

§ 46. Examples.

Ex. 1. From the rule for differentiating a function of a function (§ 28) it follows that, if u is a function of x,

$$\frac{d}{dx}(\sin u) = \cos u \frac{du}{dx}, \qquad \frac{d}{dx}(\cos u) = -\sin u \frac{du}{dx}.$$

In particular, if $u = ax + b$,

$$\frac{d}{dx}\{\sin (ax + b)\} = a \cos (ax + b),$$

$$\frac{d}{dx}\{\cos (ax + b)\} = -a \sin (ax + b),$$

and there are corresponding results for the other trigonometric functions.

Ex. 2. If $y = \sin^3 \theta$, find $dy/d\theta$.
Put $u = \sin \theta$.   Then

$$y = u^3, \qquad u = \sin \theta,$$
$$\frac{dy}{du} = 3u^2, \qquad \frac{du}{d\theta} = \cos \theta,$$
$$\therefore \frac{dy}{d\theta} = \frac{dy}{du}\frac{du}{d\theta} = 3u^2 \cos \theta = 3 \sin^2 \theta \cos \theta.$$

Ex. 3. Differentiate $\tan^2 (2x + 3)$ with respect to x.
Let $y = \tan^2 (2x + 3)$.   Put $v = \tan (2x + 3)$, $u = 2x + 3$.   Then

$$y = v^2, \qquad v = \tan u, \qquad u = 2x + 3,$$
$$\frac{dy}{dv} = 2v, \qquad \frac{dv}{du} = \sec^2 u, \qquad \frac{du}{dx} = 2,$$
$$\therefore \frac{dy}{dx} = \frac{dy}{dv}\frac{dv}{du}\frac{du}{dx} = 2v \sec^2 u \,.\, 2 = 4 \tan u \sec^2 u,$$
$$\therefore \frac{d}{dx}\{\tan^2 (2x + 3)\} = 4 \tan (2x + 3) \sec^2 (2x + 3).$$

Examples XXIX.

In Exs. 1-42 differentiate the given functions with respect to x, or θ, as the case may be :—

1. $\sin 2x.$ **2.** $\cos 3x.$ **3.** $\cos^3 x.$ **4.** $\cos (x^3).$
5. $\sin^2 x.$ **6.** $\tan^3 x.$ **7.** $\tan 4x.$ **8.** $\sec 5x.$
9. $\tan \frac{1}{2}x.$ **10.** $\sec \frac{1}{2}x.$ **11.** $\tan^2 \frac{1}{2}x.$ **12.** $\sec^2 \frac{1}{2}x.$
13. $\sin^m x.$ **14.** $\cos^n x.$ **15.** $\sin^m x \cos {}^n x.$

16. $\sin (3x + 1)$.   **17.** $\cos (a - bx)$.   **18.** $\sec (ax + b)$.

19. $\cos (1 - x)$.   **20.** $\sin n(a - x)$.   **21.** $\cot (ax + b)$.

22. $\sin^2 (2x - 1)$.   **23.** $\sec^2 (2 - x)$.   **24.** $\sqrt{(a + b \sin x)}$.

25. $x \sin x$.   **26.** $\tan^3 (mx + n)$.   **27.** $\sqrt{(1 - k^2 \sin^2 x)}$.

28. $x^2 \cos x$.   **29.** $x \sin x \cos x$.   **30.** $\sec^2 \theta - \tan^2 \theta$.

31. $\sin^2 \theta \cos \theta$.   **32.** $\theta + \sin \theta \cos \theta$.   **33.** $\frac{1}{2}\theta - \frac{1}{4} \sin 2\theta$.

34. $\sin 5\theta \cos \theta$.   **35.** $\sec \theta \tan \theta$.   **36.** $\sin \theta \sin (\theta - \alpha)$.

37. $\dfrac{\sin \theta}{\theta}$.   **38.** $\dfrac{1}{1 + \sin \theta}$.   **39.** $\dfrac{\sin \theta}{\sin (\theta + \alpha)}$.

40. $x^2 \sin \dfrac{1}{x}$.   **41.** $\dfrac{\cos \theta}{1 + \sin \theta}$.   **42.** $\dfrac{\cos \theta}{(1 + \sin \theta)^2}$.

43. If $y = \sin x$, or $y = \cos x$, prove that

$$\frac{d^2y}{dx^2} = - y, \quad \frac{d^4y}{dx^4} = y.$$

44. If $y = \tan x$, prove that

$$\frac{d^2y}{dx^2} = 2y(1 + y^2), \quad \frac{d^3y}{dx^3} = 2(1 + 3y^2)(1 + y^2).$$

45. If $y = \sin x \cos x \sqrt{(1 - a^2 \sin^2 x)}$, prove that

$$\frac{dy}{dx} = \frac{3a^2 \sin^4 x - 2(a^2 + 1) \sin^2 x + 1}{\sqrt{(1 - a^2 \sin^2 x)}}.$$

§ 47. Maxima and Minima of Trigonometric Functions.

Before finding maximum or minimum values of a periodic function, or sketching its graph, it should be noted whether the function is even or odd or neither; for if it is even or odd we need only consider it in detail over half a period.

Ex. Find the maximum and minimum values of y when

$$y = \sin x + \tfrac{1}{2} \sin 2x, \tag{i}$$

and sketch the graph of this function.

Note, firstly, that y is periodic, with period 2π (or 360°); and, secondly, that y is an odd function. Hence, we need only consider values of x from 0 to π (or 180°).

Now $$\frac{dy}{dx} = \cos x + \cos 2x. \tag{ii}$$

Hence, $dy/dx = 0$ when

$$\cos x + \cos 2x = 0,$$
$$\therefore 2 \cos^2 x + \cos x - 1 = 0,$$
$$\therefore (2 \cos x - 1)(\cos x + 1) = 0,$$
$$\therefore \cos x = \tfrac{1}{2} \text{ or } - 1,$$
$$\therefore x = 60° \text{ or } 180°.$$

Putting these values of x in (i), we find $y = 3\sqrt{3}/4$ when $x = 60°$, and $y = 0$ when $x = 180°$.

Again, from (ii),

$$\frac{d^2y}{dx^2} = - \sin x - 2 \sin 2x,$$

which is negative when $x = 60°$.   Hence

$$y_{\max} = 3\sqrt{3}/4, \text{ when } x = 60°.$$

When $x = 180°$, $d^2y/dx^2 = 0$, which does not decide the nature of the stationary point for this value of x.   But it is not necessary to examine this value further, as we now have sufficient information to sketch the graph from $x = 0$ to $x = 180°$.   It can then be continued from $x = 0$ to $x = -180°$, since y is an odd function; and then for all values of x, since y has the period 360°.

On drawing the graph, we see that the stationary point at $x = 180°$ is a point of inflexion (Fig. 32).

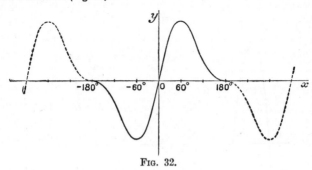

Fig. 32.

Examples XXX.

In Exs. 1-17, find the stationary values of the given functions, and the corresponding values of x.   Sketch the graphs :—

1. $y = 5 + 3 \sin x$.

2. $y = 3 \cos x + 4 \sin x$.

3. $y = 5 + 3 \sin^2 x$.

4. $y = 3 \cos^2 x + 4 \sin^2 x$.

5. $y = \cos x + \sin x$.

6. $y = \cos x + \frac{1}{2} \cos 2x$.

7. $y = \tan x + 4 \cot x$.

8. $y = 2 \sin x - \sin 2x$.

9. $y = \sin^2 x \cos x$.

10. $y = \sin x + \frac{1}{3} \sin 3x$.

11. $y = \sin x \cos^3 x$.

12. $y = 3 \sin x + \cos 2x$.

13. $y = \sin x + \frac{1}{3} \sin 3x + \frac{1}{5} \sin 5x$.

14. $y = 14 \cos^2 x - 4 \sin x \cos x + 11 \sin^2 x$.

15. $y = \cos x \cos (x - \alpha)$, where α is an acute angle.

16. $y = \sin^2 x + \sin^2 (x - \alpha)$, where α is an acute angle.

17. $y = \dfrac{\tan x}{\tan (x + \alpha)}$, where α is a positive acute angle.

18. Prove that $2 \sec \theta - \tan \theta$ is a minimum when $\theta = 30°$.

19. Prove that $\theta \sin \theta + 4 \cos \theta$ is a maximum when $\theta = 0$.

20. If $y = a \sin \theta + \frac{1}{3} \sin 3\theta$, between what values must a lie so that y may have a maximum between $\theta = 0$ and $\theta = 90°$?   Find a if y is a maximum when $\theta = 60°$.

Examples XXXI.

1. If $y = 3 \sin \omega t$, where ω is a constant, find all the values of t for which y has turning values.

2. If $y = a \sin \omega t + b \cos \omega t$, where a, b, and ω are constants, find all the values of t for which y has maximum or minimum values. What is the maximum value ?

3. ABC is a triangle in which AB = 6 ins., and AC = 10 ins. What is the maximum area of the triangle ?

4. AB is a chord of a circle, and CD is the diameter perpendicular to AB. Prove that the triangle ABC is equilateral when its area is a maximum.

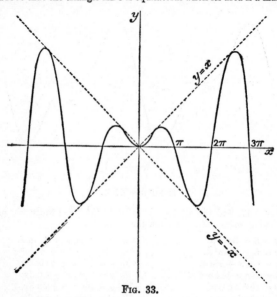

Fig. 33.

5. A cone is inscribed in a sphere of radius a. If 2θ is the angle subtended by a diameter of the base at the centre of the sphere, and if V is the volume of the cone, express V in terms of θ, and find the ratio of the maximum volume of the cone to the volume of the sphere.

6. The end A of a rod AB slides on a vertical line AD, and the rod passes through a fixed point C on a level with D. If CD = 8, AB = 27, and A is above D, find the maximum depth of the end B below the level of CD.

7. A straight line passes through the point (64, 27) and cuts the co-ordinate axes in A and B. Find the minimum length of AB.

8. A wall, of height a feet, is built parallel to the side of a house, at a distance c feet away. What is the length of the shortest ladder that will reach the house, resting on the ground on the far side of the wall ?

9. A long strip of sheet iron is shaped into a gutter whose cross-section is a circular arc subtending an angle 2θ at the centre of the circle. Find θ so that the gutter can carry away the maximum amount of water.

10. A is a point on the circumference of a fixed circle. With centre A, another circle is described, cutting the first in B and C, and B and C are joined to A. If $\angle\,\mathrm{BAC} = \theta$, prove that, when the area of the sector ABC is a maximum, $\theta = \cot\frac{1}{2}\theta$, and hence that $\theta = 74°\ 52'$ (approx.).

§ 48. Graph of $y = f(x)\sin x$.

Since $\sin x$ lies between 1 and -1, the graph of
$$y = f(x)\sin x$$
lies between the graphs of
$$y = f(x), \quad y = -f(x),$$
touching each in turn.

For example, Fig. 33 shows the graph of
$$y = x\sin x,$$
which lies between the two straight lines
$$y = x, \quad y = -x.$$
Note that $x\sin x$ is an even function; x is measured n radians.

EXAMPLES XXXII.

In Exs. 1-7 sketch the graphs of the given functions :—

1. $y = x\cos x.$ **2.** $y = x^2\sin x.$ **3.** $y = x\sin\dfrac{1}{x}.$

4. $y = \dfrac{\sin x}{x}.$ **5.** $y = \dfrac{\cos x}{x^2 + 1}.$ **6.** $y = \dfrac{x\sin x}{x^2 + 1}.$

7. $y = \sin x\sin nx, \quad y = \dfrac{\sin nx}{\sin x}, \quad (n = 2, 3, 4, \ldots).$

In Exs. 8-11, the equation $dy/dx = 0$ must be solved graphically, or by some other approximate method :—

8. If $y = x^2 - 2\sin x$, find the value of x for which y is a minimum. Sketch the graph.

9. Sketch the graph of $y = x^2 + 8\cos x$. How many turning points are there on the graph ?

10. If $y = x\sin x$, find the smallest positive value of x for which y is a maximum.

11. If $y = \dfrac{\sin x}{x}$, find the smallest positive value of x for which y is a minimum.

12. *Prove* that the graph of $y = f(x)\sin x$ touches the graphs of $y = f(x)$, $y = -f(x)$, alternately.

§ 49. Inverse Functions.—If from a given equation in x and y we derive a new equation by interchanging x and y, the new

equation defines y as a function of x which is called the *inverse* of that defined by the given equation.

For example, if the given equation is

$$y = x^2 \qquad \text{(i)}$$

the new equation obtained by interchanging x and y is

$$x = y^2, \quad \text{or } y^2 = x, \quad \text{or } y = \pm \sqrt{x},$$

which defines y as a function of x which is the inverse of that defined by (i).

§ **50. Graphs of Inverse Functions.**—From the definition of an inverse function it follows that, if we interchange the co-ordinates (a, b) of any point on the graph of a given function of x, we obtain the co-ordinates (b, a) of a point on the graph of the inverse function.

Now (see Fig. 34), the two points whose co-ordinates are (a, b) and (b, a) are the images (or reflections) of each other in the straight line $y = x$, assuming the scales to be the same along both co-ordinate axes. Hence, *the graphs of a function and its inverse function are the images of each other in the line* y = x.

The graphs of the function $y = x^2$ and its inverse function defined by $y^2 = x$ are indicated by the full-line curve and the dotted curve, respectively, in Fig. 35.

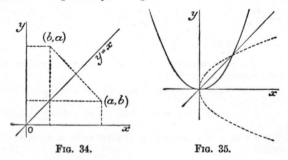

Fig. 34.   Fig. 35.

§ **51. The Inverse Sine.**—When we interchange x and y in the equation $y = \sin x$, we obtain

$$x = \sin y, \quad \text{or } \sin y = x, \quad \text{or } y = \sin^{-1} x,$$

which defines y as the *inverse sine* of x, known in Trigonometry as " the angle whose sine is x."

The graph of $\sin y = x$, or $y = \sin^{-1} x$, is shown in Fig. 36. It is the reflection of the graph of $y = \sin x$ in the line $y = x$.

Now, if x lies between 1 and -1, $\sin^{-1} x$ has an infinite number of values. Two of these lie between 0 and 2π radians, and each of the others differs from one of these two by a whole multiple of 2π radians.

Among all these values of $\sin^{-1} x$ there is always one and only one between $\frac{1}{2}\pi$ and $-\frac{1}{2}\pi$. This is called the *principal value* of $\sin^{-1} x$. It is the numerically smallest value of $\sin^{-1} x$.

For example, when $x = \frac{1}{2}$, $\sin^{-1} x$ has the two values $\pi/6$ and $5\pi/6$, and an infinite number of other values obtainable from these two by adding or subtracting whole multiples of 2π radians. The *principal value* is $\pi/6$.

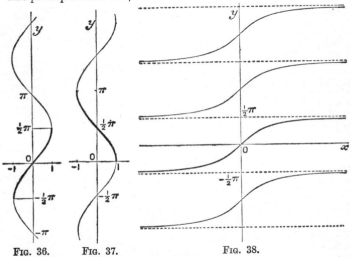

FIG. 36.   FIG. 37.   FIG. 38.

§ 52. **The Inverse Cosine.**—The equation
$$\cos y = x, \text{ or } y = \cos^{-1} x$$
defines y as the *inverse cosine* of x.

The graph of $y = \cos^{-1} x$ is shown in Fig. 37.

If x lies between 1 and -1, $\cos^{-1} x$ has an infinite number of values. The *principal value* is the one that lies between 0 and π radians. It is the smallest positive value of $\cos^{-1} x$.

§ 53. **The Inverse Tangent.**—The equation
$$\tan y = x, \text{ or } y = \tan^{-1} x$$
defines y as the *inverse tangent* of x.

The graph of $y = \tan^{-1} x$ is shown in Fig. 38.

3

If x has any value, $\tan^{-1} x$ has an infinite number of values. The *principal value* is the one that lies between $\frac{1}{2}\pi$ and $-\frac{1}{2}\pi$. It is the numerically smallest value of $\tan^{-1} x$.

§ 54. Differentiation of Inverse Trigonometric Functions. — We shall prove the first of the following standard differential coefficients of the inverse trigonometric functions. The others can be proved in a similar way :—

$$\frac{d}{dx}(\sin^{-1} x) = \frac{1}{\sqrt{(1 - x^2)}}, \quad \frac{d}{dx}\left(\sin^{-1} \frac{x}{a}\right) = \frac{1}{\sqrt{(a^2 - x^2)}}; \quad (1)$$

$$\frac{d}{dx}(\cos^{-1} x) = \frac{-1}{\sqrt{(1 - x^2)}}, \quad \frac{d}{dx}\left(\cos^{-1} \frac{x}{a}\right) = \frac{-1}{\sqrt{(a^2 - x^2)}}; \quad (2)$$

$$\frac{d}{dx}(\tan^{-1} x) = \frac{1}{1 + x^2}, \quad \frac{d}{dx}\left(\tan^{-1} \frac{x}{a}\right) = \frac{a}{a^2 + x^2}; \quad (3)$$

where the inverse functions have their principal values.

Proof. Let $y = \sin^{-1} x$. Then $x = \sin y$,

$$\therefore \frac{dx}{dy} = \cos y,$$

$$\therefore \frac{dy}{dx} = \frac{1}{\cos y}.$$

Now, since y has its principal value, it lies between $\frac{1}{2}\pi$ and $-\frac{1}{2}\pi$, and therefore $\cos y$ is positive,

$$\therefore \cos y = \sqrt{(1 - \sin^2 y)} = \sqrt{(1 - x^2)},$$

$$\therefore \frac{dy}{dx} = \frac{1}{\sqrt{(1 - x^2)}}.$$

Examples XXXIII.

In Exs. 1-14 differentiate the given functions :—

1. $\sin^{-1}(2x)$.   2. $\sin^{-1}(2x - 1)$.   3. $\tan^{-1}(ax)$.

4. $\sec^{-1} x$.   5. $\cos^{-1}(1 - x)$.   6. $\cot^{-1} x$.

7. $(\sin^{-1} x)^2$.   8. $x \sin^{-1} x$.   9. $\sin^{-1}\sqrt{x}$.

10. $\cos^{-1} \dfrac{a}{x}$.   11. $\sin^{-1}\left(\dfrac{2x - 3}{5}\right)$.   12. $\cos^{-1}\left(\dfrac{a - x}{a}\right)$.

13. $\dfrac{2x}{4 + x^2} + \tan^{-1} \dfrac{x}{2}$.   14. $x\sqrt{(a^2 - x^2)} + a^2 \sin^{-1} \dfrac{x}{a}$.

15. Prove that $\dfrac{d}{dx}\left(\tan^{-1} x + \tan^{-1} \dfrac{1}{x}\right) = 0$, and account for this result.

16. If $y = \tan^{-1}\left(\dfrac{a + x}{1 - ax}\right)$, prove that $\dfrac{dy}{dx}$ does not depend on a, and explain why.

CHAPTER VII.

RATES OF CHANGE.

§ 55. Rates of Change with respect to Time.—Let y be any function of the *time t*, and let δy be the change in y during the interval from t to $(t + \delta t)$. Then the fraction

$$\frac{\delta y}{\delta t}$$

is the average change in y per unit change in t during the interval, or the *average rate at which* y *changes* during the interval. The limit of this fraction when $\delta t \to 0$, viz.

$$\frac{dy}{dt}$$

is the rate at which y is changing *at the instant* t. Thus, *the differential coefficient of* y *with respect to* t *is the instantaneous rate at which* y *is changing.*

Illustrations are given below:—

§ 56. Linear Velocity.—Let a straight line be marked with an arrowhead to indicate a positive sense of direction on the line (Fig. 39). Let O be a fixed point, and P a variable point on the line, and let s be the distance of P from O at the time t, the distance s being counted

FIG. 39.

positive or negative according as the sense of the direction from O to P is the same as that of the arrowhead or opposed to it.

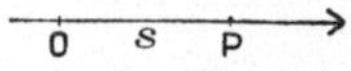

Then the differential coefficient of s with respect to t, viz.

$$\frac{ds}{dt}$$

is the rate at which s is changing at the instant t. It is called *the velocity of the point* P *at the instant* t, or briefly, *the velocity.*

Note that ds/dt is positive when s is increasing; i.e. the velocity is positive when P is moving in the positive direction of the line. The velocity is negative when P is moving in the opposite direction.

Let v denote the velocity. Then

$$v = \frac{ds}{dt}. \tag{1}$$

Since ds/dt is the gradient of the (t, s) graph (§ 23), *the velocity is equal to the gradient of the* (t, s) *graph.*

§ **57. Linear Acceleration.**—The differential coefficient of v with respect to t, viz.

$$\frac{dv}{dt},$$

is the rate at which the velocity is changing at the instant t. It is called *the acceleration of the point* P *at the instant* t, or briefly, *the acceleration.*

Note that dv/dt is positive when v is increasing; i.e. the acceleration is positive when the velocity is increasing in the positive direction of the line.

Let a denote the acceleration. Then

$$a = \frac{dv}{dt}. \tag{2}$$

Since dv/dt is the gradient of the (t, v) graph, *the acceleration is equal to the gradient of the* (t, v) *graph.*

Again, since $\frac{dv}{dt} = \frac{d}{dt}\left(\frac{ds}{dt}\right) = \frac{d^2s}{dt^2}$, we have also

$$a = \frac{d^2s}{dt^2}. \tag{3}$$

Thus, *the acceleration is the second differential coefficient of* s *with respect to* t.

From (1) and (3) it follows that, if the (t, s) graph is drawn, the *derived graph* will be the (t, v) graph, and the *second derived graph* will be the (t, a) graph (see § 33).

§ 58. **Ex.** If s is measured in feet, and t in seconds, and if

$$s = t^3 - 9t^2 + 24t, \tag{i}$$

find the velocity and acceleration when $t = 5$. Also, find the values of t when the point P is momentarily at rest.

We have $$v = \frac{ds}{dt} = 3t^2 - 18t + 24,$$ (ii)

$$\alpha = \frac{dv}{dt} = 6t - 18.$$ (iii)

When $t = 5$, from (ii),
$$v = 9 \text{ ft./sec.}$$
and from (iii),
$$\alpha = 12 \text{ ft./sec.}^2$$

From (ii), $v = 0$ when
$$3(t^2 - 6t + 8) = 0,$$
$$\therefore\ 3(t - 2)(t - 4) = 0,$$
$$\therefore\ t = 2 \text{ or } 4.$$

Hence, the point P is momentarily at rest at the instants when $t = 2$ and $t = 4$.

§ 59. **Angular Velocity.**—If a straight line is moving in a plane, and if it makes an angle θ with a fixed line in the plane, the instantaneous rate at which θ is changing is called the *angular velocity* of the moving line.

Let ω denote the angular velocity. Then

$$\omega = \frac{d\theta}{dt}.$$ (4)

§ 60. **Angular Acceleration.**—The instantaneous rate at which the angular velocity of a line is changing is called the *angular acceleration* of the line. Thus

$$\text{angular acceleration} = \frac{d\omega}{dt} = \frac{d^2\theta}{dt^2}.$$ (5)

§ 61. **The "Dot" Notation.**—Differentiation with respect to *time* is often denoted by a dot; thus

$$\dot{s} = \frac{ds}{dt}, \quad \ddot{s} = \frac{d^2s}{dt^2}, \quad \dot{v} = \frac{dv}{dt}, \quad \dot{\theta} = \frac{d\theta}{dt}, \ \cdots$$

(read : " s-dot," " s-two-dot," $\cdots$)

Examples XXXIV.

1. A point P moves on a line, and, t seconds after a certain instant, the distance of P from a fixed point O on the line is s feet. If $s = t(10 - t)$, find the average velocity of P during the interval from $t = 2$ to $t = 2 + \delta t$, and deduce the velocity of P at the instant $t = 2$.

2. Assume that, when a stone is thrown upwards with a speed of 60 miles an hour, its height h feet, at the end of t seconds, is given by $h = 88t - 16t^2$. Find its velocity at the end of (i) 2 secs., (ii) 4 secs. How high does the stone rise ?

3. If the distance, s feet, travelled by a motor-car in t seconds after the brakes are applied, is given by $s = 44t - 6t^2$, what is the speed just when

the brakes are applied ?   How far does the car travel before it stops ?
Sketch the (t, s), (t, v), and (t, α) graphs.

4. A train started from rest at one station, and stopped at another, 48
miles away, after a two hours' run.   What was the average speed ?

If the distance from the start was $12t^2(3 - t)$ miles after t hours' running,
was the speed ever 32 miles an hour, and if so, when ?   What was the maximum speed attained ?   Sketch the (t, s), (t, v), and (t, α) graphs.

5. At a certain port, t hours after high-water, the height, h feet, of the
tide above a fixed datum is given by

$$h = 10 + 7 \cos (\pi t/6).$$

At what rate, in inches per minute, is the tide falling one hour after high-
water ?

6. The current, i ampères, in an electric circuit at time t is given by
$i = \text{I} \sin (at + b)$, where I, a, b are constants.   Show that the current is
changing most rapidly when it is zero.

In Exs. 7-12, s denotes the distance in feet of a point P, moving on a
straight line, from a fixed point O on the line ; and t denotes time in seconds
measured from a certain instant.   Find the velocity and acceleration of P
when t has the given values.   Also, find the values of t when P is momentarily at rest :—

7. $s = 2t^3 - 9t^2 + 12t$; $t = 3$.   8. $s = 2 \sin 3t$; $t = 0$.

9. $s = t(3 - t)^2$; $t = 2$.   10. $s = 5 + 2 \cos \pi t$; $t = \frac{1}{6}$.

11. $s = t^2(4 - t^2)$; $t = 1$.   12. $s = 6t + 3 \cos 2t$; $t = 0$.

13. If $s = t^3 - 6t^2 + 42t$, find the minimum velocity.

14. If $s = ut + \frac{1}{2}gt^2$, and $v = ds/dt$, where u and g are constants, prove
that $v^2 - u^2 = 2gs$.

15. If $s = 4t + 2 \cos 2t$, $v = ds/dt$, $\alpha = dv/dt$, prove that

$$\alpha^2 = 32v - 4v^2.$$

16. If $s = a \sin \omega t$, where a and ω are constants, prove that

$$\frac{ds}{dt} = \pm \, \omega \sqrt{(a^2 - s^2)}, \quad \frac{d^2s}{dt^2} = - \, \omega^2 s.$$

§ 62. If y is a function of x, the rate at which y is changing
depends upon the rate at which x is changing.   In fact, by the
rule for differentiating a function of a function,

$$\frac{dy}{dt} = \frac{dy}{dx} \frac{dx}{dt}. \tag{6}$$

Hence, we can find $\dfrac{dy}{dt}$ if $\dfrac{dx}{dt}$ is given ; or $\dfrac{dx}{dt}$ if $\dfrac{dy}{dt}$ is given.

Rule.—Note the two variables, the one whose rate of change
is given, and the one whose rate of change is to be found.

Express either variable in terms of the other, by means of an
equation, and then differentiate throughout with respect to t.

Ex. 1. The radius of a circle is increasing at the rate of 3 ins./sec. How fast is the area increasing when the radius is 10 ins. ?

Let r be the radius, and A the area.

The rate at which r is changing is given, and the rate at which A is changing is to be found.

Now
$$A = \pi r^2,$$

$$\therefore \frac{dA}{dt} = \frac{dA}{dr}\frac{dr}{dt} = 2\pi r\frac{dr}{dt}.$$

But $dr/dt = 3$ ins./sec. Hence, when $r = 10$,

$$\frac{dA}{dt} = 2\pi \times 10 \times 3 = 60\pi = 188\cdot5 \text{ sq. ins./sec.}$$

Ex. 2. OA is the perpendicular from a point O on a line AB (Fig. 40). A point P moves along AB with a speed of 10 ft./sec. If OA = 5 ft., find the angular velocity of the line OP when $\angle$ AOP = 60°.

Let AP $= y$ ft., and $\angle$ AOP $= \theta$.

The rate of change of y is given, and the rate of change of θ is to be found.

Now

FIG. 40.

$$y = 5 \tan \theta,$$

$$\therefore \frac{dy}{dt} = \frac{dy}{d\theta}\frac{d\theta}{dt} = 5 \sec^2 \theta \frac{d\theta}{dt}.$$

But $dy/dt = 10$ ft./sec. Hence, when $\theta = 60°$,

$$10 = 5 \times 2^2 \times \frac{d\theta}{dt}.$$

$$\therefore \frac{d\theta}{dt} = \frac{10}{5 \times 2^2} = \frac{1}{2} \text{ rad./sec.}$$

$$= 28\cdot6 \text{ deg./sec.}$$

Examples XXXV.

1. A stone, dropped into a pond, sends out circular ripples. If the radius of the outermost ripple increases at the rate of 6 ft./sec., how fast is the disturbed area growing when the radius = 7 ft. ?

2. A circular patch of oil spreads out on water, the area growing at the rate of 6 sq. ins./min. How fast is the radius increasing when the radius = 2 ins. ?

3. The volume of a sphere is 288 cub. ins., and is increasing at the rate of 50 cub. ins./sec. How fast is the radius increasing ?

4. A metal sphere is dissolving in acid. It remains spherical and the rate at which it dissolves is proportional to the area of its surface. Prove that the radius decreases at a constant rate.

5. The height h of a cone increases at the rate of 2 ins./sec., but the slant side remains constant and equal to 9 ins. How fast is the volume changing when (i) $h = 4$ ins., (ii) $h = 6$ ins., (iii) $h = 3\sqrt{3}$ ins. ?

6. ABC is a triangle in which AB = 10 ins., AC = 12 ins., ∠BAC = θ. If θ is increasing at the rate of 6° per sec., find the rate at which the area is changing when (i) θ = 60°, (ii) θ = 90°, (iii) θ = 135°, (iv) θ = 0.

7. A rod AB, of length 10 ft., moves with the end A on the x-axis and the end B on the y-axis. Find (i) the angular velocity of the rod, and (ii) the velocity of the end B, when OA = 6 ft. and the velocity of A is 2 ft./sec.

8. A ship is anchored one mile from the nearest point A of a straight shore. A searchlight S from the ship illuminates a point B on the shore. The searchlight revolves at the rate of 2 revs./min. If ∠ASB = θ, find the velocity of B along the shore when (i) θ = 0°, (ii) θ = 60°, (iii) θ = 80°.

§ 63. Rates of Change with respect to Variables other than Time.—Suppose an iron bar is kept hot at one end and cool at the other (e.g. a poker with one end in the fire). Let P and Q be two points on the bar, at distances x and $(x + \delta x)$ inches respectively from the cool end. Let the temperatures at P and Q be T and $(T + \delta T)$ degrees, respectively. Then the fraction

$$\frac{\delta T}{\delta x} \text{ degrees per inch}$$

is the average rate at which the temperature changes *with respect to x* between P and Q.

The limit of this fraction when $\delta x \to 0$, viz.

$$\frac{dT}{dx} \text{ degrees per inch,} \tag{7}$$

is *the rate at which* T *is changing with respect to* x *at the point* P, or the *temperature gradient* at the point P.

§ 64. Every differential coefficient can be described as *the rate at which the dependent variable is changing with respect to the independent variable.*

§ 65. Gradient of a Graph.—We have seen that, on an (x, y) graph, the gradient = dy/dx. Hence, the gradient of an (x, y) graph is *the rate at which* y *is changing with respect to* x.

Since $\frac{d^2y}{dx^2} = \frac{d}{dx}\left(\frac{dy}{dx}\right)$, the second differential coefficient is *the rate at which the gradient is changing* with respect to x.

§ 66. Acceleration.—In the notation of §§ 56, 57, we have

$$\frac{dv}{dt} = \frac{dv}{ds}\frac{ds}{dt} = \frac{dv}{ds} \cdot v = v\frac{dv}{ds} = \frac{d}{ds}(\tfrac{1}{2}v^2), \tag{8}$$

$$\therefore a = \frac{d}{ds}(\tfrac{1}{2}v^2). \tag{9}$$

Thus, linear acceleration can be expressed as *the rate at which half the square of the velocity is changing with respect to s.* The three forms of acceleration, viz.

$$a = \frac{dv}{dt} = \frac{d^2s}{dt^2} = \frac{d}{ds}(\tfrac{1}{2}v^2) \qquad (10)$$

are all important in Dynamics.

§ 67. Ex. A is a fixed point, and P a variable point, on a circle of radius r ft., centre C (Fig. 41). The arc AP = s ft., and the tangent at P makes an angle ψ with the tangent at A. Find $d\psi/ds$, and give its meaning in words.

The angle between the tangents at A and P is equal to the angle between the radii CA, CP,

$$\therefore \ \psi = \angle \text{ACP} = \frac{\text{arc AP}}{\text{radius}} = \frac{s}{r}.$$

Since r is constant,

$$\frac{d\psi}{ds} = \frac{1}{r}.$$

FIG. 41.

In words, the angle ψ increases at the rate of 1/r radians per foot with respect to s when P moves round the circle.

Examples XXXVI.

In Exs. 1-5, besides finding the required differential coefficients, give their meanings in words :—

1. A prism has a square base of side 10 ins. Its height = x ins., and its volume = V cub. ins. Find dV/dx.

2. A prism has a square base of side x ins. Its height = 10 ins., and its volume = V cub. ins. Find dV/dx.

3. If s ft. is the length of the shadow of a man 6 ft. high when he stands x ft. away from a lamp 10 ft. high, find ds/dx.

4. In order to measure my distance, s yards, from a building 50 ft. high, I hold a vertical foot-rule 3 ft. from my eye, and observe the length of the scale, x ins., that subtends the same angle at my eye as the building. Find ds/dx.

5. A point of light is x ft. directly above the centre of a sphere resting on a table. If the radius of the sphere is a ft., and the area of the shadow of the sphere on the table is A sq. ft., find dA/dx.

6. If the angle θ is varying, prove that $\tan \theta$ is increasing twice as fast as $\sec \theta$ when $\theta = 30°$, and eight times as fast as $\sin \theta$ when $\theta = 60°$.

7. If ω is the angular velocity of a moving straight line which makes an angle θ with a fixed line, prove that the angular acceleration of the moving line $= \dfrac{d}{d\theta}(\tfrac{1}{2}\omega^2)$.

3 *

§ 68. Rates of Change of x and y with respect to the Arc s

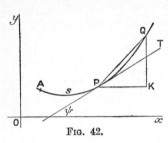

Fig. 42.

—Let A be a fixed point, and P a variable point, on a graph (Fig. 42). Let (x, y) be the co-ordinates of P, and let the tangent at P make an angle ψ with the axis of x. Let $s =$ length of arc AP. We shall prove that

$$\frac{dx}{ds} = \cos \psi, \quad \frac{dy}{ds} = \sin \psi.$$

Proof.—Let Q be the point whose co-ordinates are $(x + \delta x, y + \delta y)$, and draw PK parallel to Ox, and QK parallel to Oy.

Put $\delta s = arc$ PQ, and let $\Delta s = chord$ PQ. Then

$$\cos KPQ = \frac{PK}{PQ} = \frac{\delta x}{\Delta s} = \frac{\delta x}{\delta s} \frac{\delta s}{\Delta s},$$

$$\sin KPQ = \frac{KQ}{PQ} = \frac{\delta y}{\Delta s} = \frac{\delta y}{\delta s} \frac{\delta s}{\Delta s}.$$

Now, when Q → P, $\angle$ KPQ → ψ, and $\delta s/\Delta s$ → 1 (see § 7); hence, in the limit,

$$\cos \psi = \frac{dx}{ds}, \quad \sin \psi = \frac{dy}{ds}. \tag{11}$$

Examples XXXVII.

In Exs. 1-6, find dx/ds and dy/ds when x has the given values :—

1. $y = x^{\frac{1}{3}}$; $x = 1$.
2. $12y = 33x - 7x^2$; $x = 2$.
3. $xy = 12$; $x = 3$.
4. $3y = (x - 3)\sqrt{x}$; $x = 16$.
5. $y = \tan x$; $x = \pi/6$.
6. $y = \sin \pi x$; $x = \frac{1}{3}$.

In Exs. 7-10, find dx/ds and dy/ds in terms of x :—

7. $y = x^2$.
8. $6xy = x^4 + 3$.
9. $y = 2 \sec x$.
10. $3y = (x - 3)\sqrt{x}$.

In Exs. 11-16, $\dot{s} = \dfrac{ds}{dt}$, $\dot{x} = \dfrac{dx}{dt}$, $\dot{y} = \dfrac{dy}{dt}$. A point P moves along the given curve. The velocity of P along the curve is $\dot{s}$, and $\dot{x}$ and $\dot{y}$ are its component velocities parallel to the axes of x and y respectively :—

11. Prove that $\dot{x} = \dot{s} \cos \psi$, $\dot{y} = \dot{s} \sin \psi$.
12. $y = x^{\frac{3}{4}}$. If $\dot{s} = 10$, find $\dot{x}$ and $\dot{y}$, when $x = 1$.
13. $y = \sin 2\pi x$. If $\dot{s} = 10$, find $\dot{x}$ and $\dot{y}$, when $x = \frac{1}{4}$.

14. $4y = x^2 - x + 1$. If $\dot{x} = 12$, find $\dot{y}$ and $\dot{s}$, when $x = 2$.

15. $x^2y = 18$. If $\dot{y} = 8$, find $\dot{x}$ and $\dot{s}$, when $x = 3$.

16. $xy = y^2 + 1$. If $\dot{s} = 20$, find $\dot{x}$ and $\dot{y}$, when $y = 2$.

§ 69. Increasing and Decreasing Functions.

—If the rate of change of y with respect to x is positive, y is increasing as x increases. If the rate of change is negative, y is decreasing as x increases.

Accordingly, if dy/dx is positive (or zero) for all values of x from $x = a$ to $x = b$, then y is called an *increasing function* from $x = a$ to $x = b$. But, if dy/dx is negative (or zero) for all values of x from $x = a$ to $x = b$, then y is called a *decreasing function* from $x = a$ to $x = b$.

Ex. Prove that $x^3 - 3x^2 + 15x - 20$ is an increasing function for all values of x.

Put
$$y = x^3 - 3x^2 + 15x - 20,$$
$$\therefore \frac{dy}{dx} = 3x^2 - 6x + 15$$
$$= 3(x^2 - 2x + 5)$$
$$= 3\{(x - 1)^2 + 4\}.$$

Now $(x - 1)^2$, being a square, is positive for all values of x, positive or negative, and therefore dy/dx is positive for all values of x. Hence, y is an increasing function for all values of x.

Examples XXXVIII.

In Exs. 1-6, prove that the given functions either increase for all values of x, or decrease for all values of x :—

1. x^3. **2.** $x^5 + 2x$. **3.** $5 - x - x^2 - x^3$.

4. $x + \cos x$. **5.** $6x - 8 \sin x + \sin 2x$.

6. $x^3 + 3(2 - x^2) \sin x - 6x \cos x$.

In Exs. 7-9, do the given functions decrease for all values of x ?

7. $\dfrac{2x + 1}{2x - 1}$. **8.** $\dfrac{x(x - 2)}{(x - 1)(x - 3)}$. **9.** $x - \tan x$.

10. Prove that $\dfrac{5 \sin x}{3 + 2 \cos x} - x$ is an increasing function from $x = -1{\cdot}82$ to $+ 1{\cdot}82$.

11. Find the condition that $x^3 + ax^2 + bx + c$ should be an increasing function for all values of x.

12. Find the condition that $\dfrac{ax + b}{cx + d}$ should be an increasing function for every value of x (except $x = -d/c$).

13. Prove that $(\sin x - x)$ is a decreasing function for all values of x; and deduce that $\sin x < x$, when x is positive.

14. Prove that $(\cos x - 1 + \frac{1}{2}x^2)$ is an increasing function of x when x is positive ; and deduce that $\cos x > 1 - \frac{1}{2}x^2$, for all values of x.

15. Prove that $\sin x > x - \frac{1}{6}x^3$, when x is positive.

§ 70. Points of Inflexion.

An (x, y) graph is said to be *concave upwards* at points where the gradient is increasing as x increases (e.g. from A to I, Fig. 43), but *concave downwards* at points where the gradient is decreasing as x increases (e.g. from I to J).

Now d^2y/dx^2 is the rate of change of the gradient (§ 65). Hence, a graph is concave upwards where d^2y/dx^2 is positive, but concave downwards where d^2y/dx^2 is negative.

A *point of inflexion* is a point where a graph ceases to be concave upwards and begins to be concave downwards, or vice-versa (e.g. the point I or J). Hence, at a point of inflexion the gradient ceases to increase and begins to decrease, or vice-versa. A point of inflexion is therefore one where *the gradient* dy/dx *is a maximum or a minimum*.

Now (§ 37), dy/dx is a maximum or minimum when $x = a$ if $d^2y/dx^2 = 0$ when $x = a$, and if d^2y/dx^2 changes sign as x passes through the value a. Hence the rule :—

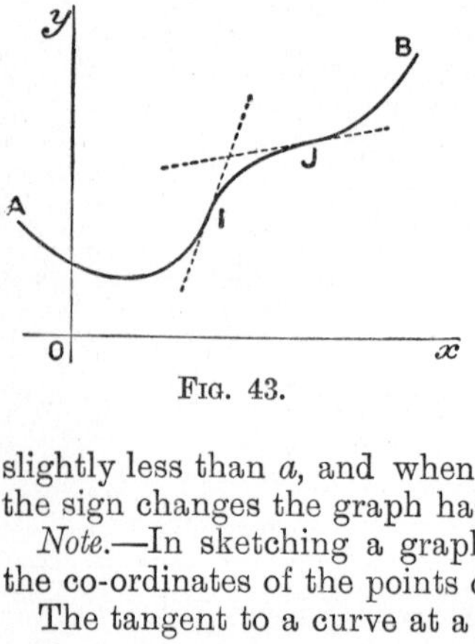

FIG. 43.

Rule.—To find the values of x where a graph has points of inflexion :—

Solve the equation $d^2y/dx^2 = 0$, and consider its roots. These are the values of x where the *gradient* is stationary.

Let a be one root. Examine the *sign* of d^2y/dx^2 when x is slightly less than a, and when x is slightly greater than a. If the sign changes the graph has a point of inflexion at $x = a$.

Note.—In sketching a graph it is sometimes helpful to find the co-ordinates of the points of inflexion.

The tangent to a curve at a point of inflexion *crosses the curve*.

Ex. Consider the graphs of (i) $y = x^3$, (ii) $y = x^4$.

(i) If $y = x^3$, $\qquad\qquad \dfrac{d^2y}{dx^2} = 6x$,

$\therefore \dfrac{d^2y}{dx^2} = 0$ when $x = 0$, and the sign of $\dfrac{d^2y}{dx^2}$ changes from $-$ to $+$ when x increases through the value 0. Hence, there is a point of inflexion at $x = 0$, i.e. at the origin.

(ii) If $y = x^4$, $\qquad\qquad \dfrac{d^2y}{dx^2} = 12x^2$,

$\therefore \dfrac{d^2y}{dx^2} = 0$ when $x = 0$, but the sign of $\dfrac{d^2y}{dx^2}$ is positive both when $x < 0$ and when $x > 0$. In this case, there is no point of inflexion at $x = 0$.

Examples XXXIX.

In Exs. 1-3, find for what values of x the graph is (i) concave upwards, (ii) concave downwards :—

 1. $y = x^2$.   2. $y = 3x^2 - x^3$.   3. $y = x^2(6 - x^2)$.

In Exs. 4-13, find the co-ordinates of the points of inflexion, and sketch the graphs of the given functions :—

 4. $y = x^2(6 - x)$.   5. $y = x + x^3$.   6. $y = 3x^5 - 10x^3$.

 7. $y = \dfrac{1}{1 + x^2}$.   8. $y = \dfrac{2x}{1 + x^2}$.   9. $y = \dfrac{1}{x} - \dfrac{1}{x^2}$.

 10. $y = \sin x$.   11. $y = \sin^2 x$.   12. $y = \sin^3 x$.   13. $y = \sin^4 x$.

 14. Find the minimum value of the angle between the x-axis and a tangent to the curve $y = 2 + 2x + x^2 + \frac{1}{3}x^3$.

 15. Show that the curve $y = a + bx + cx^2 + dx^3$ has one point of inflexion, and that, when the origin is taken at this point, the equation of the curve has the form $y = \alpha x + \beta x^3$.

§ 71. **Curvature of a Curve.**—Let A be a fixed point on a curve, P and Q two variable points (Fig. 44). Let arc AP $= s$,

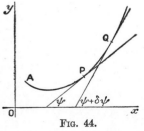

Fig. 44.

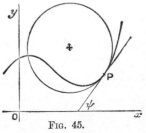

Fig. 45.

arc AQ $= s + \delta s$, and let the tangents at P and Q make angles ψ and $(\psi + \delta\psi)$ respectively with the x-axis. Then $\delta\psi$ is the change that occurs in ψ when the change δs occurs in s, and the fraction $\delta\psi/\delta s$ is the average rate (e.g. in radians per foot) at which ψ changes with respect to s between P and Q. It is called the *average curvature* of the arc PQ.

The limit of this fraction when $\delta s \to 0$, viz.

$$\frac{d\psi}{ds},\qquad\qquad(1)$$

is called the *curvature* of the curve at the point P.

In particular (see § 67), when the curve is a circle, $\dfrac{d\psi}{ds} = \dfrac{1}{r}$, where r is the radius. Hence, *the curvature of a circle at any point is equal to the reciprocal of the radius.*

§ 72. Circle of Curvature and Radius of Curvature.

—Suppose the curve is not a circle, but let a circle be drawn touching the curve at P and *having the same curvature* as the curve at P (Fig. 45). Then the angle ψ is changing at the same rate along this circle as along the curve at P. For this reason this circle has closer contact with the curve near P than any other circle, and is called the *circle of closest contact,* or the *osculating circle,* at P. It is also called the *circle of curvature* at P.

The centre of the circle of curvature at P is called the *centre of curvature,* and its radius the *radius of curvature,* of the curve at P.

Let ρ be the radius of curvature at P. Then the curvature of the circle of curvature is $1/\rho$ and the curvature of the curve is $d\psi/ds$, and since these are equal,

$$\frac{1}{\rho} = \frac{d\psi}{ds}, \quad \text{or} \quad \rho = \frac{ds}{d\psi}. \tag{2}$$

§ 73. Formula for Curvature.

—Let $y' = dy/dx$, $y'' = d^2y/dx^2$. We shall prove that the radius of curvature ρ is given by the formula

$$\frac{1}{\rho} = \frac{y''}{(1 + y'^2)^{\frac{3}{2}}}.$$

Proof.—Since

$$\frac{dy}{dx} = \tan \psi, \quad \text{and} \quad \frac{ds}{dx} = \sec \psi,$$

$$\therefore \frac{d^2y}{dx^2} = \sec^2 \psi \frac{d\psi}{dx} = \sec^2 \psi \frac{d\psi}{ds} \frac{ds}{dx} = \sec^3 \psi \frac{d\psi}{ds},$$

$$\therefore \frac{d\psi}{ds} = \frac{\dfrac{d^2y}{dx^2}}{\sec^3 \psi} = \frac{\dfrac{d^2y}{dx^2}}{(1 + \tan^2 \psi)^{\frac{3}{2}}},$$

$$\therefore \frac{1}{\rho} = \frac{y''}{(1 + y'^2)^{\frac{3}{2}}}. \tag{3}$$

Corollary (1).—At points where $\dfrac{d^2y}{dx^2} = 0$, $\dfrac{1}{\rho} = 0$, $\therefore \rho = \infty$. In particular, $\rho = \infty$ at points of inflexion.

Corollary (2).—At points where $\frac{dy}{dx}$ is so small that $\left(\frac{dy}{dx}\right)^2$ is small compared with 1,

$$\frac{1}{\rho} \doteqdot \frac{d^2y}{dx^2}.$$

This approximation is important in the application of the theory of elasticity to slightly bent beams.

Note that formula (3) makes ρ positive or negative according as y'' is positive or negative; i.e. according as the graph is concave upwards or downwards (§ 70).

Ex. Find the radius of curvature of the graph of $y = x^2$ at any point (x, y), and in particular at the point where $x = \frac{2}{3}$.

Since $y = x^2$, $\therefore y' = 2x$, $y'' = 2$,

$$\therefore \frac{1}{\rho} = \frac{2}{(1 + 4x^2)^{\frac{3}{2}}},$$

$$\therefore \rho = \tfrac{1}{2}(1 + 4x^2)^{\frac{3}{2}}.$$

In particular, when $x = \frac{2}{3}$, we find $\rho = 2\frac{17}{54}$.

Examples XL.

In Exs. 1-10, find the radius of curvature of the given curves at the points where x has the given values :—

1. $y = x^2$; $x = 0$.   2. $y = 3\sqrt{x}$; $x = 4$.
3. $y = \sin x$; $x = 0$.   4. $y = \sqrt[3]{(x^4)}$; $x = 1$.
5. $y = \cos x$; $x = 0$.   6. $y = \tan x$; $x = \pi/6$.
7. $y = \sin^2 x$; $x = 0$.   8. $y = ax + bx^2$; $x = 0$.
9. $y = \dfrac{1}{x^2 + 1}$; $x = 0$.   10. $y = \dfrac{x^2}{a} + \dfrac{x^3}{b^2}$; $x = 0$.

In Exs. 11-16, find the radius of curvature at any point in terms of x :—

11. $y = x^3$.   12. $y^2 = 4ax$.   13. $3y = (x - 3)\sqrt{x}$.
14. $y = 2 \sec x$.   15. $y = \sqrt{(a^2 - x^2)}$.   16. $6xy = x^4 + 3$.

17. At any point P on the rectangular hyperbola $xy = c^2$, prove that $\rho = r^3/2c^2$, where r is the distance of P from the origin.

18. If the curve $y = a + bx + cx^2$ passes through the point $(3, 4)$, and at that point has the same circle of curvature as the curve $xy = 12$, find the values of a, b, c.

19. If x is regarded as a function of y, prove that

$$\frac{1}{\rho} = \frac{d^2x}{dy^2} \bigg/ \left\{ 1 + \left(\frac{dx}{dy}\right)^2 \right\}^{\frac{3}{2}}.$$

Find the radius of curvature of the parabola $y^2 = 4ax$ at the origin.

20. Find the radius of curvature of the curve $y = x^n$ at the origin, considering all positive values of n.

CHAPTER VIII.

SMALL CHANGES. DIFFERENTIALS.

§ 74. **Proportional Change. — Percentage Change.** — When a small change δx occurs in a variable x,

$\dfrac{\delta x}{x}$ is called the *proportional*, or *relative*, *change ;*

$\dfrac{100\delta x}{x}$ is called the *percentage change.*

§ 75. **Small Change in a Function caused by a Small Change in the Independent Variable.** — Let y be a function of x, and let δy be the change in y caused by a change δx in x. We shall prove that, when δx is small enough,

$$\delta y \doteqdot \frac{dy}{dx}\delta x, \tag{1}$$

provided that $dy/dx \neq 0$. In words, the small change δy in y, caused by a small change δx in x, is approximately equal to δx multiplied by the derivative of y with respect to x.

Proof.—If $dy/dx \neq 0$, we have

$$\frac{\delta y}{\dfrac{dy}{dx}\delta x} = \frac{\dfrac{\delta y}{\delta x}}{\dfrac{dy}{dx}},$$

which approaches the limit 1 when $\delta x \to 0$, since $\dfrac{\delta y}{\delta x} \to \dfrac{dy}{dx}$.

Hence, the ratio of δy to $\dfrac{dy}{dx}\delta x$ approaches the limit 1 when $\delta x \to 0$, and it follows from the definition in § 8 that δy is approximately equal to $\dfrac{dy}{dx}\delta x$ when δx is small enough.

Ex. Calculate the difference for $1'$ in a four-figure table of values of $\tan\theta$, when $\theta = 30°$.

The difference required is the small change caused in $\tan\theta$ when θ changes from $30°$ to $30°\ 1'$.

Put
$$y = \tan\theta,$$
$$\therefore\ \delta y \doteqdot \frac{dy}{d\theta}\delta\theta = \sec^2\theta\ \delta\theta.$$

If $\theta = 30°$,
$$\sec^2\theta = \sec^2 30° = \tfrac{4}{3}\ ;$$

and
$$\delta\theta = 1' = \frac{1}{60}\cdot\frac{\pi}{180}\ \text{radians};$$

$$\therefore\ \delta y \doteqdot \frac{4}{3}\cdot\frac{1}{60}\cdot\frac{\pi}{180} = 0\!\cdot\!0004.$$

§ 76. Small Errors.

Ex. Prove that a small error made in measuring an edge of a cube leads to three times as great a percentage error in the calculated volume (approximately).

Let V be the volume, x the length of an edge ; and let δV be the error in V due to an error δx in x.   Then
$$V = x^3, \tag{i}$$
$$\therefore\ \delta V \doteqdot \frac{dV}{dx}\delta x = 3x^2\delta x. \tag{ii}$$

Dividing (ii) by (i), and multiplying by 100, we get
$$\frac{100\delta V}{V} \doteqdot 3 \times \frac{100\delta x}{x},$$

i.e. the percentage error in V is three times that in x (approx.).

Examples XLI.

In Exs. 1-6, write down the approximate change δy, in y, when the independent variable changes from x to $x + \delta x$, where δx is small :—

1. $y = 3x^2$.   **2.** $y = x^{-1}$.   **3.** $y = 3x + 1$.

4. $y = \sin x$.   **5.** $y = \sec x$.   **6.** $y = \cos^2 x$.

7. If A is the area of a circle, find approximately the change δA in A, when the radius changes from r to $(r + \delta r)$, where δr is small.

8. If V is the volume of a sphere, find approximately the change δV in V, when the radius changes from r to $(r + \delta r)$, where δr is small.

9. If $pv = C$, find approximately the change δp in p due to a small change δv in v.

10. Calculate the difference for $2'$ in a four-figure table of values of $\sin\theta$, when $\theta = 60°$.

11. Calculate the difference for $1'$ in a four-figure table of values of $\cot\theta$, when (i) $\theta = 45°$, (ii) $\theta = 30°$, (iii) $\theta = 70°$.

12. Show that the percentage change in x^n when x increases by α per cent. is approximately $n\alpha$, if α is small.

13. Find the percentage change in $\sqrt{x}$ when x increases by δx.   What percentage error do we make if we replace $\sqrt{(388)}$ by $\sqrt{(400)}$?

14. What percentage error do we make if we replace

(i) $\sqrt[3]{x}$ by $\sqrt[3]{(x + \delta x)}$, (ii) $\sqrt[3]{(8120)}$ by $\sqrt[3]{(8000)}$?

15. How much does the shadow of a 6-ft. man shorten when the sun's altitude increases from 30 to $(30 + \alpha)$ degrees, where α is small ?

16. The formula $S = \frac{1}{2}ab \sin C$ is used to calculate the area of a triangle. Find the percentage error in S caused by a small error α degrees in C.

17. The formula $i = k \tan \theta$ is used to calculate electric current i, where θ is the deflection of a tangent galvanometer, and k is a constant. Find the percentage error in i due to a small error α degrees in θ.

18. If the distance s feet travelled by a point in t seconds is given by $s = t \sin^2 (\pi t/12)$, how far does it move in the interval from $t = 3$ to $t = 3 + \delta t$, where δt is small ?

19. A metal plate, of area A square feet, is parallel to a horizontal table, at a distance x feet above it. A point of light, above the plate, is a feet above the table. If S is the area of the shadow of the plate on the table, find approximately the change δS in S when the plate is raised a small distance δx.

20. Two lines OA, OB, including an angle of $60°$, were once drawn on a sheet of paper, which has since shrunk α per cent. along all lines parallel to OA, where α is small. What does the angle measure now, approximately, in degrees ?

§ 77. Differentials.—If $y = x^3$, instead of $\dfrac{dy}{dx} = 3x^2$ we sometimes write

$$dy = 3x^2 dx, \tag{i}$$

which can be interpreted in either of the following ways :—

(1) We can regard (i) as the ultimate form of the approximation $\delta y \doteqdot 3x^2 \delta x$, when δx and δy are infinitely small; in the sense that the relative error in this approximation approaches zero as $\delta x \to 0$.

(2) We can regard dx as *any* change in x. Then, since $3x^2$ is the rate at which y is changing with respect to x at the beginning of the change from x to $(x + dx)$, it follows that dy, as given by (i), is *the change that would occur in* y *if the rate of change remained constant and equal to its value at the beginning of the change.*

When the form (i) is used, dx and dy are called *differentials*, and dy is called the differential of y with respect to x.

In general, if $y = f(x)$, the *differential* of y with respect to x is denoted by dy and is defined by the equation

$$dy = \frac{dy}{dx} dx, \tag{ii}$$

or $$dy = f'(x) dx. \tag{iii}$$

In words, the differential of y with respect to x is the differential dx multiplied by the coefficient dy/dx (hence the name "differential coefficient").

§ 78. **Graphical Meaning.**—In Fig. 46 let P and Q be two points on a graph. Let PK be the perpendicular from P on the ordinate through Q, and let the tangent at P meet KQ in T.

Let $PK = dx$, $\angle KPT = \psi$. Then

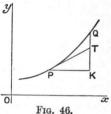

$$KT = PK \tan \psi = dx \cdot \frac{dy}{dx} = \frac{dy}{dx}dx,$$

$$\therefore \ dy = KT.$$

Thus, the differential dy is *the change that would occur in* y, *due to the change* dx *in* x, *if the graph were replaced by its tangent at* P.

The *actual* change in $y = \delta y = KQ$.

Plainly, $KT \doteqdot KQ$, that is, $dy \doteqdot \delta y$, when the change dx is small enough.

Fig. 46.

Ex.
$$df(x) = f'(x)dx \ ;$$
$$d(x^n) = nx^{n-1}dx \ ;$$
$$d\left(\frac{1}{x}\right) = -\frac{1}{x^2}dx \ ; \qquad d(\sqrt{x}) = \frac{1}{2\sqrt{x}}dx \ ;$$
$$d(\sin x) = \cos x \, dx \ ; \quad d(\tan x) = \sec^2 x \, dx \ ; \text{ etc.}$$

Again, if u, v, w are functions of x, and du, dv, dw their differentials with respect to x, and a a constant,

$$d(a) = 0 \ ; \qquad d(ax) = a \, dx \ ; \qquad d(au) = a \, du \ ;$$
$$d(u + v - w) = du + dv - dw \ ;$$
$$d(uv) = u \, dv + v \, du \ ; \quad d\left(\frac{u}{v}\right) = \frac{v \, du - u \, dv}{v^2}.$$

Examples XLII.

Express the given differentials in the form $f'(x)dx$ or $f'(\theta)d\theta$, as the case may be :—

1. $d(2x^3)$.   **2.** $d(x^{-3})$.   **3.** $d(a - x)$.   **4.** $d(ax^2 + c)$.

5. $d\left(\frac{1}{\sqrt{x}}\right)$.   **6.** $d\left(\frac{1}{x^n}\right)$.   **7.** $d\left(x + \frac{1}{x}\right)$.   **8.** $d\left(\frac{\alpha x + \beta}{\gamma x + \delta}\right)$.

9. $d(2\theta)$.   **10.** $d(\frac{1}{2}\theta)$.   **11.** $d(\sec \theta)$.   **12.** $d(\tan \frac{1}{2}\theta)$.

13. $d(\sin^2 \theta)$.   **14.** $d(\cos^n \theta)$.   **15.** $d(\tan^n \theta)$.

16. $d(\sin^{-1} x)$.   **17.** $d(\sin^{-1} x)^2$.   **18.** $d(\tan^{-1} x)$.

§ 79. **Differential Coefficients obtained Geometrically.** — The chief use of differentials occurs in the applications of the Calculus to Geometry, Physics, etc., when it is necessary to find a differential coefficient dy/dx *before the function* y *is* *known in terms of x*. This we can sometimes do by considering *small* changes, which naturally lead to the notation of differentials. The success of many applications of the Calculus depends, in fact, upon our degree of insight into what happens during infinitesimal changes in the variables concerned. In this connection the following theorems are useful :—

(1) If δy lies between $z\delta x$ and $(z + \delta z)\delta x$, where z is a function of x, then

$$dy = z\,dx, \quad \text{or} \quad \frac{dy}{dx} = z.$$

Proof.—Since δy lies between $z\delta x$ and $(z + \delta z)\delta x$,

$$\therefore \frac{\delta y}{\delta x} \text{ lies between } z \text{ and } (z + \delta z).$$

But $\delta z \to 0$ when $\delta x \to 0$; hence, in the limit,

$$\frac{dy}{dx} = z, \quad \text{or} \quad dy = z\,dx.$$

In the functional notation, the same theorem is :—
If δy lies between $f(x)\delta x$ and $f(x + \delta x)\delta x$, then

$$dy = f(x)dx, \quad \text{or} \quad \frac{dy}{dx} = f(x).$$

(2) If $\delta y = z\delta x + \epsilon$, where z is a function of x, and ϵ is so small that $\epsilon/\delta x \to 0$ when $\delta x \to 0$, then

$$dy = z\,dx, \quad \text{or} \quad \frac{dy}{dx} = z.$$

Proof.—Since $\qquad \delta y = z\delta x + \epsilon,$

$$\therefore \frac{\delta y}{\delta x} = z + \frac{\epsilon}{\delta x}.$$

But $\epsilon/\delta x \to 0$, when $\delta x \to 0$; hence, in the limit,

$$\frac{dy}{dx} = z, \quad \text{or} \quad dy = z\,dx.$$

Ex. 1. If A is the area of a circle of radius r, prove that

$$\frac{dA}{dr} = 2\pi r,$$

given that the circumference $= 2\pi r$, but *without using the formula* $A = \pi r^2$.

Let $\delta A =$ the area of the annulus between two concentric circles of radii r and $r + \delta r$ (Fig. 47).

Then plainly δA lies between the areas of two rectangular strips, one of length $2\pi r$, the other of length $2\pi(r + \delta r)$, and both of breadth δr. That is,

$$\delta A \text{ lies between } 2\pi r \delta r \text{ and } 2\pi(r + \delta r)\delta r.$$

Hence, by theorem (1) above,

$$dA = 2\pi r \, dr, \quad \text{or} \quad \frac{dA}{dr} = 2\pi r.$$

Ex. 2. If V is the volume of water in a bowl of any shape when the depth of water is y (Fig. 48), and if A is the area of the surface of the water, prove that

$$\frac{dV}{dy} = A.$$

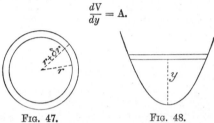

FIG. 47.   FIG. 48.

Let δV be the change in V, and δA the change in A, when the depth of water changes from y to $(y + \delta y)$.

Then, whatever the shape of the bowl, if δy is small enough, δV lies between the volumes of two discs, one of base area A, the other of base area $(A + \delta A)$, and both of thickness δy. That is,

$$\delta V \text{ lies between } A\delta y \text{ and } (A + \delta A)\delta y.$$

Hence, by theorem (1) above,

$$dV = A \, dy, \quad \text{or} \quad \frac{dV}{dy} = A.$$

Ex. 3. If $y = \sin \theta$, prove geometrically that $dy/d\theta = \cos \theta$.

In Fig. 49, let OA and OB be two perpendicular radii of a circle of radius 1.

Let P and Q be two points on the circle, and let PQ meet OB in R.

Let $\angle AOP = \theta$, $\angle AOQ = \theta + \delta\theta$.

Let arc PQ $= \delta s$, $chord$ PQ $= \varDelta s$. Then

$$y + \delta y = \sin(\theta + \delta\theta) = NQ,$$
$$y = \sin \theta \qquad = MP,$$
$$\therefore \delta y = NQ - MP = NQ - NK = KQ.$$

But

$$KQ = PQ \cos \angle KQP = PQ \cos \angle ORP,$$
$$\therefore \delta y = \varDelta s \,.\, \cos \angle ORP.$$

Now $\varDelta s \doteqdot \delta s = \delta\theta$ (since the radius $= 1$), and $\angle ORP \to \theta$ when $\delta\theta \to 0$,

$$\therefore \delta y \doteqdot \delta\theta \cos \theta + \ldots$$

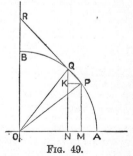

FIG. 49.

where the term omitted on the right is unknown, but is so small that it cannot affect the limit of $\delta y/\delta\theta$ when $\delta\theta \to 0$. Hence, in the limit,

$$dy = d\theta \cos \theta, \quad \text{or} \quad \frac{dy}{d\theta} = \cos \theta.$$

The above reasoning is given as an illustration of the method of differentials. It was not, however, essential to use that method here. We could have reasoned as follows :—

Since $\delta\theta = \delta s$,

$$\therefore \frac{\delta y}{\delta\theta} = \frac{\delta y}{\delta s} = \frac{\delta y}{\Delta s} \cdot \frac{\Delta s}{\delta s} = \frac{\Delta s}{\delta s} \cos \angle KQP = \frac{\Delta s}{\delta s} \cos \angle ORP.$$

But, when $\delta\theta \to 0$, $\angle ORP \to \theta$, and $\Delta s/\delta s \to 1$,

$$\therefore \frac{dy}{d\theta} = \cos \theta.$$

Examples XLIII.

1. If V is the volume, and S the surface area, of a sphere of radius r, prove geometrically that $dV = Sdr$.

2. If V is the volume of a cone of height x and semi-angle $30°$, prove geometrically that $dV/dx = \frac{1}{3}\pi x^2$.

3. Differentiate $\cos \theta$ geometrically.

4. Differentiate (i) $\tan \theta$, (ii) $\sec \theta$, geometrically. [Begin with a right-angled triangle OAP, in which OA $= 1$, $\angle AOP = \theta$, and $\angle OAP =$ a right angle.]

5. A circle of radius a is divided into two segments by a chord drawn at a distance x from the centre. If A is the area of the major segment, prove geometrically that

$$\frac{dA}{dx} = 2\sqrt{(a^2 - x^2)}.$$

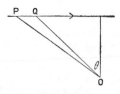

FIG. 50.   FIG. 51.

6. In the circle $x^2 + y^2 = a^2$ (see Fig. 50), if $s =$ arc AP, $\theta = \angle AOP$, prove that

(i) $x\,ds = a\,dy$, (ii) $y\,ds = -a\,dx$,

where dx, dy, ds denote differentials with respect to θ.

7. P and Q are two points close together on the trajectory of a shell travelling at 1600 ft./sec. (Fig. 51). Calculate the angle θ if the noise of the shell reaches O from P and Q simultaneously. [Velocity of sound$=1100$ ft./sec.]

8. The area of the horizontal section of a ship at the water-line is 25,000 square feet, and the weight of the ship is 20,000 tons. Find the change in its draught when it passes from a river to the sea. [Sea-water weighs 64, and fresh water $62\frac{1}{2}$ lbs./cub. ft. approx.]

9. Water pours into a vessel of any shape at the rate of q cub. ft./sec. How fast is the water level rising when the area of the surface of the water is A square feet ?

10. Water is pouring into a hemispherical bowl of diameter 30 ins. When the depth is 6 ins. the level is rising at the rate of one-tenth of an inch per second. How fast is the water pouring in ?

11. The vertical section of a bowl, by a plane passing through its axis, has the shape of the graph of $y = x^4$ between the points $(1, 1)$ and $(-1, 1)$, x and y being measured in feet.

When the bowl contains water to a depth of y feet, it flows out through a hole in the bottom at the rate of $6\sqrt{y}$ cub. ins./sec. Show that the water level falls at a constant rate, and find how long the bowl will take to empty if it is full to begin with.

12. If A is the area common to two circles, each of radius x, and if $2a$ is the distance between their centres, express A in terms of a and x. Find dA/dx, and verify geometrically.

13. If x, y are the lengths of the diagonals of a parallelogram formed by four inextensible jointed bars, prove that when the parallelogram undergoes a small deformation

$$y dy = - x dx.$$

[*Hint :* The sum of the squares on the diagonals of a parallelogram is equal to the sum of the squares on the sides.]

14. ABCD is a quadrilateral formed by four inextensible jointed bars, and P, Q, R, S are the mid points of the sides AB, BC, CD, DA respectively.

If $x = $ PR, $y = $ QS, prove that when the quadrilateral undergoes a small deformation

$$y dy = x dx.$$

[*Hint :* $x^2 - y^2 = \frac{1}{2}(b^2 + d^2 - a^2 - c^2)$

where $a = $ AB, $b = $ BC, $c = $ CD, $d = $ DA.]

CHAPTER IX.

INTEGRALS.

§ 80. Indefinite Integrals.—We now turn to the process which is the reverse of differentiation.

The sign $\int$ is called the *integral sign*. The expression

$$\int f(x)dx$$

[read: "integral $f(x)dx$"] is called the *indefinite integral* of the differential $f(x)dx$; it denotes *a function of* x *whose differential coefficient with respect to* x *is* f(x), or, a function whose differential with respect to x is $f(x)dx$.

In this indefinite integral, $f(x)$ is called the *integrand*, and dx the differential of the *variable of integration*.

By definition, the differential coefficient of an indefinite integral with respect to the variable of integration is the integrand; thus,

$$\frac{d}{dx}\int f(x)dx = f(x). \tag{1}$$

§ 81. To *evaluate* a given indefinite integral, we have to find a function whose differential coefficient is the integrand. The process of finding an indefinite integral is therefore the reverse of finding a differential coefficient.

There is a general rule for finding differential coefficients (§ 20), but none for finding integrals. To find an integral we have to rely, to begin with, upon our familiarity with the reverse process of differentiation.

§ 82. Ex. Evaluate the indefinite integral $\int 3x^2 dx$.

The integrand is $3x^2$, which we know to be the differential coefficient of x^3,

$$\therefore \int 3x^2 dx = x^3.$$

But we could also put

$$\int 3x^2 dx = x^3 + \mathrm{C},$$

where C is any constant, because $3x^2$ is also the differential coefficient of $(x^3 + \mathrm{C})$, since the differential coefficient of a constant is zero. It is on account of this latitude in its meaning that the integral is called *indefinite*.

The constant C is called an *arbitrary constant*, or the *constant of integration* (see § 94).

§ 83. **The Integral** $\int x^n\, dx$.—By differentiation we have, provided $(n + 1) \neq 0$,

$$\frac{d}{dx}\left(\frac{x^{n+1}}{n+1}\right) = x^n.$$

It follows that, provided $n \neq -1$,

$$\int x^n\, dx = \frac{x^{n+1}}{n+1}.$$

Rule.—If the integrand is a power of the variable of integration, with a constant index, *add 1 to the index and divide by the new index.*

Ex. 1. $\int x^5\, dx = \dfrac{x^6}{6}.$

Ex. 2. $\int \dfrac{dx}{\sqrt{x}} = \int x^{-\frac{1}{2}}\, dx = \dfrac{x^{\frac{1}{2}}}{\frac{1}{2}} = 2\sqrt{x}.$

Ex. 3. $\int \dfrac{dx}{x^2} = \int x^{-2}\, dx = \dfrac{x^{-1}}{-1} = -\dfrac{1}{x}.$

Note.—We have excepted the case $n = -1$. When $n = -1$,

$$\int x^n\, dx = \int x^{-1}\, dx = \int \frac{1}{x} dx = \log_e x,$$

as we shall see later (§ 174).

§ 84. **Standard Integrals.**—In this and the next two chapters we shall rely upon the following *standard integrals* :—

$$\int x^n dx = \frac{x^{n+1}}{n+1}, \qquad (1)$$

$$\int \cos x\, dx = \sin x, \qquad \int \cos (ax + b)dx = \frac{\sin (ax + b)}{a}, \qquad (2)$$

$$\int \sin x\, dx = -\cos x, \qquad \int \sin (ax + b)dx = -\frac{\cos (ax + b)}{a}. \qquad (3)$$

To prove (2) and (3) it is only necessary to show that the differential coefficients of the right-hand sides are equal to the integrands on the left-hand sides.

§ 85. **Two Rules.**—(1) *A constant factor in the integrand can be written before the integral sign.* That is, if a is a constant, and u a function of x,

$$\int au\, dx = a\int u\, dx. \qquad (4)$$

(2) *Rule for finding an integral whose integrand is a sum or difference :* If u, v, w are functions of x,

$$\int (u + v - w)dx = \int u\, dx + \int v\, dx - \int w\, dx. \qquad (5)$$

Proof.—In both cases, the derivative of the left side is equal to that of the right side, by the definition of an indefinite integral and the rules of differentiation.

Ex. Evaluate (i) $\int \dfrac{x^4 + 1}{x^2} dx$, (ii) $\int \cos 5x \cos 3x \, dx$.

(i) $\int \dfrac{x^4 + 1}{x^2} dx = \int \left(x^2 + \dfrac{1}{x^2} \right) d \, x = \int x^2 \, dx + \int \dfrac{dx}{x^2} = \dfrac{x^3}{3} - \dfrac{1}{x}.$

(ii) $\int \cos 5x \cos 3x \, dx = \tfrac{1}{2} \int (\cos 8x + \cos 2x) dx$, by trigonometry,

$$= \dfrac{1}{2} \left(\dfrac{\sin 8x}{8} + \dfrac{\sin 2x}{2} \right).$$

Examples XLIV.

Evaluate the given indefinite integrals :—

1. $\int x^4 \, dx$.
2. $\int 6x^2 \, dx$.
3. $\int x \, dx$.
4. $\int dx$.
5. $\int x^{-4} \, dx$.
6. $\int 6x^{-2} \, dx$.
7. $\int x^{1.4} \, dx$.
8. $\int x^{-1.4} \, dx$.
9. $\int \dfrac{dx}{x^3}$.
10. $\int \dfrac{dx}{\sqrt{x}}$.
11. $\int \dfrac{5dx}{x^2}$.
12. $\int \dfrac{dx}{ax^n}$.
13. $\int (x^2 + x) dx$.
14. $\int (x^3 - a^3) dx$.
15. $\int (ax^2 + bx + c) dx$.
16. $\int \left(x - \dfrac{1}{x} \right)^2 dx$.
17. $\int \dfrac{2x - 3}{x^3} dx$.
18. $\int \dfrac{ax^2 + bx + c}{x^4} dx$.
19. $\int \dfrac{x + 1}{\sqrt{x}} dx$.
20. $\int (1 + \sqrt[3]{x^2}) dx$.
21. $\int (1 + x)^2 \sqrt{x} \, dx$.
22. $\int a \sin \omega t \, dt$.
23. $\int \cos (1 + 3x) dx$.
24. $\int \sin (1 - x) dx$.
25. $\int \sin 2x \cos 2x \, dx$.
26. $\int \sin x \sin 3x \, dx$.
27. $\int \cos mx \cos nx \, dx$.
28. $\int a \sin \omega t \, . \, b \cos (\omega t - \alpha) \, dt$.

§ 86. Methods of Integration are methods by which the evaluation of integrals, which are not themselves standard integrals, can be made to depend on standard integrals. One such method is to *change the variable of integration* by means of a *substitution*.

§ 87. Substitutions of the form $v = \phi(x)$.—We shall prove that, if v is a function of x,

$$\int f(v) \dfrac{dv}{dx} dx = \int f(v) dv. \qquad (1)$$

Proof.—Let $z = \int f(v) dv$. Then $\dfrac{dz}{dv} = f(v)$,

$$\therefore \dfrac{dz}{dx} = \dfrac{dz}{dv} \dfrac{dv}{dx} = f(v) \dfrac{dv}{dx},$$

$$\therefore z = \int f(v)\frac{dv}{dx}dx,$$

$$\therefore \int f(v)\frac{dv}{dx}dx = z = \int f(v)dv.$$

Ex. 1. Evaluate $\int(x^3 + x^2)^{-\frac{1}{2}}(3x^2 + 2x)dx, = z$, say.

Since $d(x^3 + x^2) = (3x^2 + 2x)dx$, we make the substitution

$$v = x^3 + x^2, \qquad dv = (3x^2 + 2x)dx,$$

$$\therefore z = \int v^{-\frac{1}{2}} \, dv = \frac{v^{\frac{1}{2}}}{\frac{1}{2}} = 2v^{\frac{1}{2}},$$

$$\therefore z = 2(x^3 + x^2)^{\frac{1}{2}}.$$

Ex. 2. Evaluate $\int x(x^2 + a^2)^n \, dx, = z$, say.

Multiplying and dividing by 2, which does not affect the value of the integrand, we can put z in the form

$$z = \tfrac{1}{2}\int(x^2 + a^2)^n \cdot 2x \, dx.$$

Since $d(x^2 + a^2) = 2x \, dx$, we make the substitution

$$v = x^2 + a^2, \qquad dv = 2x \, dx,$$

$$\therefore z = \tfrac{1}{2}\int v^n \, dv = \frac{v^{n+1}}{2(n + 1)},$$

$$\therefore z = \frac{(x^2 + a^2)^{n+1}}{2(n + 1)}.$$

Examples XLV.

Evaluate the given integrals :—

1. $\int(x^2 + 4)^5 \cdot 2x \, dx.$
2. $\int 2x\sqrt{(x^2 - 1)}dx.$
3. $\int(2x - 1)^{\frac{1}{3}} \, dx.$
4. $\int x\sqrt{(a^2 - x^2)} \, dx.$
5. $\int x(ax^2 + b)^n \, dx.$
6. $\int(ax + b)^4 \, dx.$
7. $\int x^2(a + bx^3)^{\frac{1}{2}} \, dx.$
8. $\int(ax^2 + bx)^n(2ax + b)dx.$
9. $\int \frac{2dx}{\sqrt{(2x + 3)}}.$
10. $\int \frac{dx}{(1 - 3x)^3}.$
11. $\int \frac{dx}{(ax + b)^2}.$
12. $\int \frac{3x^2 \, dx}{(a^3 + x^3)^2}.$
13. $\int \frac{x \, dx}{\sqrt{(1 - x^2)}}.$
14. $\int \frac{dx}{\sqrt[3]{(ax + b)}}.$
15. $\int \frac{x^5 \, dx}{(x^6 + 1)^3}.$
16. $\int \frac{(1 + \sqrt{x})^n}{\sqrt{x}} \, dx.$
17. $\int \left(\frac{1}{a} - \frac{1}{x}\right)^n \frac{dx}{x^2}.$
18. $\int \frac{(x + 1)dx}{\sqrt{(x^2 + 2x - 1)}}.$
19. $\int \frac{(3x + 2)dx}{(3x^2 + 4x + 2)^4}.$

§ 88. The integral $\int\sin^m \theta \cos^n \theta \, d\theta$.—Here the integrand is a product of powers of the sine and cosine of the variable of integration.

To evaluate an integral of this kind, we notice, for the present, the following methods (see also § 187, and p. 243) :—

(1) *Cosine index odd.* Make the substitution

$$v = \sin \theta, \qquad dv = \cos \theta \, d\theta, \qquad \cos^2 \theta = 1 - v^2.$$

(2) *Sine index odd.* Make the substitution

$$v = \cos \theta, \qquad dv = - \sin \theta \, d\theta, \qquad \sin^2 \theta = 1 - v^2.$$

(3) *Both indices even.* Apply the double-angle formulæ :—

$$\cos^2 \theta = \tfrac{1}{2}(1 + \cos 2\theta), \quad \sin^2 \theta = \tfrac{1}{2}(1 - \cos 2\theta), \quad \sin \theta \cos \theta = \tfrac{1}{2} \sin 2\theta,$$

repeatedly, if necessary.

Ex. 1. Evaluate (i) $\int \sin^2 \theta \cos \theta \, d\theta$, (ii) $\int \sin^3 \theta \, d\theta$.
(i) Put

$$v = \sin \theta, \qquad dv = \cos \theta \, d\theta,$$
$$\therefore \int \sin^2 \theta \cos \theta \, d\theta = \int v^2 dv = \frac{v^3}{3} = \frac{\sin^3 \theta}{3}.$$

Briefly,

$$\int \sin^2 \theta \cos \theta \, d\theta = \int \sin^2 \theta \, d(\sin \theta) = \tfrac{1}{3} \sin^3 \theta.$$

(ii) Put

$$v = \cos \theta, \quad dv = - \sin \theta \, d\theta, \quad \sin^2 \theta = 1 - v^2,$$
$$\therefore \int \sin^3 \theta \, d\theta = \int \sin^2 \theta \sin \theta \, d\theta = \int (1 - v^2)(- dv).$$
$$\therefore \int \sin^3 \theta \, d\theta = - v + \tfrac{1}{3} v^3 = - \cos \theta + \tfrac{1}{3} \cos^3 \theta.$$

Ex. 2. Evaluate (i) $\int \cos^2 \theta \, d\theta$, (ii) $\int \sin^2 \theta \, d\theta$, (iii) $\int \sin^2 \theta \cos^2 \theta \, d\theta$.

(i) $\int \cos^2 \theta \, d\theta = \tfrac{1}{2} \int (1 + \cos 2\theta) d\theta = \tfrac{1}{2} \left(\theta + \dfrac{\sin 2\theta}{2} \right)$,

$$\therefore \int \cos^2 \theta \, d\theta = \tfrac{1}{2}(\theta + \sin \theta \cos \theta).$$

(ii) Similarly,

$$\int \sin^2 \theta \, d\theta = \tfrac{1}{2}(\theta - \sin \theta \cos \theta).$$

(iii) $\int \sin^2 \theta \cos^2 \theta \, d\theta = \int (\tfrac{1}{2} \sin 2\theta)^2 d\theta = \tfrac{1}{8} \int (1 - \cos 4\theta) d\theta$,

$$\therefore \int \sin^2 \theta \cos^2 \theta \, d\theta = \frac{1}{8} \left(\theta - \frac{\sin 4\theta}{4} \right).$$

§ 89. Integrals differing by a Constant.—Different methods of evaluating the same integral may lead to different results, but these can only differ by a constant.

Ex. $\int \sin \theta \cos \theta \, d\theta = \int \sin \theta \, d(\sin \theta) = \dfrac{\sin^2 \theta}{2}.$

Also, $\int \sin \theta \cos \theta \, d\theta = \int \dfrac{\sin 2\theta}{2} d\theta = - \dfrac{\cos 2\theta}{4}.$

Thus, for the same integral, we have two results, but these only differ by a constant, as may be verified by trigonometry.

Examples XLVI.

Evaluate the given indefinite integrals :—

1. $\int \cos^3 \theta \, d\theta.$ **2.** $\int \sin^3 \theta \cos \theta \, d\theta.$ **3.** $\int \cos^2 \theta \sin \theta \, d\theta.$

4. $\int \sin^5 \theta \, d\theta.$ **5.** $\int \sin^3 \theta \cos^3 \theta \, d\theta.$ **6.** $\int \sin 2\theta \cos \theta \, d\theta.$

7. $\int \sin^4 \theta \, d\theta.$ **8.** $\int \sin^2 \theta \cos^4 \theta \, d\theta.$ **9.** $\int \cos 2\theta \cos^2 \theta \, d\theta.$

10. $\int \dfrac{\sin \theta \, d\theta}{\cos^2 \theta}.$ **11.** $\int \dfrac{\cos \theta \, d\theta}{\sqrt{(\sin \theta)}}.$ **12.** $\int \dfrac{\cos^3 \theta \, d\theta}{\sin^4 \theta}.$

13. $\int (1 + \sin \theta)^2 d\theta.$ **14.** $\int (2 + \sin \theta)^3 \cos \theta \, d\theta.$

15. $\int (\cos \theta + 2 \sin \theta)^2 d\theta.$ **16.** $\int (\cos \theta + \cos 2\theta)^2 d\theta.$

§ 90. Substitutions of the form $x = \phi(v).$—From (1), § 87, we deduce, by a change of notation, that, if x is a function of v,

$$\int f(x) dx = \int f(x) \frac{dx}{dv} dv. \qquad (2)$$

Hence, to change the variable of integration from x to v by a substitution of the form $x = \phi(v)$, we have the rule :—

Rule.—Express the integrand in terms of v, and replace dx by $\dfrac{dx}{dv} dv.$

Ex. Evaluate $\int \dfrac{x \, dx}{(2x + 1)^3}$, $= z$, say.

Put $2x + 1 = v, \;\; \therefore \; x = \tfrac{1}{2}(v - 1), \;\; dx = \tfrac{1}{2} dv,$

$$\therefore z = \int \frac{\tfrac{1}{2}(v - 1) \cdot \tfrac{1}{2} dv}{v^3} = \frac{1}{4} \int \left(\frac{1}{v^2} - \frac{1}{v^3} \right) dv,$$

$$\therefore z = \frac{1}{4} \left(-\frac{1}{v} + \frac{1}{2v^2} \right) = \frac{-2v + 1}{8v^2},$$

$$\therefore z = -\frac{4x + 1}{8(2x + 1)^2}.$$

§ 91. Square-roots in the Integrand.—Often the object of a substitution is, in the first place, to get rid of a square-root sign in the integrand.

Rule.—When the square-root of a *linear* function, $\sqrt{(ax + b)}$ occurs in the integrand, make the substitution

$$\sqrt{(ax + b)} = v, \;\; \therefore \; ax + b = v^2, \;\; x = \frac{v^2 - b}{a}, \;\; dx = \frac{2v \, dv}{a}.$$

Ex. Evaluate $\int \dfrac{x \, dx}{\sqrt{(x - 1)}}$, $= z$, say.

Put $\sqrt{(x - 1)} = v, \;\; \therefore \; x - 1 = v^2, \;\; x = v^2 + 1, \;\; dx = 2v \, dv,$

$$\therefore z = \int \frac{(v^2 + 1) 2v \, dv}{v} = 2 \int (v^2 + 1) dv,$$

$$\therefore z = 2 \left(\frac{v^3}{3} + v \right) = \frac{2v}{3} (v^2 + 3),$$

$$\therefore z = \tfrac{2}{3}(x + 2)\sqrt{(x - 1)}.$$

§ 92. When $\sqrt{(a^2 - x^2)}$ occurs in an integrand, it is often best to make the *trigonometric* substitution

$$x = a \sin \theta, \quad dx = a \cos \theta \, d\theta, \quad \sqrt{(a^2 - x^2)} = a \cos \theta.$$
$$[\sqrt{(a^2 - x^2)} = \sqrt{(a^2 - a^2 \sin^2 \theta)} = \sqrt{(a^2 \cos^2 \theta)} = a \cos \theta.]$$

This is a particular case of the square-root of a *quadratic* function in the integrand.

Ex. Evaluate (i) $\int \dfrac{dx}{\sqrt{(a^2 - x^2)}}$, (ii) $\int \sqrt{(a^2 - x^2)} dx$.

In each case we make the above substitution.

(i) 　　　　$\int \dfrac{dx}{\sqrt{(a^2 - x^2)}} = \int \dfrac{a \cos \theta \, d\theta}{a \cos \theta} = \int d\theta = \theta,$

　　　　$\therefore \int \dfrac{dx}{\sqrt{(a^2 - x^2)}} = \sin^{-1} \dfrac{x}{a}.$

This **is a** standard integral, which also follows immediately from (1), § 54.

(ii) 　　　　$\int \sqrt{(a^2 - x^2)} dx = \int a \cos \theta \cdot a \cos \theta \, d\theta$
　　　　　　　　$= a^2 \int \cos^2 \theta \, d\theta$
　　　　　　　　$= \tfrac{1}{2} a^2 (\theta + \sin \theta \cos \theta),$

by Ex. 2, § 88 ; hence, making use of Fig. 52,

$$\int \sqrt{(a^2 - x^2)} dx = \tfrac{1}{2} a^2 \sin^{-1} \dfrac{x}{a} + \tfrac{1}{2} x \sqrt{(a^2 - x^2)}.$$

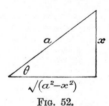

Fig. 52.

Examples XLVII.

Evaluate the given indefinite integrals :—

1. $\int x(x - 1)^5 \, dx$.
2. $\int \dfrac{x \, dx}{(x - 1)^4}$.
3. $\int \dfrac{x^2 \, dx}{(x - 1)^4}$.
4. $\int x \sqrt{(x - 1)} dx$.
5. $\int (x + 2) \sqrt{(2x + 3)} dx$.
6. $\int \dfrac{x \, dx}{\sqrt{(x + 2)}}$.
7. $\int \dfrac{x^2 \, dx}{\sqrt{(x - 1)}}$.
8. $\int \dfrac{4x^2 + 1}{\sqrt{(2x + 1)}} dx$.
9. $\int \dfrac{dx}{\sqrt{(4 - x^2)}}$.
10. $\int \dfrac{x \, dx}{\sqrt{(4 - x^2)}}$.
11. $\int \dfrac{x^2 \, dx}{\sqrt{(a^2 - x^2)}}$.
12. $\int \dfrac{dx}{\sqrt{(1 - x^2)}}$.
13. $\int \dfrac{dx}{\sqrt{(1 - a^2 x^2)}}$.
14. $\int \dfrac{dx}{\sqrt{(9 - 4x^2)}}$.
15. $\int \sqrt{(4 - x^2)} dx$.
16. $\int x \sqrt{(1 - x^2)} dx$.
17. $\int x^2 \sqrt{(a^2 - x^2)} dx$.

§ 93. **Integration by Parts.**—We shall prove that

$$\int u\, dv = uv - \int v\, du. \qquad (3)$$

Proof.—Since

$$d(uv) = u\, dv + v\, du,$$
$$\therefore uv = \int u\, dv + \int v\, du,$$
$$\therefore \int u\, dv = uv - \int v\, du.$$

This formula has many applications. For our present purpose it is useful when $\int v\, du$ is easier to evaluate than $\int u\, dv$. Applying this formula is called *integrating by parts*.

Ex. 1. Evaluate $\int x \cos x\, dx$, $= z$, say.
Since
$$\cos x\, dx = d(\sin x),$$
$$\therefore z = \int x\, d(\sin x) = x \sin x - \int \sin x\, dx$$
$$= x \sin x + \cos x.$$

Ex. 2. Evaluate $\int (x^2 + 1) \cos x\, dx$, $= z$, say.
$$z = \int (x^2 + 1)\, d(\sin x) = (x^2 + 1) \sin x - \int \sin x\, d(x^2 + 1)$$
$$= (x^2 + 1) \sin x - 2\int x \sin x\, dx.$$
Integrating by parts again,
$$\int x \sin x\, dx = \int x\, d(-\cos x) = x(-\cos x) - \int (-\cos x)dx$$
$$= -x \cos x + \sin x.$$
$$\therefore z = (x^2 + 1) \sin x - 2(-x \cos x + \sin x)$$
$$= (x^2 - 1) \sin x + 2x \cos x.$$

Examples XLVIII.

Evaluate the given integrals :—

1. $\int x \sin x\, dx$.
2. $\int x^2 \sin x\, dx$.
3. $\int 2x \cos 2x\, dx$.
4. $\int x^3 \cos x\, dx$.
5. $\int x \cos^2 x\, dx$.
6. $\int (x - x^2) \cos x\, dx$.
7. $\int (1 - 2x) \sin 2x\, dx$.
8. $\int x \sin x \cos x\, dx$.
9. $\int (x + 1)^2 \cos 2x\, dx$.
10. $\int 2x \cos 3x \cos x\, dx$.

§ 94. **The General Integral.**—We shall first prove that $(x^3 + C)$ is the *most general* value of the indefinite integral $\int 3x^2\, dx$. In other words, *every* function whose derivative is $3x^2$ is included in $(x^3 + C)$, where C denotes any constant.

Proof.—Let v be *any* function whose derivative is $3x^2$, and consider the difference $(v - x^3)$. Since

$$\frac{d}{dx}(v - x^3) = \frac{dv}{dx} - 3x^2 = 3x^2 - 3x^2 = 0,$$

the rate of change of the function $(v - x^3)$, with respect to x, is zero for all values of x,

$$\therefore v - x^3 = \text{a constant},$$
$$\therefore v = x^3 + \text{a constant}.$$

Hence, $(x^3 + C)$ includes every function whose derivative is $3x^2$, and is called the *general integral* of $3x^2\, dx$.

§ 95. Next, let $F(x)$ be any function whose differential coefficient is $f(x)$. Then we could prove in a similar way that the most general value of the indefinite integral $\int f(x)dx$ is given by

$$\int f(x)dx = F(x) + C,$$

where C denotes any constant. Hence, $F(x) + C$ is called the *general integral* of $f(x)dx$. It follows that, if

$$\frac{dy}{dx} = f(x),$$

then
$$y = \int f(x)dx + C,$$

where C is *some* constant.

Ex. 1. The gradient at any point of a certain curve is $2x$, and the curve passes through the point (2, 7). Find its equation.

Since
$$\frac{dy}{dx} = 2x,$$
$$\therefore y = \int 2x\, dx + C,$$
$$\therefore y = x^2 + C,$$

where C is some constant.

But $y = 7$ when $x = 2$, since the point (2, 7) is on the curve,
$$\therefore 7 = 2^2 + C = 4 + C,$$
$$\therefore C = 3,$$
$$\therefore y = x^2 + 3.$$

This is the equation of the curve.

Ex. 2. Given that $\frac{d^2y}{dx^2} = 6(1 - x)$, that $\frac{dy}{dx} = 2$ when $x = 0$, and that $y = 4$ when $x = 1$, express y in terms of x.

Since
$$\frac{d}{dx}\left(\frac{dy}{dx}\right) = \frac{d^2y}{dx^2} = 6(1 - x),$$
$$\therefore \frac{dy}{dx} = \int (6 - 6x)dx + C,$$
$$= 6x - 3x^2 + C,$$

where C is some constant.

But $dy/dx = 2$ when $x = 0$,
$$\therefore 2 = 0 - 0 + C,$$
$$\therefore C = 2,$$
$$\therefore \frac{dy}{dx} = 2 + 6x - 3x^2,$$
$$\therefore y = \int (2 + 6x - 3x^2)dx + A,$$
$$= 2x + 3x^2 - x^3 + A,$$

where A is another constant.

But $y = 4$ when $x = 1$,
$$\therefore 4 = 2 + 3 - 1 + A = 4 + A,$$
$$\therefore A = 0,$$
$$\therefore y = 2x + 3x^2 - x^3.$$

§ **96.** Let a point move along a straight line, and let s, v, a, and t have their usual meanings (§§ 56, 57) :—

Since $\qquad \dfrac{ds}{dt} = v, \qquad \therefore s = \int v\,dt + C.$ $\qquad$ (1)

Since $\qquad \dfrac{dv}{dt} = a, \qquad \therefore v = \int a\,dt + C.$ $\qquad$ (2)

Since $\qquad \dfrac{d}{ds}(\tfrac{1}{2}v^2) = a, \quad \therefore \tfrac{1}{2}v^2 = \int a\,ds + C.$ $\qquad$ (3)

Before the integrals in (1) and (2) can be evaluated, v and a must be known *in terms of t;* before the integral in (3) can be evaluated, a must be known *in terms of s.*

Examples XLIX.

In Exs. 1-6, express y in terms of x :—

1. $\dfrac{dy}{dx} = 6x^2$; $y = 1$ when $x = 0$. $\quad$ 2. $\dfrac{dy}{dx} = \sin x$; $y = 0$ when $x = 0$.

3. $\dfrac{dy}{dx} = \dfrac{6}{x^4}$; $y = 0$ when $x = 1$. $\quad$ 4. $\dfrac{dy}{dx} = \dfrac{-14}{(4x-1)^2}$; $y = 1$ when $x = 2$.

5. $\dfrac{d^2y}{dx^2} = 1 - x$; $\dfrac{dy}{dx} = 0$ and $y = 0$, when $x = 0$.

6. $\dfrac{d^2y}{dx^2} = x(1 - x)$; $y = 0$ when $x = 0$ and when $x = 1$.

In Exs. 7-12, s, v, a, and t have their usual meanings :—

7. $a = 2t - 5$; $v = 10$ when $t = 3$. Express v in terms of t, and find v when $t = 6$.

8. $v = a \sin \pi t$; $s = 0$ when $t = 0$. Express s in terms of t, and find s when $t = 1$.

9. $a = g$; $v = u$ when $t = 0$, and $s = 0$ when $t = 0$; where g is a constant. Express v and s in terms of t.

10. $a = 4 \sin 2t$; $v = 0$ when $t = 0$, and $s = 3$ when $t = 0$. Express v and s in terms of t.

11. $a = g$; $v = u$ when $s = 0$; where g is a constant. Express v in terms of s.

12. $a = -k/s^2$; $v = 0$ when $s = a$; where k is a constant. Express v in terms of s.

13. If $EI\dfrac{d^2y}{dx^2} = W(l - x)$, where E, I, W, l are constants ; and if $y = 0$ and $dy/dx = 0$ when $x = 0$, express y in terms of x, and find the value of y when $x = l$.

14. If $\dfrac{dy}{dx} = -k(a^2 - x^2)$, and $\dfrac{dz}{dx} = -y$, where k and a are constants ; and if $y = 0$ and $z = 0$ when $x = a$, prove that
$$z = \tfrac{1}{12} k(a - x)^3(3a + x).$$

4

§ 97. **Definite Integrals.**—The expression $\int_a^b f(x)dx$, which we read "integral $f(x)dx$ from a to b," is called a *definite integral*. It denotes the change (§ 15) in the indefinite integral $\int f(x)dx$ when x changes from a to b. Let $\int f(x)dx = F(x)$; then, since $F(x)$ changes from $F(a)$ to $F(b)$ when x changes from a to b,

$$\int_a^b f(x)dx = F(b) - F(a).$$

The range of variation of x, from a to b, is called the *range of integration*; a and b are called the *limits of integration*, a being called the *lower limit* and b the *upper limit*. (The meaning of the word "limit" here is quite distinct from its meaning in § 5. The limits a and b are simply the first and last values of the range of variation of x.)

The difference $F(b) - F(a)$ is also denoted by $\left[F(x) \right]_a^b$, so that

$$\int_a^b f(x)dx = \left[F(x) \right]_a^b = F(b) - F(a).$$

Rule. To evaluate the definite integral $\int_a^b f(x)dx$:—

Find the indefinite integral $F(x)$, and then subtract the value of $F(x)$ when $x = a$ from its value when $x = b$.

Ex. Evaluate (i) $\int_3^5 x\,dx$, (ii) $\int_0^\pi \sin^2\theta\,d\theta$.

(i)
$$\int_3^5 x\,dx = \left[\frac{x^2}{2}\right]_3^5 = \frac{5^2}{2} - \frac{3^2}{2} = 8.$$

(ii) Since $\int \sin^2\theta\,d\theta = \frac{1}{2}(\theta - \sin\theta\cos\theta)$, by Ex. 2, § 88,

$$\therefore \int_0^\pi \sin^2\theta\,d\theta = \frac{1}{2}\left[\theta - \sin\theta\cos\theta\right]_0^\pi$$
$$= \frac{1}{2}[(\pi - \sin\pi\cos\pi) - (0 - 0)]$$
$$= \frac{1}{2}\pi.$$

Examples L.

Evaluate the given definite integrals :—

1. $\int_3^6 x^2 dx.$

2. $\int_0^1 \sqrt{x}\,dx.$

3. $\int_{-6}^6 (x^2 - x^3)dx.$

4. $\int_a^b dx.$

5. $\int_{-a}^a x\,dx.$

6. $\int_{-a}^a (a^2 - x^2)dx.$

7. $\int_1^{10} \frac{dx}{x^2}.$

8. $\int_1^2 \frac{x-1}{x^3}dx.$

9. $\int_4^9 \frac{x+1}{\sqrt{x}}dx.$

10. $\int_0^{\frac{\pi}{2}} \sin \theta \, d\theta.$ **11.** $\int_0^{\frac{\pi}{2}} \cos^2 \theta \, d\theta.$ **12.** $\int_0^4 \sqrt{(9 + 4x)} dx.$

13. $\int_{-\alpha}^{\alpha} \cos \theta \, d\theta.$ **14.** $\int_0^{\pi} \sin^3 \theta \, d\theta.$ **15.** $\int_0^{\pi} \cos^2 \theta \sin \theta \, d\theta.$

16. $\int_0^{\pi} x \sin x \, dx.$ **17.** $\int_0^{\frac{\pi}{2}} x \cos x \, dx.$ **18.** $\int_0^{2\pi} (1 - \cos \theta)^2 d\theta.$

19. $\int_0^{\pi} \sin^4 \theta \, d\theta.$ **20.** $\int_0^{\pi} \cos^2 \frac{x}{3} \, dx.$ **21.** $\int_0^{\pi} \cos 3x \cos 5x \, dx.$

§ 98. **Meaning of a Definite Integral on the Graph of the Integrand.**—Assume that $f(x)$ is positive from $x = a$ to $x = b$, and does not become infinite for any value of x between a and b, and that $a < b$.

We shall prove that $\int_a^b f(x) dx =$ the area bounded by the graph of $y = f(x)$, the x-axis, and the ordinates $x = a$, $x = b$.

Proof. Let the curve in Fig. 53 be the graph of $y = f(x)$. Let $OA = a$, $OB = b$, $OM = x$, $ON = x + \delta x$. Draw the ordinates AD, MP, NQ, BC.

Then $MP = y$, $NQ = y + \delta y$.
Let $A =$ area ABCD.
Let $z =$ area AMPD. Then z is a function of x, such that $z = 0$ when $x = a$, $z = A$ when $x = b$, and $\delta z =$ area of strip MNQP.

Let PK be the perpendicular from P on NQ, and QH the perpendicular from Q on MP.

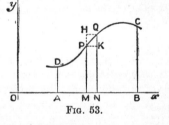

Fig. 53.

Now, if MN is small enough, the area MNQP lies between the areas of the rectangles MNKP and MNQH; that is,

$$\delta z \text{ lies between } y\delta x \text{ and } (y + \delta y)\delta x,$$

$$\therefore \frac{\delta z}{\delta x} \text{ lies between } y \text{ and } (y + \delta y).$$

But $\delta y \to 0$ when $\delta x \to 0$; hence, in the limit,

$$\frac{dz}{dx} = y = f(x),$$

$$\therefore z = \int f(x) dx + C,$$

where C is some constant.

Let $\int f(x)dx = F(x)$.   Then $z = F(x) + C$.
But $z = A$ when $x = b$, $\therefore A = F(b) + C$.
Also $z = 0$ when $x = a$, $\therefore 0 = F(a) + C$.
Hence, by subtraction, $A = F(b) - F(a)$,

$$\therefore A = \int_a^b f(x)dx.$$

§ 99. **Calculation of Areas.**—The result just proved can be used to calculate the area bounded by the graph of a given function, the axis of x, and the ordinates $x = a$, $x = b$.

Ex. Calculate the area bounded by the graph of $y = x^3$, the axis of x, and the ordinates $x = 2$, $x = 6$.
Let A be the required area.   Then

$$A = \int_2^6 x^3 dx = \left[\frac{x^4}{4}\right]_2^6 = \frac{6^4}{4} - \frac{2^4}{4} = 320.$$

Examples LI.

In Exs. 1-16, calculate the areas bounded by the given curves and the x-axis, between the given values of x :—

1. $y = x$; $x = 2, x = 6$.
2. $y = 9 - x^2$; $x = -3, x = 3$.
3. $ay = bx$; $x = 0, x = a$.
4. $y = 2x(3 - x)$; $x = 1, x = 2$.
5. $y = \dfrac{6}{x^2}$; $x = 1, x = 3$.
6. $y = \dfrac{x}{2} + \dfrac{2}{x^4}$; $x = \frac{1}{2}, x = 2$.
7. $y = 2\sqrt{x}$; $x = 4, x = 9$.
8. $y = 2x^2 + 2x + 5$; $x = 0, x = 3$.
9. $y = \sin \frac{1}{2}x$; $x = 0, x = \frac{1}{2}\pi$.
10. $y = 1 + \sin x$; $x = 0, x = \pi$.
11. $\dfrac{y}{b} = \sin\dfrac{\pi x}{a}$; $x = 0, x = \dfrac{a}{2}$.
12. $y = \cos^2 \dfrac{x}{3}$; $x = 0, x = \pi$.
13. $y = x \sin x$; $x = 0, x = \frac{1}{2}\pi$.
14. $y = 1 - \cos^3 x$; $x = 0, x = 2\pi$.
15. $y = 3 \sin^2 x + 5 \cos^2 x$; $x = 0, x = \pi$.
16. $y = \sin x + \frac{1}{3} \sin 3x$; $x = 0, x = \pi$.

17. Find the area of the loop of the curve $y^2 = x(1 - x)^2$.

18. If A is the area between the graphs of $y = x$ and $y = x^n$, find A when n is positive. Prove that $A \to \frac{1}{2}$ when $n \to \infty$, and explain this result graphically.

19. The origin and the point (a, a) are opposite corners of a square. Calculate the ratio of the areas of the two parts into which the parabola $\sqrt{x} + \sqrt{y} = \sqrt{a}$ divides the square.

20. In the parabola $y^2 = 4ax$, PQ is a chord parallel to the y-axis, and PM, QN are perpendiculars from P and Q on the y-axis. Prove that the area bounded by the curve and the chord PQ is two-thirds that of the rectangle PMNQ.

§ **100. Three Properties of Definite Integrals.**—(1) A *definite integral does not depend upon the particular letter that is used for the variable of integration.* Thus

$$\int_a^b f(x)dx = \int_a^b f(u)du = \int_a^b f(t)dt = \ldots$$

(2) *The limits may be interchanged if the sign of the integral is changed.* Thus

$$\int_a^b f(x)dx = -\int_b^a f(x)dx.$$

Proof.—Let $\int f(x)dx = F(x)$. Then we have to prove that

$$F(b) - F(a) = -\{F(a) - F(b)\},$$

which is plainly true.

(3) *If* c *is a third limit between (or not between) the limits* a *and* b, *then*

$$\int_a^b f(x)dx = \int_a^c f(x)dx + \int_c^b f(x)dx.$$

Proof.—We have to prove that

$$F(b) - F(a) = \{F(c) - F(a)\} + \{F(b) - F(c)\},$$

which is plainly true.

§ **101. Meaning of a Definite Integral on the Graph of the Integrand** (*continued*).—In § 98 we considered the meaning of a definite integral on the graph of the integrand in the case when the integrand is positive, and the lower limit less than the upper limit. We shall now notice other cases, repeating the first case for the sake of completeness.

Case I. Integrand positive ; lower limit < upper limit. If $f(x)$ is positive, and $a < b$ (see Fig. 54),

$$\int_a^b f(x)dx = + \text{ (area ABCD)}.$$

Case II. Integrand positive ; lower limit > upper limit. If $f(x)$ is positive, and $a > b$ (see Fig. 55),

$$\int_a^b f(x)dx = - \text{ (area BADC)}.$$

Ex. $\qquad \int_5^3 x\,dx = \left[\frac{x^2}{2}\right]_5^3 = \frac{3^2}{2} - \frac{5^2}{2} = -8.$

Case III. Integrand negative; lower limit $<$ upper limit. If $f(x)$ is negative, and $a < b$ (see Fig. 56),

$$\int_a^b f(x)dx = - \text{ (area ADCB)}.$$

Ex. $\int_3^5 (-x)dx = \left[-\frac{x^2}{2} \right]_3^5 = -\frac{5^2}{2} + \frac{3^2}{2} = -8.$

Case IV. Integrand negative; lower limit $>$ upper limit. If $f(x)$ is negative, and $a > b$ (see Fig. 57),

$$\int_a^b f(x)dx = + \text{ (area BCDA)}.$$

Ex. $\int_5^3 (-x)dx = \left[-\frac{x^2}{2} \right]_5^3 = -\frac{3^2}{2} + \frac{5^2}{2} = 8.$

General Rule for Cases I.-IV.—If $f(x)$ has the same sign from $x = a$ to $x = b$, the value of the definite integral $\int_a^b f(x)dx$ is represented on the graph of $y = f(x)$ by the area bounded by the graph, the x-axis, and the ordinates $x = a, x = b$, with the $+$ or $-$ sign prefixed according as the order of the letters ABCD round the area indicates a positive or negative sense of rotation.

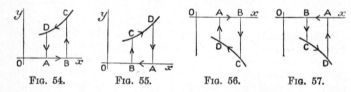

FIG. 54.   FIG. 55.   FIG. 56.   FIG. 57.

§ **102.** *Case V. Integrand positive in parts of the range, negative in other parts; lower limit $<$ upper limit* (Fig. 58).

Let c lie between a and b, $(a < c < b)$, and let $f(x)$ be positive from $x = a$ to $x = c$, negative from $x = c$ to $x = b$.

Now, by (3), § 100,

$$\int_a^b f(x)dx = \int_a^c f(x)dx + \int_c^b f(x)dx,$$

and it follows, from cases I. and II., that

$$\int_a^b f(x)dx = + \text{ (area above the x-axis)}$$
$$- \text{ (area below the x-axis)}.$$

Case VI.   Integrand positive in parts of the range, negative in other parts ; lower limit > upper limit (Fig. 59).

In this case we could show in a similar way that

$$\int_a^b f(x)dx = + \text{ (area below the axis of } x)$$
$$- \text{ (area above the axis of } x).$$

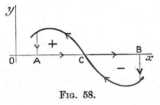

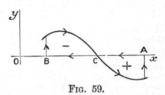

Fig. 58.   Fig. 59.

§ 103. Limits Equal in Magnitude but Opposite in Sign.—From the meaning of a definite integral on the graph of the integrand, we deduce the following two results, in which the range of integration is from − a to + a, so that the limits are equal in magnitude but opposite in sign :—

(1) If the integrand is *even* (Fig. 60),

$$\int_{-a}^a f(x)dx = 2\int_0^a f(x)dx.$$

(2) If the integrand is *odd* (Fig. 61),

$$\int_{-a}^a f(x)dx = 0.$$

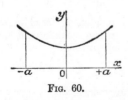

Fig. 60.

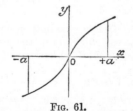

Fig. 61.

Ex.
$$\int_{-\pi}^\pi x \sin x \, dx = 2\int_0^\pi x \sin x \, dx \,;$$
$$\int_{-\pi}^\pi x^2 \sin x \, dx = 0 \,;$$

since the integrand is even in the first integral, odd in the second.

Examples LII.

Evaluate each of the following integrals, and explain its meaning on the graph of the integrand :—

1. $\int_0^2 (1 - x)dx.$ 2. $\int_0^2 (x - 3)dx.$ 3. $\int_{-1}^{-3} 3x^2\ dx.$

4. $\int_0^\pi \cos x\ dx.$ 5. $\int_{2\pi}^\pi \sin x\ dx.$ 6. $\int_0^2 x(x-1)(x-2)dx.$

7. $\int_\pi^{2\pi} x \sin x\ dx.$ 8. $\int_{-a}^a (a^2 + x^2)dx.$ 9. $\int_{-a}^a (a^2x + x^3)dx.$

10. $\int_{-\pi}^\pi \sin^5 \theta\ d\theta.$ 11. $\int_{-\pi}^\pi x^2 \cos x\ dx.$ 12. $\int_{-\pi}^\pi x^3 \cos x\ dx.$

§ 104. **Change of Variable in a Definite Integral.**—Let $z = \int f(x)dx$, and suppose the variable of integration changed from x to v. Then, by (2), § 90,

$$z = \int f(x)dx = \int f(x)\frac{dx}{dv}dv.$$

When $x = a$, let $v = a$ and $z = A$.
When $x = b$, let $v = \beta$ and $z = B$.
Then $(B - A)$ is the change in z when x changes from a to b,

$$\therefore B - A = \int_a^b f(x)dx. \tag{i}$$

Also, $(B - A)$ is the change in z when v changes from a to β,

$$\therefore B - A = \int_a^\beta f(x)\frac{dx}{dv}dv. \tag{ii}$$

From (i) and (ii),

$$\int_a^b f(x)dx = \int_a^\beta f(x)\frac{dx}{dv}dv.$$

Rule.—When a definite integral is evaluated by changing the variable of integration, the limits in the transformed integral must be those of *the new variable of integration.*

Ex. 1. Evaluate $\int_0^4 \frac{x\,dx}{\sqrt{(x^2 + 9)}}.$

Put $v = x^2 + 9, \ \therefore dv = 2x\,dx, \ x\,dx = \frac{1}{2}dv.$
When $x = 0, v = 9$; when $x = 4, v = 25$;

$$\therefore \int_0^4 \frac{x\,dx}{\sqrt{(x^2 + 9)}} = \int_9^{25} \frac{dv}{2\sqrt{v}} = \left[\sqrt{v}\right]_9^{25} = 5 - 3 = \mathbf{2}.$$

Ex. 2. Find the area of the circle $x^2 + y^2 = a^2$.
Let $A =$ the area of the circle.
Then $A =$ four times the area of the first quadrant.

Hence, since $y = \sqrt{(a^2 - x^2)}$,

$$A = 4 \int_0^a \sqrt{(a^2 - x^2)}dx.$$

As in § 92, put
$$x = a \sin \theta, \quad dx = a \cos \theta \, d\theta,$$
$$\sqrt{(a^2 - x^2)} = a \cos \theta \,;$$
the angle θ is shown in Fig. 62.
When $x = 0$, $\theta = 0$;   when $x = a$, $\theta = \frac{1}{2}\pi$;

$$\therefore A = 4a^2 \int_0^{\frac{\pi}{2}} \cos^2 \theta \, d\theta$$

$$= 2a^2 \left[\theta + \sin \theta \cos \theta \right]_0^{\frac{\pi}{2}}$$

$$= \pi a^2.$$

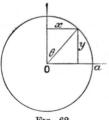

Fig. 62.

Examples LIII.

In Exs. 1-14, evaluate the given definite integrals :—

1. $\int_1^2 x(x - 1)^4 dx.$ **2.** $\int_0^2 x\sqrt{(2x^2 + 1)}dx.$ **3.** $\int_0^1 x\sqrt{(2 - x)}dx.$

4. $\int_1^2 \sqrt{(4 - x^2)}dx.$ **5.** $\int_0^1 x^3\sqrt{(1 - x^2)}dx.$ **6.** $\int_0^1 x^2\sqrt{(1 - x^2)}dx.$

7. $\int_0^2 \dfrac{x \, dx}{\sqrt{(9 - 2x^2)}}.$ **8.** $\int_0^1 \dfrac{x^2 + 1}{(x + 1)^4}dx.$ **9.** $\int_0^2 \dfrac{x \, dx}{(x^2 + 1)^2}.$

10. $\int_0^a \dfrac{dx}{\sqrt{(a^2 - x^2)}}.$ **11.** $\int_0^{\frac{1}{2}} \dfrac{dx}{\sqrt{(1 - x^2)}}.$ **12.** $\int_0^1 \dfrac{x^2 dx}{\sqrt{(4 - x^2)}}.$

13. $\int_0^4 \dfrac{x^3 dx}{\sqrt{(3x^2 + 1)}}.$ **14.** $\int_0^a \dfrac{dx}{a^2 + x^2}.$ [Put $x = a \tan \theta$.]

15. Find the area of the circle $x^2 + y^2 = a^2$, using the substitution $x = a \cos \theta$ to evaluate the integral.

16. A chord of a circle of radius a subtends an angle 2α at the centre. Find the areas of the two segments into which the chord divides the circle.

17. A chord of a circle of radius a is drawn at a distance c from the centre.   Find the areas of the two segments into which the chord divides the circle.

18. Find the area enclosed by the ellipse $\dfrac{x^2}{a^2} + \dfrac{y^2}{b^2} = 1.$

19. Sketch the curve $y^2 = x^2(1 - x)$.   Find the area of the loop.
20. Sketch the curve $y^2 = x^2(1 - x)^3$.   Find the area of the loop.
21. Sketch the curve $y^2 = x^4(x + 1)$.   Find the area of the loop.
22. Sketch the curve $b^2y^2 = x^2(a^2 - x^2)$.   Find the area of a loop.

§ **105. Infinite Limits.   Infinities in the Integrand.**—So far we have supposed the limits of integration to be finite, and the integrand to be finite for every value of x within the range of integration.

(1) If the upper limit is infinite, or if the integrand is infinite at the upper limit: that is, if $b = \infty$, or if $f(b) = \infty$, the following definition may be used:—

$$\int_a^b f(x)dx = \lim_{x \to b} [\mathrm{F}(x) - \mathrm{F}(a)],$$

provided this limit exists; where $\mathrm{F}(x) = \int f(x)dx$.

(2) If the lower limit is infinite, or if the integrand is infinite at the lower limit: that is, if $a = \infty$, or if $f(a) = \infty$, the corresponding definition is

$$\int_a^b f(x)dx = \lim_{x \to a} [\mathrm{F}(b) - \mathrm{F}(x)].$$

(3) If the integrand is infinite for some value of x within the range of integration: that is, if $f(c) = \infty$, where c lies between a and b, the following definition is used:—

$$\int_a^b f(x)dx = \int_a^c f(x)dx + \int_c^b f(x)dx,$$

provided both the integrals on the right have meanings under definitions (1) and (2).

Ex. Consider (i) $\int_2^\infty \dfrac{dx}{x^2}$, (ii) $\int_0^3 \dfrac{dx}{x^2}$, (iii) $\int_{-1}^1 \dfrac{dx}{x^2}$.

(i) The upper limit is infinite. Now $\int \dfrac{dx}{x^2} = -\dfrac{1}{x}$,

$$\therefore \int_2^\infty \dfrac{dx}{x^2} = \lim_{x \to \infty} \left[-\dfrac{1}{x} + \dfrac{1}{2} \right] = \dfrac{1}{2}.$$

(ii) The integrand is infinite at the lower limit. In this case,

$$\int_0^3 \dfrac{dx}{x^2} = \lim_{x \to 0} \left[-\dfrac{1}{3} + \dfrac{1}{x} \right],$$

provided this limit exists. But it does not exist, for $1/x$ approaches infinity when $x \to 0$. Hence the integral has no finite meaning. The area bounded by the graph of $y = 1/x^2$, the x-axis, and two ordinates $x = a$, $x = b$, approaches infinity when $a \to 0$.

(iii) The integrand is infinite when $x = 0$, i.e. for a value of x between the limits -1 and 1,

$$\therefore \int_{-1}^1 \dfrac{dx}{x^2} = \int_{-1}^0 \dfrac{dx}{x^2} + \int_0^1 \dfrac{dx}{x^2},$$

provided both the integrals on the right have meanings. But neither has a meaning [see (ii) above]; so the integral on the left has no meaning.

Note that such a statement as

$$\int_{-1}^{1} \frac{dx}{x^2} = \left[-\frac{1}{x} \right]_{-1}^{1} = -1 - 1 = -2$$

is plainly absurd, since the integrand is positive.

Examples LIV.

Evaluate the given integrals, where possible, noticing the infinities in the limits or in the integrand :—

1. $\int_{0}^{1} \frac{dx}{\sqrt{x}}$. 2. $\int_{1}^{\infty} \frac{dx}{\sqrt{x}}$. 3. $\int_{-1}^{1} \frac{dx}{\sqrt[3]{(x^2)}}$. 4. $\int_{0}^{1} \frac{dx}{x^n}$.

5. $\int_{0}^{1} \frac{dx}{(1-x)^2}$. 6. $\int_{0}^{3} \frac{dx}{(x-1)^2}$. 7. $\int_{0}^{a} \frac{x\,dx}{\sqrt{(a-x)}}$.

8. $\int_{0}^{\frac{\pi}{2}} \frac{\cos\theta\,d\theta}{\sin^2\theta}$. 9. $\int_{0}^{\frac{\pi}{2}} \frac{\cos^3\theta\,d\theta}{\sqrt{(\sin\theta)}}$. 10. $\int_{-a}^{a} \frac{dx}{\sqrt{(a^2-x^2)}}$.

11. $\int_{0}^{\infty} \frac{dx}{(x+2)^2}$. 12. $\int_{0}^{\infty} \frac{x\,dx}{(2x+1)^3}$. 13. $\int_{0}^{\infty} \frac{x\,dx}{(x^2+a^2)^2}$.

14. $\int_{1}^{\infty} \frac{dx}{x^2+1}$. 15. $\int_{-\infty}^{\infty} \frac{dx}{(x^2+1)^2}$. [Put $x = \tan\theta$.]

$$\to \text{but} \int_{-1}^{1} \frac{dx}{x^2} = \int_{-1}^{0-\epsilon} \frac{dx}{x^2} + \int_{0+\eta}^{1} \frac{dx}{x^2}$$

$$\text{where } 0 < \epsilon, \eta < 1$$

$$\Rightarrow \frac{1}{\epsilon} - 1 - 1 + \frac{1}{\eta} = \frac{1}{\epsilon} + \frac{1}{\eta} > 2 \text{ which is } > 0 \ !$$

CHAPTER X.

INTEGRATION.

§ **106. Integration** means the adding together of small parts. The leading idea in integration in mathematics is that a magnitude can sometimes be calculated by supposing it dissected into an infinite number of infinitely small parts, and adding the parts together. (The words "infinite," "infinitely small," are, of course, used in a conventional sense, which will appear as we proceed.)

We shall first show how the area bounded by the graph of $y = f(x)$, the x-axis, and the ordinates $x = a$, $x = b$, can be regarded as the sum of an infinite number of infinitely narrow rectangles; assuming, to begin with, that y is positive and increasing from $x = a$ to $x = b$:—

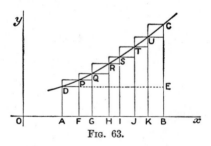

Fig. 63.

In Fig. 63, let $OA = a$, $OB = b$; and let the area ABCD be divided into a large number of narrow strips by ordinates FP, GQ, HR, . . . parallel to the axis of y.

Through D, P, Q, R, . . . draw lines parallel to the axis of x, thus forming a series of rectangles.

Let S = sum of areas of the rectangles AP, FQ, GR, . . .

s = sum of areas of the rectangles DF, PG, QH. . . .

We first prove that the difference (S $\sim$ s) approaches zero when the number of strips approaches infinity and the width of every strip approaches zero:—

108

Proof.—Let DE be the perpendicular from D on BC.

Let h be any length, and let the width of every strip be less than h. Then, when $h \to 0$, the width of every strip will approach zero, and the number of strips will approach infinity.

Now $(S - s) =$ the sum of the areas of the rectangles DP, PQ, QR, . . . But the sum of the heights of these rectangles is EC, and the width of each of them is less than h,

$$\therefore S - s < h \cdot EC.$$

It follows that $(S - s) \to 0$, when $h \to 0$, since EC is constant.

Next, let A = area ABCD. Then, plainly, A lies between s and S, and since the difference $(S - s)$ approaches zero, it follows that s and S both approach the limit A when $h \to 0$. That is,

$$\lim_{h \to 0} (s) = \lim_{h \to 0} (S) = A. \tag{1}$$

Having in mind the limit when $h \to 0$, we express this result conventionally as follows: The area A is equal to the sum of the areas of the infinitely narrow rectangles DF, PG, QH, . . .; or, the area A is equal to the sum of the areas of the infinitely narrow rectangles AP, FQ, GR, . . .

§ 107. **Analytical Statement.**—We shall now express (1) analytically. Let

$$AF = \delta x_1, \quad FG = \delta x_2, \quad GH = \delta x_3, \ldots$$
$$AD = y_1, \quad FP = y_2, \quad GQ = y_3, \quad HR = y_4, \ldots$$

Also, let

$$y_2 = y_1 + \delta y_1, \quad y_3 = y_2 + \delta y_2, \quad y_4 = y_3 + \delta y_3, \ldots$$

Then

$$s = y_1 \delta x_1 + y_2 \delta x_2 + y_3 \delta x_3 + \ldots$$
$$S = (y_1 + \delta y_1)\delta x_1 + (y_2 + \delta y_2)\delta x_2 + (y_3 + \delta y_3)\delta x_3 + \ldots.$$

Since the range from $x = a$ to $x = b$ is divided up into the intervals $\delta x_1, \delta x_2, \delta x_3, \ldots$ we use the abbreviations

$$s = \sum_{x=a}^{x=b} y\delta x, \quad S = \sum_{x=a}^{x=b} (y + \delta y)\delta x.$$

The analytical statement of (1) is therefore

$$\lim_{h \to 0} \sum_{x=a}^{x=b} y\delta x = \lim_{h \to 0} \sum_{x=a}^{x=b} (y + \delta y)\delta x = A. \tag{2}$$

$\delta x \to 0$?

§ 108. The Fundamental Theorem of Integration.—Since $A = \int_a^b y\, dx$, it follows from (2) that

$$\lim_{h \to 0} \sum_{x=a}^{x=b} y\delta x = \int_a^b y\, dx. \tag{3}$$

This result has been arrived at by a consideration of the area under the graph of y. But, in its final form, the result has no reference to areas. It is called the *fundamental theorem of integration*. Since $y = f(x)$, we can also express it as follows:

$$\lim_{h \to 0} \sum_{x=a}^{x=b} f(x)\delta x = \int_a^b f(x)\, dx. \tag{4}$$

§ 109. Method of Application.—The way in which the fundamental theorem is applied to certain practical problems will now be indicated:—

Suppose a magnitude U is to be calculated. In the kind of problems that arise, the magnitude U can be dissected into a large number of small parts, or "elements," in such a way that, at the same time, the range of a certain variable x, from $x = a$ to $x = b$, is divided into an equal number of corresponding elements, each less than h, where h is any number, however small.

Let δU be a typical element of U, and δx the corresponding element of x. Then, it can be proved that, if δx is small enough,

δU lies between $y\delta x$ and $(y + \delta y)\delta x$,

where y is a certain function of x.

Still supposing y positive and increasing from $x = a$ to $x = b$, we deduce, by summation, that

$\Sigma\delta U$ lies between the two sums $\sum_{x=a}^{x=b} y\delta x, \sum_{x=a}^{x=b} (y + \delta y)\delta x.$

But $\Sigma\delta U = U$, and since these two sums have the same limit $\int_a^b y\, dx$, it follows that

$$U = \int_a^b y\, dx.$$

The reasons for some of the terms employed in the last chapter will now be evident. Thus, "integrals" are so called on account of their close connection with problems of integration. The " variable of integration " is a variable introduced in order to effect an integration.

Generalisation.—So far we have supposed y to be positive and increasing from $x = a$ to $x = b$. But the same kind of reasoning could be applied to prove the fundamental theorem whenever y, or $f(x)$, is an ordinary function.

Rule.—If U is the magnitude to be calculated, and if δU is a typical element of U, and δx the corresponding element of the variable of integration; and if, further,

$$\delta \text{U lies between } y\delta x \text{ and } (y + \delta y)\delta x$$

when δx is small enough, then

$$\text{U} = \int_a^b y\, dx,$$

where a and b are the limits of the range of integration.

In practice we say conventionally : Let the magnitude U be dissected into an infinite number of infinitely small elements, and let dU be a typical element corresponding to the element dx of the variable of integration. Then, if

$$d\text{U} = y\, dx,$$

the magnitude U is given by the formula

$$\text{U} = \int_a^b y\, dx.$$

§ 110. **Areas.**—As first applications, we give further examples of calculating areas, now treated from the present point of view of integration.

I. Find a formula for the area A bounded by a graph, the x-axis, and the ordinates $x = a$, $x = b$ (Fig. 64).

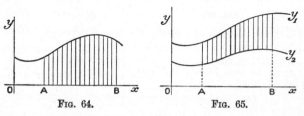

Fig. 64.   Fig. 65.

Dissect the area A into strips, by means of ordinates parallel to the y-axis. Let δA be the area of the strip between the ordinates at distances x and $(x + \delta x)$ from the y-axis. Then, if δx is small enough,

δA lies between $y\delta x$ and $(y + \delta y)\delta x$,

$$\therefore \; A = \int_a^b y \, dx. \qquad (1)$$

In practice we say conventionally: Dissect the area A into infinitely narrow strips, parallel to the y-axis. Let dA be the area of a typical strip, of length y and width dx. Then

$$dA = y \, dx,$$
$$\therefore \; A = \int_a^b y \, dx.$$

II. If y_1, y_2 are two functions of x, find a formula for the area A, bounded by their graphs and the ordinates $x = a$, $x = b$ (Fig. 65).

Dissect the area A into infinitely narrow strips parallel to the y-axis. Let dA be the area of a typical strip, of width dx. Assuming $y_1 > y_2$, the length of this strip is $(y_1 - y_2)$,

$$\therefore \; dA = (y_1 - y_2)dx,$$
$$\therefore \; A = \int_a^b (y_1 - y_2)dx. \qquad (2)$$

III. Find a formula for the area A bounded by a graph, the y-axis, and the lines $y = c$, $y = d$ (Fig. 66).

Dissecting the area into strips parallel to the x-axis, we find

$$A = \int_c^d x \, dy. \qquad (3)$$

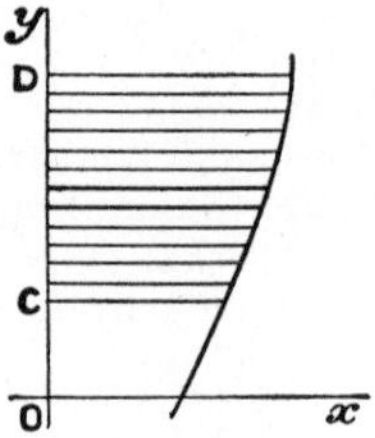

FIG. 66.

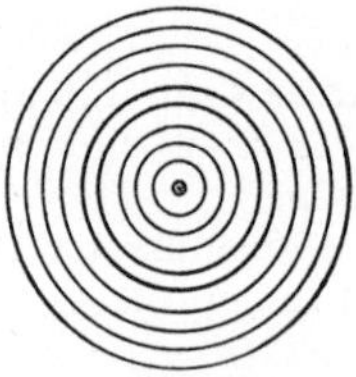

FIG. 67.

IV. Find the area of a circle of radius a (Fig. 67).

Dissect the circle into a large number of annular rings by means of circles concentric with the given circle.

Let δA be the area of the annulus whose inner radius is r and outer radius $(r + \delta r)$. Then

δA lies between $2\pi r\delta r$ and $2\pi(r + \delta r)\delta r$,

$$\therefore \; A = \int_0^a 2\pi r \, dr,$$
$$\therefore \; A = \left[\pi r^2 \right]_0^a = \pi a^2.$$

In practice we say conventionally : Dissect the circle into infinitely narrow rings by circles concentric with the given circle. Let dA be the area of the ring of radius r and width dr. Then

$$dA = 2\pi r\, dr,$$

$$\therefore A = \int_0^a 2\pi r\, dr = \pi a^2.$$

Examples LV.

In Exs. 1-6, find the closed areas bounded by the given curves and lines (sketch graphs in all cases) :—

1. $y = ax^n$, $x = b$, $x = c$, $y = 0$.
2. $x = 1 + y + \tfrac{1}{2}y^2$, $x = 0$, $y = 0$, $y = 6$.
3. $y^2 = ax$, $x^2 = by$.   4. $y^2 = 3x$, $y = x(x - 2)$.
5. $y^2 = 4x$, $x = 0$, $y = 12$.   6. $y = x + x^3$, $x = 3$, $y = 2$.
7. Find the area in the first quadrant bounded by the curves
$$x^2 y = 36, \quad y = 37 - x^2.$$

8. Find the area bounded by the circle $x^2 + y^2 = 4$ and the parabolas $y^2 = 3x$, $x^2 = 3y$, in the first quadrant of the circle.

9. What fraction of the area of the circle $x^2 + y^2 = 4$ lies outside the parabola $y^2 = 4(1 - x)$?

10. Find by integration the area of a circular annulus of inner radius a and outer radius b.

11. Find by integration the area of a triangle of base a and altitude h, dissecting the triangle into strips parallel to the base.

12. If a, b are the lengths of the two parallel sides of a trapezium, and h the distance between them, find the area by integration, dissecting the trapezium into strips parallel to the parallel sides.

§ **111. Volumes of Revolution about the x-axis.**—Let V be the volume generated when the area bounded by a graph, the x-axis, and the ordinates $x = a$, $x = b$, makes one revolution about the x-axis.

Let this volume be dissected into a number of discs by planes perpendicular to the x-axis (Fig. 68). Let A, $A + \delta A$ be the areas of the cross-sections made by planes at distances x, $x + \delta x$ from the origin, and let δV be the volume of the disc between these planes. Then, if δx is small enough,

$$\delta V \text{ lies between } A\delta x \text{ and } (A + \delta A)\delta x,$$

$$\therefore V = \int_a^b A\, dx.$$

But $A = \pi y^2$,

$$\therefore V = \int_a^b \pi y^2\, dx. \tag{4}$$

In practice we say conventionally : Let the volume V be dissected into infinitely thin discs by planes perpendicular to the x-axis. Let dV be the volume, dx the thickness, and A the area of a typical disc. Then

$$dV = A\,dx,$$

$$\therefore V = \int_a^b A\,dx = \int_a^b \pi y^2\,dx.$$

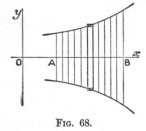

Fig. 68.

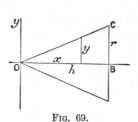

Fig. 69.

Ex. Find the volume of a cone of height h and base-radius r.

In Fig. 69, let OBC be a right-angled triangle in which OB $= h$, BC $= r$. Then the cone can be regarded as generated by the revolution of this triangle about the x-axis.

Now, if (x, y) are the co-ordinates of any point on the line OC, by similar triangles

$$\frac{y}{x} = \frac{r}{h}, \quad \therefore\ y = \frac{rx}{h}.$$

Hence, if V is the volume of the cone,

$$V = \int_0^h \pi y^2\,dx = \int_0^h \pi\left(\frac{rx}{h}\right)^2 dx = \frac{\pi r^2}{h^2}\int_0^h x^2\,dx = \tfrac{1}{3}\pi r^2 h.$$

§ 112. **Volumes of Revolution about the y-Axis.**—Let V be the volume generated when the area bounded by a graph, the y-axis, and the lines $y = c$, $y = d$, revolves about the y-axis. Then we find

$$V = \int_c^d \pi x^2\,dy. \tag{5}$$

Ex. Find the volume generated by rotating about the y-axis the area bounded by the co-ordinate axes and the graph of $y = \cos x$ from $x = 0$ to $x = \tfrac{1}{2}\pi$.

Instead of using the formula just given, we shall, for the sake of illustration, use an alternative method.

Let V $=$ the required volume. Dissect this volume into infinitely thin hollow cylinders having the common axis Oy (Fig. 70). Let dV be the volume, dx the thickness, and y the height of a typical one of these cylinders.

Then $$dV = 2\pi x\,dx\,.\,y = 2\pi xy\,dx,$$

$$\therefore\ V = \int_0^{\frac{\pi}{2}} 2\pi xy\,dx = 2\pi\int_0^{\frac{\pi}{2}} x\cos x\,dx.$$

Integrating by parts, we find

$$V = 2\pi\Big[\,x\sin x + \cos x\,\Big]_0^{\frac{\pi}{2}} = \pi(\pi - 2) = 3\cdot58\,\ldots$$

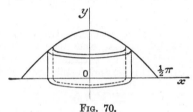

Fig. 70.

Examples LVI.

In Exs. 1-10 find the volumes generated when the areas under the given curves, between the given values of x, revolve about the x-axis :—

1. $y = x$; $x = 2, x = 4$.
2. $2y = x + 4$; $x = 0, x = 8$.
3. $y = x^2$; $x = 0, x = 5$.
4. $y = x(2 - x)$; $x = 0, x = 2$.
5. $xy = 6$; $x = 2, x = 9$.
6. $x^2 - y^2 = a^2$; $x = a, x = 2a$.
7. $y = \sin x$; $x = 0, x = \pi$.
8. $y = 1 - \cos 2x$; $x = 0, x = \pi$.
9. $y = \dfrac{a^3}{a^2 + x^2}$; $x = 0, x = \infty$.
10. $\dfrac{x^2}{a^2} + \dfrac{y^2}{b^2} = 1$; $x = -a, x = a$.

In Exs. 11-16 find the volumes generated when the areas bounded by the given curves and lines revolve about the y-axis :—

11. $y^2 = x^3,\ x = 0,\ y = 8$.
12. $y^2 = 4 - x,\ x = 0,\ y = 0$.
13. $y = x^2,\ y = 0,\ x = 2$.
14. $xy = 1,\ x = 0,\ x = 1,\ y = 0$.
15. $x^2 = y(2a - y)$.
16. $3a^2x^2 = y^3(4a - y)$.

17. The area bounded by the graph of $y = (3 - x)(x - 1)$, the lines $x = 1, x = 3$, and the line $y = 2$, revolves about the line $y = 2$. Find the volume generated.

18. The smaller segment cut from the circle $x^2 + y^2 = 4$ by the line $y = 1$ revolves about that line. Find the volume generated.

19. The radii of the ends of a frustum of a cone are a and b, and the height is h. Prove that its volume V is given by $V = \frac{1}{3}\pi h(a^2 + ab + b^2)$.

Examples 20-24 relate to the sphere :—

20. Find by integration the volume of a sphere of radius a, dissecting it into concentric spherical shells.

21. Find by integration the volume of a hollow sphere of inner radius a, outer radius b.

22. Find by integration the volume of the sphere generated when the circle $x^2 + y^2 = a^2$ revolves about the x-axis, dissecting the sphere into discs perpendicular to the x-axis.

23. A cylindrical hole of length $2r$ is bored through any sphere of radius greater than r, the axis of the hole passing through the centre of the sphere. Prove that the volume of the part that remains is $\frac{4}{3}\pi r^3$.

24. A sphere of radius a is divided into two parts by a plane at a distance c from the centre. Find the volumes of the two parts. Also, find approximately the ratio of c to a when the volumes of the two parts are in the ratio $1:3$.

§ 113. Volumes not of Revolution.—Let V be the volume of any solid. Let Ox be any axis, and dissect the volume V into infinitely thin layers by planes perpendicular to Ox. Let dV be the volume, dx the thickness, and A the area, of a typical thin layer. Then

$$d\mathrm{V} = \mathrm{A}\,dx.$$

Hence, if the whole volume is included between the planes $x = a$, $x = b$,

$$\mathrm{V} = \int_a^b \mathrm{A}\,dx. \qquad (6)$$

Ex. Find the volume V of any pyramid of height h and base area S.

Dissect the pyramid into infinitely thin layers parallel to the base (Fig. 71). Let dV be the volume, dx the thickness, and A the area of the layer whose perpendicular distance from the apex O is x.

Now A is proportional to x^2, and A = S when $x = h$,

Fig. 71.

$$\therefore \frac{\mathrm{A}}{x^2} = \frac{\mathrm{S}}{h^2}, \quad \therefore \mathrm{A} = \frac{\mathrm{S}x^2}{h^2}.$$

Hence 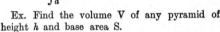 $$\mathrm{V} = \int_0^h \mathrm{A}\,dx = \int_0^h \frac{\mathrm{S}x^2\,dx}{h^2} = \frac{\mathrm{S}}{h^2}\int_0^h x^2\,dx,$$

$$\therefore \mathrm{V} = \tfrac{1}{3}\mathrm{S}h = \tfrac{1}{3}(\text{base-area})(\text{height}).$$

Examples LVII.

1. The base of a trough is a rectangle 2 ft. long by 6 ins. wide. The top is a rectangle 3 ft. long by 12 ins. wide. If the depth is 1 ft., find the volume of water in the trough when full.

2. A railway embankment, built on a level plain, rises with a steady grade of 1 in 50. The top of the bank is 20 ft. wide, and the sides have a gradient of 1 in 3. Find the volume of the bank between two sections where the heights are 10 and 50 ft.

3. Four vertical poles, of lengths 5, 6, 8, 7 ft., stand at the corners of a square of side 4 ft., in order round the square. Show that the tops of the poles lie in a plane.

Find the volume of the tent made by stretching plane sheets of canvas between the poles and across their tops.

4. The axes of two equal circular cylinders, of radius a, intersect at right angles. Find the volume common to both.

[First show that the cross-section of the common volume by a plane parallel to the axes is a square.]

5. The axes of two equal circular cylinders, of radius a, intersect at an angle α. Find their common volume.

6. Prove that the section of a tetrahedron, by a plane parallel to two opposite edges, is a parallelogram.

If a, b are the lengths of two opposite edges, h the shortest distance between them, and θ the angle between their directions, prove that the volume of the tetrahedron is $\frac{1}{6}abh \sin \theta$.

§ 114. Length of a Curve.

Let s be the length of a graph from a point A where $x = a$ to a point B where $x = b$ (Fig. 72).

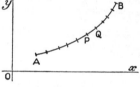

Dissect the arc AB into a number of elements of arc, such as PQ. Let $\delta s = $ arc PQ. Let x, $x + \delta x$ be the abscissæ of the points P, Q; and let the tangents at P, Q make angles ψ, $\psi + \delta \psi$ with the axis of x, respectively.

Fig. 72.

The gradient must be either increasing or decreasing from P to Q, if PQ is small enough. Suppose it is increasing. Then, we may assume that δs is greater than it would be if the gradient were constant along PQ and equal to its value at P; hence $\delta s > \delta x \sec \psi$.

Also, δs is less than it would be if the gradient were constant along PQ and equal to its value at Q; hence $\delta s < \delta x \sec (\psi + \delta \psi)$.

Hence, if δx is small enough, δs lies between $\delta x \sec \psi$ and $\delta x \sec (\psi + \delta \psi)$. Therefore (§ 109)

$$s = \int_a^b \sec \psi \,\, \delta x. \tag{7}$$

But

$$\sec \psi = (1 + \tan^2 \psi)^{\frac{1}{2}} = \left\{ 1 + \left(\frac{dy}{dx}\right)^2 \right\}^{\frac{1}{2}},$$

$$\therefore s = \int_a^b \left\{ 1 + \left(\frac{dy}{dx}\right)^2 \right\}^{\frac{1}{2}} dx. \tag{8}$$

In practice we say conventionally : Divide the arc AB into infinitely small elements. Let ds be the length of a typical element of arc, and let (x, y), $(x + dx, y + dy)$ be the co-ordinates of the ends of this element. Then dx, dy, ds are the sides and hypotenuse of an infinitesimal right-angled triangle,

$$\therefore \; ds^2 = dx^2 + dy^2,$$

$$\therefore \; ds = (dx^2 + dy^2)^{\frac{1}{2}} = \left\{ 1 + \left(\frac{dy}{dx} \right)^2 \right\}^{\frac{1}{2}} dx,$$

$$\therefore \; s = \int_a^b \left\{ 1 + \left(\frac{dy}{dx} \right)^2 \right\}^{\frac{1}{2}} dx.$$

Examples LVIII.

In Exs. 1-4 find the lengths of the given curves between the points where x has the given values :—

1. $4y^2 = x^3$; $x = 0, x = 1$.   2. $y = 6 - 3x^{\frac{1}{2}} + \frac{1}{9}x^{\frac{3}{2}}$; $x = 0, x = 9$.
3. $6xy = x^4 + 3$; $x = 1, x = 3$.   4. $3y = (x - 3)\sqrt{x}$; $x = 4, x = 9$.
5. Verify, by integration, that the length of the circumference of the circle $x^2 + y^2 = a^2$ is $2\pi a$.
6. Find the length of the loop of the curve $9ay^2 = x(3a - x)^2$.

§ 115. Areas of Surfaces of Revolution.—When the arc of a graph from a point A, where $x = a$, to a point B, where $x = b$, revolves about the x-axis, a surface of revolution is generated by the arc AB. Let S = the area of this surface.

Dissect the arc AB into a number of elements of arc, such as PQ (Fig. 73). Let δs be the length of the element PQ, and δS the area of the element of surface generated by δs.

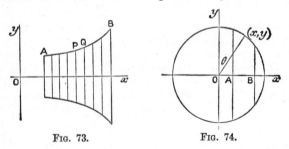

Fig. 73.   Fig. 74.

Let (x, y) be the co-ordinates of P, and $(x + \delta x, y + \delta y)$ those of Q ; and suppose y to be increasing from P to Q. Then we may assume that the surface generated by the element PQ is greater than it would be if every point of the element were at a distance y from the x-axis, but less than it would be if every point were at a distance $(y + \delta y)$ from the x-axis.   Hence,

$$\delta S \text{ lies between } 2\pi y \delta s \text{ and } 2\pi (y + \delta y)\delta s,$$

$$\therefore \ S = \int 2\pi y \, ds, \tag{9}$$

$$\therefore \ S = \int_a^b 2\pi y \left\{ 1 + \left(\frac{dy}{dx}\right)^2 \right\}^{\frac{1}{2}} dx. \tag{10}$$

In practice we say conventionally : Dissect the arc AB into infinitely small elements.   Let dS be the element of surface generated by a typical element of arc ds.   Then

$$dS = 2\pi y \, ds,$$
$$\therefore \ S = \int 2\pi y \, ds.$$

§ 116. Area of a Spherical Zone.—

Ex. A sphere of radius a is cut by two parallel planes at a distance h apart.   Prove that the area of the spherical zone included between the planes is $2\pi ah$ (the same as that of the curved surface of a cylinder of radius a, height h).

Let the spherical surface be generated by the revolution of the circle $x^2 + y^2 = a^2$ about the x-axis.

Let the two parallel planes be at distances α and β from the centre.   Then

$$h = \beta - \alpha.$$

Let S be the area of the zone between these planes.

Put $x = a \sin \theta$, $y = a \cos \theta$ (the angle θ is shown in Fig. 74).

Then
$$dx = a \cos \theta \, d\theta, \quad dy = - a \sin \theta \, d\theta,$$
$$\therefore \ ds = \sqrt{(dx^2 + dy^2)} = a \, d\theta,$$
$$\therefore \ y \, ds = a \cos \theta \, . \, a \, d\theta = a \, . \, a \cos \theta \, d\theta = a \, dx, \tag{11}$$
$$\therefore \ S = \int 2\pi y \, ds = \int_\alpha^\beta 2\pi a \, dx = 2\pi a(\beta - \alpha),$$
$$\therefore \ S = 2\pi ah. \tag{12}$$

Examples LIX.

In Exs. 1-5 find the areas of the surfaces generated when the given curves, between the given values of x, revolve about the x-axis :—

1. $4y = 3x$; $x = 0, x = 8$.   **2.** $3y = 12 + 4x$; $x = 0, x = 3$.
3. $4y = x^3$; $x = 0, x = 1$.   **4.** $6xy = x^4 + 3$; $x = 1, x = 3$.
5. $3x^2 + 4y^2 = 12$; $x = -2, x = 2$.

In Exs. 6-9 find the areas of the surfaces generated when the given curves, between the given values of y, revolve about the y-axis :—

6. $y = 2x$; $y = 0, y = 10$.   **7.** $3x + 4y = 12$; $y = 0, y = 9$.
8. $y = x^2$; $y = 20, y = 30$.   **9.** $4x^2 + y^2 = 1$; $y = -1, y = 1$.

10. Prove that the area of the curved surface of a cone of base-radius r is πrl, where l is the length of the slant side.

11. Prove that the area of the curved surface of a frustum of a cone is $\pi(a + b)l$, where a, b are the end radii and l is the length of the slant side.

12. Find the area of the surface generated by revolving the parabola $y^2 = 4ax$, from $x = 0$ to $x = h$, about the x-axis.

A parabolic mirror is 12 ins. wide and 4 ins. deep. Find the area of its surface.

13. Find the area of the surface generated when the loop of the curve $9ay^2 = x(3a - x)^2$ revolves about the x-axis.

Examples 14-18 *relate to the sphere* :—

14. Find, by applying formula (10), the area of the surface of the sphere generated by the revolution of the circle $x^2 + y^2 = a^2$ about a diameter.

15. A cone of semi-angle α has its apex at the centre of a sphere of radius a. Find the area of the portion of the surface of the sphere within the cone.

16. Prove that the area of the curved surface of a spherical segment is πr^2, where r is the distance of the central point of the curved surface from any point on the edge. Find the area of a spherical mirror 6 ins. wide, 1 in. deep.

17. If h is the height, and c the radius of the flat surface, of a segment of a sphere, prove that the area A of the whole surface, and the volume V, are given by

$$A = \pi(h^2 + 2c^2), \quad V = \frac{\pi h^3}{6} + \frac{\pi c^2 h}{2}.$$

18. A sphere of radius a is viewed from a point at a distance x from the nearest point of the surface. If S is the area of the visible part of the surface, prove that

$$S = \frac{2\pi a^2 x}{a + x}.$$

§ 117. Volume Density.

When a body is not homogeneous, the ratio of the total mass to the total volume is called the *average density*.

The density *at any point* P is defined as follows :—

Let δm be the mass of a small volume δv surrounding P. Then the ratio $\delta m/\delta v$ is the average density throughout this small volume, and the limit of this ratio, when δv shrinks to zero, is called *the density at the point* P. Hence, if ρ = the density at the point P,

$$\rho = \lim_{\delta v \to 0} \left(\frac{\delta m}{\delta v} \right). \tag{1}$$

In the notation of differentials, if dm is the mass of an infinitely small volume dv at P,

$$dm = \rho \, dv. \tag{2}$$

§ 118. Surface Density.—When a surface is covered with a layer of matter, the *surface density* (mass per unit area) at any point P is defined as follows :—

Let δm be the element of mass covering an element of surface δS at P. Then, if σ = the surface density at P,

$$\sigma = \lim_{\delta S \to 0} \left(\frac{\delta m}{\delta S} \right). \qquad (3)$$

In differentials, if dm is the mass covering an infinitely small element of surface dS at P,

$$dm = \sigma \, dS. \qquad (4)$$

§ 119. Line Density.—When matter is distributed along a line or curve, the *line density* (mass per unit length) at any point P is defined as follows :—

Let δm be the mass of an element δs of the curve at P. Then, if λ = the line density at P,

$$\lambda = \lim_{\delta s \to 0} \left(\frac{\delta m}{\delta s} \right). \qquad (5)$$

In differentials, if dm is the mass of an infinitely small element ds at P,

$$dm = \lambda \, ds. \qquad (6)$$

Ex. The density at any point of a solid sphere, of radius a, is proportional to the distance of the point from the centre. If ρ_1 = the density at the surface, find the total mass and the average density.

Let M = the total mass, $\bar{\rho}$ = the average density.

Let ρ = the density at radius r. Then $\rho = kr$, where k is a constant.

But $\qquad \rho = \rho_1$ when $r = a$, $\quad \therefore \rho_1 = ka$, $\quad \therefore k = \rho_1/a$. $\qquad$ (i)

Dissect the sphere into infinitely thin spherical shells. Let dm be the mass, and dv the volume, of the thin shell of radius r and thickness dr. Then

$$dm = \rho \, dv = kr \, . \, 4\pi r^2 \, dr = 4\pi kr^3 \, dr,$$

$$\therefore \; M = 4\pi k \int_0^a r^3 \, dr = \pi ka^4.$$

Hence, by (i),

$$M = \pi a^3 \rho_1,$$

and

$$\bar{\rho} = \frac{M}{\frac{4}{3}\pi a^3} = \tfrac{3}{4}\rho_1.$$

Examples LX.

1. The density at any point of a solid sphere, of radius a, is inversely proportional to the distance of the point from the centre. If ρ_1 = the density at the surface, find the total mass and the average density.

2. A sphere, of radius a, is surrounded by an atmosphere, of radius b, at any point of which the density is inversely proportional to the distance from the centre. If M is the total mass of the atmosphere, find the density at radius r.

3. The weight per unit volume at any point of a solid hemisphere is wx/a, where x is the perpendicular distance of the point from the base, a is the radius, and w is a constant.   Find the total weight.

4. A spherical globe of radius a is filled with a gas.   Supposing the density of the gas at any point to be proportional to the depth below the top of the globe, and the density at the bottom to be ρ_1, find the total mass of the gas, and the average density.

5. When a disc of radius a is charged with electricity, the surface density of the charge at radius r is inversely proportional to $\sqrt{(a^2 - r^2)}$.   If Q is the total charge, find the surface density at the centre.

6. If the weight per unit length of a rod varies as the square of the distance from one end, prove that the weight per unit length at the middle is three-quarters of the average weight per unit length.

7. A triangle ABC is covered with a layer of matter, so that the surface density at any point is proportional to the square of its distance from the base BC.   If $\bar{\sigma}$ is the average surface density, find the surface density at A.

8. A circle is covered with a layer of matter.   If the surface density at radius r is a linear function of r, equal to σ_0 at the centre, and equal to σ_1 at the circumference, find the average surface density.

§ 120. The Mean Value of a Function.

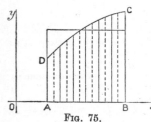

FIG. 75.

—Let the area under the graph of $y = f(x)$, from $x = a$ to $x = b$, be divided into n strips of equal widths ; let $y_1, y_2, \ldots y_n$ be the mid-ordinates of the successive strips (Fig. 75), and let $\bar{y}_n$ be the *average* or *mean* of these ordinates.   Then

$$\bar{y}_n = \frac{y_1 + y_2 + \ldots + y_n}{n}.$$

Let $\bar{y}$ denote the limit of $\bar{y}_n$ when $n \to \infty$.   Then $\bar{y}$ is called *the average or mean value of the function* y, *with respect to* x, *over the range from* x = a *to* x = b.

Let δx be the width of each strip, and multiply numerator and denominator of $\bar{y}_n$ by δx.   Then, since $n\delta x = b - a$,

$$\bar{y}_n = \frac{y_1\,\delta x + y_2\,\delta x + \ldots + y_n\,\delta x}{n\,\delta x} = \frac{\Sigma y\,\delta x}{b - a}.$$

Hence, in the limit when $n \to \infty$ and $\delta x \to 0$,

$$\bar{y} = \frac{\int_a^b y\,dx}{b - a} = \frac{\text{area ABCD}}{\text{AB}}. \tag{1}$$

Ex. 1. Find the average value of x^2 from $x = 1$ to $x = 4$.

Let $\bar{y}$ be the required average value.   Then

$$\bar{y} = \frac{\int_1^4 x^2\, dx}{4 - 1} = \frac{\int_1^4 x^2\, dx}{3} = 7.$$

Ex. 2. If $y = a + bx + cx^2 + dx^3$, prove that the average ordinate on the (x, y) graph over any range is given by

$$\bar{y} = \tfrac{1}{6}(y_1 + 4y_2 + y_3),$$

where y_1 and y_3 are the first and last ordinates, and y_2 is the middle ordinate.

Take the origin at the foot of the middle ordinate.   Referred to this origin, let the equation of the curve be

$$y = \alpha + \beta x + \gamma x^2 + \delta x^3. \tag{i}$$

Let the range of integration be from $-h$ to h.   Then

$$\bar{y} = \frac{1}{2h}\int_{-h}^{h} (\alpha + \beta x + \gamma x^2 + \delta x^3)dx = \alpha + \tfrac{1}{3}\gamma h^2.$$

But, putting $x = -h$, 0, h, in turn in (i), we get
$$y_1 = \alpha - \beta h + \gamma h^2 - \delta h^3, \quad y_2 = \alpha, \quad y_3 = \alpha + \beta h + \gamma h^2 + \delta h^3,$$
$$\therefore\ y_1 + 4y_2 + y_3 = 6\alpha + 2\gamma h^2 = 6(\alpha + \tfrac{1}{3}\gamma h^2),$$
$$\therefore\ \bar{y} = \tfrac{1}{6}(y_1 + 4y_2 + y_3).$$

§ 121. By the average value of a *periodic* function we mean its average value *over a period*, unless some other range is specified.

Ex. 1. The average value of $\cos nx$ or $\sin nx$ is zero (over a period).   **This is evident from a graph, and may be verified by integration.**

Ex. 2. Prove that, between $x = 0$ and $x = \pi$, the average value of $\cos^2 nx$ or $\sin^2 nx$ is $\tfrac{1}{2}$, if n is an integer.

Proof.—The average value of $\cos^2 nx$ over the given range is

$$\frac{1}{\pi}\int_0^\pi \cos^2 nx\, dx = \frac{1}{2\pi}\int_0^\pi (1 + \cos 2nx)dx = \frac{1}{2\pi}\cdot \pi = \tfrac{1}{2}.$$

Similarly, the average value of $\sin^2 nx$ is $\tfrac{1}{2}$, over the same range.

Ex. 3. Prove that, between $x = 0$ and $x = \pi$, the average value of $\cos mx \cos nx$ or $\sin mx \sin nx$ is zero, if m and n are unequal positive integers.

Proof.—The average value of $\cos mx \cos nx$ over this range is

$$\frac{1}{\pi}\int_0^\pi \cos mx \cos nx\, dx = \frac{1}{2\pi}\int_0^\pi \{\cos (m + n)x + \cos (m - n)x\}dx$$
$$= \frac{1}{2\pi}\left[\frac{\sin (m + n)x}{m + n} + \frac{\sin (m - n)x}{m - n}\right]_0^\pi$$

provided $m \neq \pm n$.   Since the sine of any whole multiple of π is zero, the desired result follows.   Similarly, the average value of $\sin mx \sin nx$ is zero over the same range.

§ **122.** It should be noted that the mean value of a function depends upon the independent variable.

For example, let v be the velocity of a body falling freely under gravity. It is known from Mechanics that, if it falls s ft. in t secs., starting from rest, we have approximately

$$v = 32t, \qquad s = 16t^2, \qquad v^2 = 64s.$$

First, let $\bar{v}_t$ be the mean velocity *with respect to* t during the first second. Then

$$\bar{v}_t = \frac{1}{1-0} \int_0^1 v \, dt = \int_0^1 32t \, dt = 16 \text{ ft./sec.}$$

Next, let $\bar{v}_s$ be the mean velocity *with respect to* s in the same interval. Then, since the body falls 16 ft. in this interval,

$$\bar{v}_s = \frac{1}{16-0} \int_0^{16} v \, ds = \frac{1}{16} \int_0^{16} 8 \sqrt{s} \, ds = 21\tfrac{1}{3} \text{ ft./sec.}$$

Thus the average value of v depends upon whether v is regarded as a function of t or of s.

Examples LXI.

In Exs. 1-14 find the average values of the given functions over the ranges indicated by the given values of the independent variables :—

1. $x(2-x)$; $x = 0, x = 2$.   2. x^n ; $x = 0, x = 1$. $(n > -1)$.
3. $\sin x$; $x = 0, x = 2\pi$.   4. $\sin x$; $x = 0, x = \pi$.
5. $\sin pt$; $t = 0, t = 2\pi/p$.   6. $\sin^2 pt$; $t = 0, t = 2\pi/p$.
7. $\cos^2 x$; $x = 0, x = \pi/4$.   8. $\sin^2 \theta \cos^3 \theta$; $\theta = 0, \theta = \pi/2$.
9. $\sin^2 (\theta - \alpha)$; $\theta = 0, \theta = \pi$.   10. $t \sin \omega t$; $t = 0, t = \pi/\omega$.
11. $\sin \theta \cos (\theta - \alpha)$; $\theta = 0, \theta = \pi$.
12. $a + b \sin nx$; $x = 0, x = 2\pi/n$, and $x = 0, x = \pi/n$.
13. $a + b \sin^2 x$; $x = 0, x = n\pi/2$, where n is an integer.
14. $a \sin x + b \sin 3x$; $x = 0, x = 2\pi$, and $x = 0, x = \pi$.

15. If $s = a \sin \omega t$, and $v = ds/dt$, prove that $v = + \omega \sqrt{(a^2 - s^2)}$ when t lies between 0 and $\pi/2\omega$. Over this interval, find the average value of v with respect to t, and also with respect to s.

16. Find the mean value of $x(a-x)$ from $x = 0$ to $x = a$,

    (i) with respect to x,   (ii) with respect to $\sqrt{x}$,

    (iii) with respect to x^2,   (iv) with respect to x^n.

§ **123. Evaluation of a Definite Integral when the Average Value of the Integrand is known.**—From (1), § 120, follows

$$\int_a^b y \, dx = \bar{y}(b-a)$$

$$= \text{(average value of the integrand)}$$
$$\times \text{(the range of integration)}.$$

This result is useful when the average value of the integrand is known over the range of integration.

Ex. Evaluate $\int_0^\pi (3\cos\theta + \cos 3\theta)^2\, d\theta,\ = z$, say.

Squaring out the integrand, we get

$$z = 9\int_0^\pi \cos^2\theta\, d\theta + 6\int_0^\pi \cos\theta \cos 3\theta\, d\theta + \int_0^\pi \cos^2 3\theta\, d\theta.$$

By Exs. 2 and 3, § 121, the average value of the integrand is $\frac{1}{2}$ in the first and third integrals, 0 in the second,

$$\therefore z = 9 \cdot \tfrac{1}{2} \cdot \pi + 0 + \tfrac{1}{2}\pi = 5\pi.$$

§ 124. The Root-Mean-Square (R.M.S.) Value of a Function.—

The square-root of the mean value of y^2, between $x = a$ and $x = b$, is called the *root-mean-square value* of y between $x = a$ and $x = b$.

By the R.M.S. value of a periodic function we mean the R.M.S. value *over a period*, unless some other range is specified.

Ex. 1. Find the R.M.S. value of x from $x = 0$ to $x = a$.

Here $y = x$, and the R.M.S. value is

$$\left\{\frac{1}{a}\int_0^a y^2\, dx\right\}^{\frac{1}{2}} = \left\{\frac{1}{a}\int_0^a x^2\, dx\right\}^{\frac{1}{2}} = \left(\frac{a^2}{3}\right)^{\frac{1}{2}} = \frac{a}{\sqrt 3}.$$

Ex. 2. If $i = \mathrm{I}\sin pt$, find the R.M.S. value of i.

The mean value of $i^2 =$ the mean value of $\mathrm{I}^2\sin^2 pt = \mathrm{I}^2 \times \frac{1}{2}$.

Hence the R.M.S. value of $i = \left(\dfrac{\mathrm{I}^2}{2}\right)^{\frac{1}{2}} = \dfrac{\mathrm{I}}{\sqrt 2}.$

Examples LXII.

In Exs. 1-5 evaluate the given definite integrals :—

1. $\displaystyle\int_0^{2\pi} (1 + \sin x)^2 dx.$
2. $\displaystyle\int_0^\pi (\sin x + 2\sin 3x)^2\, dx.$

3. $\displaystyle\int_0^\pi (\cos\theta + \cos 2\theta)^2 d\theta.$
4. $\displaystyle\int_0^\pi (\cos\theta + \sin 2\theta)^2\, d\theta.$

5. $\displaystyle\int_0^\pi (\cos\theta + 2\cos 2\theta + 3\cos 3\theta)^2\, d\theta.$

6. The curve $y = \sin x + \frac{1}{3}\sin 3x + \frac{1}{5}\sin 5x$, from $x = 0$ to $x = \pi$, revolves about the x-axis. Find the volume generated.

7. If $v = \mathrm{V}\cos pt$, and $i = \mathrm{I}\cos(pt - \alpha)$, find the average value of the product vi over a period.

8. If $v = \mathrm{V}(1 + \sin pt)$, and $i = \mathrm{I}(1 + \sin pt)$, find the average value of the product vi over a period.

In Exs. 9-13 find the R.M.S. values of the given functions over the range from $x = 0$ to $x = 2\pi$:—

9. $a + b\sin x.$
10. $a + b\sin x + c\cos x.$
11. $a\sin x + b\sin 3x.$
12. $a + b\cos x + c\cos 2x.$
13. $a_0 + a_1\cos x + a_2\cos 2x + \ldots + a_n\cos nx.$

In Exs. 14-16 find the ratios of the R.M.S. values of the given functions to their mean values, between $\theta = 0$ and $\theta = \pi$:—

14. $\sin\theta.$
15. $a + b\sin 2\theta.$
16. $\sin^2\theta.$

§ 125. Approximate Integration.　Simpson's Rule.—*Simpson's Rule* is a rule by which we can calculate the *approximate* value of a definite integral when the indefinite integral is not known. It will now be explained :—

The definite integral $\int_a^b y \, dx$ is equal to the area bounded by the graph of the integrand, the x-axis, and the ordinates $x = a$, $x = b$.

Divide this area into an *even* number of strips, each of width h, by means of ordinates parallel to the y-axis.

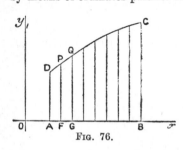

FIG. 76.

Let $2n =$ the number of strips. Then the number of ordinates, including the first and the last, is $2n + 1$. Let the lengths of the ordinates be $y_1, y_2, y_3, \ldots y_{2n+1}$. Let AD, FP, GQ be the first three ordinates, and consider the double strip AGQD (Fig. 76).

In general, a curve of the form

$$y = a + bx + cx^2 + dx^3$$

can be drawn through the points D, P, Q, fitting the original curve very closely (the shorter the arc DQ, the better will be the fit).

Now, by Ex. 2, § 120, the average ordinate between D and Q on this new curve is $\frac{1}{6}(y_1 + 4y_2 + y_3)$, which is therefore a good *approximation* to the average ordinate between D and Q on the original curve.　Since the width of the double strip AGQD is $2h$, it follows that the area of this double strip is approximately

$$\tfrac{1}{3}h(y_1 + 4y_2 + y_3).$$

Similarly, the area of the next double-strip is approximately

$$\tfrac{1}{3}h(y_3 + 4y_4 + y_5) ;$$

and so on.

By addition, the whole area between $x = a$ and $x = b$ is approximately

$$\begin{aligned}
&\tfrac{1}{3}h(y_1 + 4y_2 + y_3 \\
&\qquad + y_3 + 4y_4 + y_5 \\
&\qquad\qquad + y_5 + 4y_6 + y_7 \\
&\qquad\qquad\qquad + \ldots) \\
&= \tfrac{1}{3}h(y_1 + 4y_2 + 2y_3 + 4y_4 + 2y_5 + \ldots + 4y_{2n} + y_{2n+1}) \\
&= \tfrac{1}{3}h\{(y_1 + y_{2n+1}) + 2(y_3 + y_5 + \ldots) + 4(y_2 + y_4 + \ldots)\}.
\end{aligned}$$

Finally, we have the following approximation

$$\int_a^b y\,dx \doteq \tfrac{1}{3}h(\mathrm{X} + 2\mathrm{O} + 4\mathrm{E}).$$

In words, the approximate value of the definite integral is equal to *one-third the width of a strip multiplied by the sum of the two extreme ordinates, twice the sum of the odd ordinates (except the first and last), and four times the sum of the even ordinates.*

Ex. Evaluate $\int_9^{25} \sqrt{x}\,dx$ by Simpson's Rule, using 8 strips.

Here $y_1 = \sqrt{9}$, $y_2 = \sqrt{11}$, $y_3 = \sqrt{13}, \ldots y_9 = \sqrt{25}$.
From a table of square-roots, we find

$y_1 = 3{\cdot}000$	$y_3 = 3{\cdot}606$	$y_2 = 3{\cdot}317$
$y_9 = 5{\cdot}000$	$y_5 = 4{\cdot}123$	$y_4 = 3{\cdot}873$
	$y_7 = 4{\cdot}583$	$y_6 = 4{\cdot}359$
$\mathrm{X} = 8{\cdot}000$		$y_8 = 4{\cdot}796$
	$\mathrm{O} = 12{\cdot}312$	
	$2\mathrm{O} = 24{\cdot}624$	$\mathrm{E} = 16{\cdot}345$
		$4\mathrm{E} = 65{\cdot}380$

Hence, since $h = 2$,

$$\int_9^{25} \sqrt{x}\,dx = \tfrac{2}{3}(8{\cdot}000 + 24{\cdot}624 + 65{\cdot}380) = 65{\cdot}33.$$

In this case we can evaluate the integral in the usual way, and so test the accuracy of Simpson's Rule :—

$$\int_9^{25} \sqrt{x}\,dx = \left[\tfrac{2}{3}x^{\frac{3}{2}} \right]_9^{25} = \tfrac{2}{3}[125 - 27] = 65{\cdot}333 \ldots$$

Thus the approximate result is correct to four figures.

Examples LXIII.

Evaluate the given integrals by Simpson's Rule, using the number of strips indicated in brackets :—

1. $\int_4^{16} \sqrt{x}\,dx$; (6).

2. $\int_4^{12} \dfrac{1}{x}\,dx$; (8).

3. $\int_0^4 \sqrt{(x^4 + 1)}\,dx$; (4).

4. $\int_6^{10} (\log_{10} x)\,dx$; (4).

5. $\int_0^\pi \sqrt{(\sin \theta)}\,d\theta$; (12)

6. $\int_0^\pi \sqrt{(1 - \tfrac{3}{4}\sin^2 \theta)}\,d\theta$; (6).

CHAPTER XI.

PHYSICAL APPLICATIONS.

§ 126. Rectilinear Motion.—Let s, v, a, t have their usual meanings (§§ 56, 57). Let $s = s_1$ when $t = t_1$, and $s = s_2$ when $t = t_2$. Then $(s_2 - s_1)$ is the distance moved in the interval from t_1 to t_2.

Let this distance be divided into small elements, and let δs be the element of distance moved in the interval from t to $(t + \delta t)$, while the velocity changes from v to $(v + \delta v)$. Then, if δt is small enough,

$\qquad \delta s$ lies between $v \delta t$ and $(v + \delta v) \delta t$.

Hence, by § 109,

$$s_2 - s_1 = \int_{t_1}^{t_2} v\, dt. \tag{1}$$

It follows that the distance moved in the interval from t_1 to t_2 is represented on the (t, v) graph by the area between the graph, the t-axis, and the ordinates $t = t_1$, $t = t_2$ (Fig. 77).

In practice we say conventionally: Let ds be the distance moved in the infinitely short interval dt, when the velocity is v. Then $ds = v\, dt$, and hence follows (1).

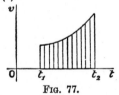

FIG. 77.

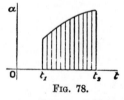

FIG. 78.

§ 127. Again, let $v = v_1$ when $t = t_1$, and $v = v_2$ when $t = t_2$. Then $(v_2 - v_1)$ is the change in v in the interval from t_1 to t_2.

Let δv be the change in v in the interval from t to $(t + \delta t)$, while the acceleration changes from a to $(a + \delta a)$. Then, if δt is small enough,

$\qquad \delta v$ lies between $a \delta t$ and $(a + \delta a) \delta t$,

$$\therefore \quad v_2 - v_1 = \int_{t_1}^{t_2} a\, dt. \tag{2}$$

It follows that the change in v in the interval from t_1 to t_2 is represented on the (t, a) graph by the area between the graph, the t-axis, and the ordinates $t = t_1$, $t = t_2$ (Fig. 78).

In practice we say conventionally : Let dv be the change in v in the infinitely short interval dt, when the acceleration is α. Then $dv = \alpha\, dt$, and hence follows (2).

§ 128. **Work done by a Force on a Body.**—Still considering the motion of a body in a straight line, let W be the work done on the body by one of the forces acting on it, while s changes from s_1 to s_2.

Let δW be the element of work done while the body moves a distance δs and the force changes from F to $(F + \delta F)$. Then, if δs is small enough,

$$\delta W \text{ lies between } F\delta s \text{ and } (F + \delta F)\delta s,$$

$$\therefore \; W = \int_{s_1}^{s_2} F\, ds. \tag{3}$$

The work done is represented on the (s, F) graph by the area between the graph, the s-axis, and the ordinates $s = s_1$, $s = s_2$ (Fig. 79).

In practice we say conventionally : Let dW be the element of work done while the body moves the infinitely short distance ds. Then dW $= F\, ds$, and hence follows (3).

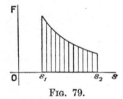

FIG. 79.

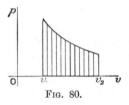

FIG. 80.

§ 129. **Work done by Expanding Gas.**—Let a gas be confined in a cylinder, closed by a movable piston of area a. Let p be the pressure, and v the volume, of the gas when the length of the cylinder is x.

Let W be the work done by the gas on the piston while the gas expands and the length of the cylinder changes from x_1 to x_2. Then, since pa is the force exerted by the gas on the piston, we have, by (3),

$$W = \int_{x_1}^{x_2} pa\, dx.$$

5

But $a\,dx = dv$, since $v = ax$. Hence, if $v = v_1$ when $x = x_1$, and $v = v_2$ when $x = x_2$,

$$W = \int_{v_1}^{v_2} p\,dv. \tag{4}$$

It follows that the work done by a gas while its volume expands from v_1 to v_2 is represented on the (v, p) graph by the area between the graph, the axis of v, and the ordinates $v = v_1$, $v = v_2$ (Fig. 80).

Examples LXIV.

1. The velocity of a body, t seconds after a certain instant, is $(10t^2 + 5)$ ft./sec. Find how far it moves in the interval from $t = 3$ to $t = 6$.

2. The speed of a train, t minutes after it starts from rest, is $30\sin^2(\pi t/10)$ mls./hr. How far does it travel in the first five minutes ?

3. The acceleration of a car, t seconds after the beginning of an interval of one minute, is $5\cos(\pi t/60)$ ft./sec.^{2} Show that the velocity of the car at the end of the minute is the same as it was at the beginning.

4. A body of mass m moves with simple harmonic motion on the axis of x, its distance from the origin at time t being given by $x = a\sin\omega t$. Find its maximum kinetic energy, and its average kinetic energy with respect to t.

5. If T is the tension in an elastic rod when it is extended a distance x beyond its natural length, it is known that $T = kx$, where k is a constant (Hooke's Law).

Find the work done on the rod when the extension is increased from x_1 to x_2; and show that the average force required to cause this increase is half the sum of the initial and final tensions.

6. A charge E of electricity repels a charge e with a force equal to Ee/x^2, when x is the distance between them. Find the work that must be done on a charge e in bringing it from infinity to a point at a distance r from a charge E.

7. A gas expands, from volume v_1 to v_2, according to the law $pv^n = C$, where n and C are constants. Find the work done by the gas, and prove that the average pressure with respect to v during the expansion is

$$\frac{p_1v_1 - p_2v_2}{(n-1)(v_2 - v_1)},$$

where p_1, p_2 are the initial and final values of p.

8. The weight per unit length of a horizontal rod varies as the square of the distance from one end, which is fixed to a smooth hinge. Show that the least vertical force, acting at the middle, that will turn the rod about the hinge is $3W/2$, where W is the total weight of the rod.

9. A circular disc, of weight W, can turn about a smooth pivot through its centre on a rough horizontal table. The pressure of the disc on the table is uniformly distributed. Show that the least force that will turn the disc round the pivot is $2\mu W/3$, where μ is the coefficient of friction.

10. A uniform rod, of length l and weight W, suspended freely from one end, is held at an angle θ to the vertical by a couple. Find the moment of

the couple. If the rod hangs at rest initially, and is then turned, by a couple alone, through 180° until it is at rest in the upright position, find by integration the work done by the couple on the rod. [If the rod turns through an angle $d\theta$ while a couple of moment M acts upon it, the work done by the couple on the rod is $Md\theta$.]

CENTRES OF GRAVITY.

§ 130. Let a set of masses m_1, m_2, m_3 . . . all have their centres of gravity on the axis of x, at distances x_1, x_2, x_3, . . . from the origin. Let M be the total mass, so that

$$M = m_1 + m_2 + m_3 + \ldots = \Sigma m. \tag{1}$$

Also, let $\bar{x}$ be the distance of the centre of gravity G of the whole set from the origin. Then

$$M\bar{x} = m_1x_1 + m_2x_2 + m_3x_3 + \ldots = \Sigma mx. \tag{2}$$

In the language of mechanics : *the moment about the origin of the total mass, supposed concentrated at G, is equal to the sum of the moments of the separate masses.*

From (2) it follows that $\bar{x}$ is given by

$$\bar{x} = \frac{m_1x_1 + m_2x_2 + m_3x_3 + \ldots}{M} = \frac{\Sigma mx}{M}. \tag{3}$$

§ 131. Two Properties of the Centre of Gravity.

(1) *If the separate masses are equal, $\bar{x}$ is the average of x_1, x_2, x_3, . . .*
Proof. Let there be n masses, each equal to m. Then

$$M\bar{x} = m(x_1 + x_2 + \ldots + x_n).$$

But

$$M = nm.$$

By division,

$$\bar{x} = \frac{x_1 + x_2 + \ldots + x_n}{n}.$$

(2) *If the centre of gravity is at the origin, $\Sigma mx = 0$.*
Proof. If G is at the origin, $\bar{x} = 0$; $\therefore \Sigma mx = 0$, by (2).

§ 132. Body Symmetrical about the x-axis.—Let G be the centre of gravity of a body of uniform density, symmetrical about the x-axis (e.g. a solid or surface of revolution). Then G lies on the x-axis, by symmetry. Let $OG = \bar{x}$.

Dissect the body into infinitely small elements of mass by means of planes perpendicular to the x-axis. Let dm be a typical element of mass, and let its centre of gravity, which lies on the x-axis, be at a distance x from O.

The moment of this element about $O = dm \cdot x = x\,dm$. Hence, by integration, the sum of the moments of all the elements is $\int x\,dm$,

$$\therefore\ M\bar{x} = \int x\,dm. \tag{4}$$

But

$$M = \int dm.$$

By division,

$$\bar{x} = \frac{\int x\,dm}{\int dm}. \tag{5}$$

Rule.—Write down a typical element of mass dm.

Write down the moment of this element about O.

Find the sum of the moments of all the elements, in the form of a *definite* integral. Equate this to $M\bar{x}$.

Find M, in general by integration.

Deduce $\bar{x}$, by division.

§ 133. Centre of Gravity of a Uniform Solid Cone.—Let $r =$ the base-radius, $h =$ the height, $\rho =$ the density.

Let the cone be placed with its apex at the origin, and its axis along the x-axis (Fig. 81), and dissect the cone into infinitely thin discs perpendicular to the x-axis. Let x be the distance from O of the centre of a typical disc, of thickness dx, radius y, volume dv, and mass dm. Then (cf. **Ex.**, § 111)

$$dm = \rho\,dv = \rho\pi y^2\,dx = \pi\rho\left(\frac{rx}{h}\right)^2 dx.$$

The moment of this element of mass about O is

$$dm \cdot x = \frac{\pi\rho r^2}{h^2}x^3\,dx,$$

$$\therefore\ M\bar{x} = \frac{\pi\rho r^2}{h^2}\int_0^h x^3\,dx = \frac{\pi\rho r^2\,h^2}{4}.$$

But

$$M = \frac{\pi r^2\,h\rho}{3}.$$

By division,

$$\bar{x} = \frac{3h}{4}. \tag{6}$$

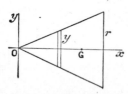

Fig. 81.   Fig. 82.

§ 134. Centre of Gravity of a Thin Hemispherical Shell.—

Let a = the radius, σ = the mass per unit area.

Let the shell be placed with the centre of the base at the origin, and the base perpendicular to the x-axis (Fig. 82).

Dissect the shell into infinitely narrow zones by means of planes parallel to the base, and let dS be the area, dm the mass, of a typical zone. Then

$$dm = \sigma \, dS = \sigma \,.\, 2\pi y \, ds = 2\pi\sigma a \, dx, \text{ by (11), § 116 ;}$$

$$\therefore \; dm \,.\, x = 2\pi\sigma a x \, dx,$$

$$\therefore \; M\bar{x} = 2\pi\sigma a \int_0^a x \, dx = \pi\sigma a^3.$$

But

$$M = 2\pi a^2 \sigma.$$

By division,

$$\bar{x} = \frac{a}{2}. \tag{7}$$

§ 135. Centre of Gravity of a Homogeneous Solid Hemisphere.—

Let a = the radius, ρ = the density.

Dissect the hemisphere into infinitely thin concentric hemispherical shells, and let dm be the mass, dv the volume, of the shell of radius r, thickness dr. Then

$$dm = \rho \, dv = \rho \,.\, 2\pi r^2 \, dr = 2\pi\rho r^2 \, dr.$$

The distance of the centre of gravity of this shell from O is $\frac{1}{2}r$, by § 134. Hence its moment about O is

$$dm \,.\, \tfrac{1}{2}r = \pi\rho r^3 \, dr,$$

$$\therefore \; M\bar{x} = \pi\rho \int_0^a r^3 \, dr = \frac{\pi\rho a^4}{4}.$$

But

$$M = \frac{2\pi a^3 \rho}{3}.$$

By division,

$$\bar{x} = \frac{3a}{8}. \tag{8}$$

§ 136. Example of Variable Density.

Ex. The density at any point of a solid hemisphere, of radius a, is proportional to the perpendicular distance of the point from the base. Find the position of the centre of gravity.

Let the hemisphere be placed with the centre of the base at the origin, and the base perpendicular to the x-axis.

Dissect the hemisphere into discs parallel to the base.

Let ρ be the density of the typical disc, and x the distance of its centre from the origin. Then $\rho = kx$, where k is a constant. Let y be the radius of this disc, dm its mass, dv its volume, dx its thickness. Then

$$dm = \rho \, dv = \rho \,.\, \pi y^2 \, dx = \pi\rho(a^2 - x^2)dx = \pi kx(a^2 - x^2)dx,$$

$$\therefore \; dm \,.\, x = \pi kx^2(a^2 - x^2)dx,$$

$$\therefore \; M\bar{x} = \pi k \int_0^a x^2(a^2 - x^2)dx = \frac{2\pi ka^5}{15}.$$

But

$$M = \pi k \int_0^a x(a^2 - x^2)dx = \frac{\pi ka^4}{4}.$$

By division,

$$\bar{x} = \frac{8a}{15}.$$

Examples LXV.

1. Find the distance of the centre of gravity of a solid hemisphere, of radius a, from the centre of the base; dissecting the hemisphere into discs parallel to the base.

2. Find the centre of gravity of the volume generated when the curve $y = x^2$, from $x = 0$ to $x = 6$, revolves about the x-axis.

3. A bowl, formed by rotating the parabola $y = x^2$ about the y-axis, is filled with water to a depth h. Find the height of the c.g. of the water above the bottom of the bowl.

4. A hemispherical cup, of radius a, is filled with water to a depth $\frac{1}{2}a$. Find the depth of the centre of gravity of the water below the water surface.

5. A sphere of radius a is divided into two segments by a plane at a distance c from the centre. Find the distance of the c.g. of the smaller segment from the centre. Test your answer by putting $c = 0$ and $c = a$.

6. A hollow sphere of inner radius a, outer radius b, is cut by two parallel planes, one passing through the centre and the other touching the inner surface. Find the distance from the centre to the c.g. of the solid between the planes.

7. The mass per unit length at any point of a straight rod, of length l, is proportional to the square of the distance of the point from one end. Find the distance of the c.g. from that end.

8. The density at any point of a solid hemisphere, of radius a, is proportional to the square of the distance of the point from the centre of the base. Find the distance of the c.g. from the base.

9. A hollow sphere, of inner radius a, outer radius b, is cut into two halves by a plane through the centre. Find the distance from the centre to the c.g. of either half.

10. Using the result of Ex. 9, find approximately the ratio of a to b when the c.g. lies on the inner surface.

11. The radii of the ends of a frustum of a solid cone are a and b, and the height of the frustum is h. Find the distance of the c.g. from the end of radius a.

12. Prove that the centre of gravity of the surface of a spherical zone bisects the line joining the centres of the two circles which form the boundary of the zone.

13. Find the distance from the apex to the centre of gravity of the curved surface of a cone of height h.

14. The loop of the curve $9y^2 = x(3 - x)^2$ revolves about the x-axis. Find the distance from the origin to the centre of gravity of the surface of revolution generated.

15. The parabola $y^2 = 4x$, from $x = 0$ to $x = 3$, revolves about the x-axis. Find the distance from the origin to the centre of gravity of the surface of revolution generated.

§ **137.** Let a set of masses m_1, m_2, m_3, . . . have their centres of gravity at the points (x_1, y_1), (x_2, y_2), (x_3, y_3) . . . respectively.

Let $(\bar{x}, \bar{y})$ be the co-ordinates of G, the centre of gravity of the whole set of masses, and let M be the total mass. Then

$$M\bar{x} = m_1x_1 + m_2x_2 + m_3x_3 + \ldots = \Sigma mx,$$
$$M\bar{y} = m_1y_1 + m_2y_2 + m_3y_3 + \ldots = \Sigma my.$$

In mechanics, we can regard these equations as the results of taking moments about the axes of y and x respectively, supposing gravity to act perpendicularly to the plane of the axes. It follows that $\bar{x}$ and $\bar{y}$ are given by

$$\bar{x} = \frac{\Sigma mx}{M}, \quad \bar{y} = \frac{\Sigma my}{M} \tag{9}$$

For continuous bodies, the summations must be replaced by definite integrals.

§ 138. Centre of Gravity of a Circular Arc.

Ex. Find the centre of gravity of a uniform wire bent into an arc of a circle, of radius a, and subtending an angle 2α at the centre of the circle.

Let AB be the arc, C its middle point, P any point on it, O the centre of the circle, OC the x-axis, and $\angle COP = \theta$. Then G lies on OC, by symmetry (Fig. 83).

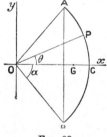
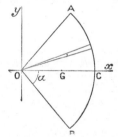

FIG. 83.   FIG. 84.

Dissect the arc AB into infinitely small arcs, and let dm be the mass of an infinitely small arc ds at P, subtending an angle $d\theta$ at O. Then, if $\lambda =$ the line density,

$$dm = \lambda \, ds = \lambda a \, d\theta.$$

The moment of this element about the y-axis is

$$dm \, . \, x = \lambda a \, d\theta \, . \, a \cos \theta = \lambda a^2 \cos \theta \, d\theta,$$
$$\therefore \; M\bar{x} = \lambda a^2 \int_{-a}^{a} \cos \theta \, d\theta = 2\lambda a^2 \sin \alpha.$$

But $$M = 2a\alpha \cdot \lambda.$$

By division, $$\bar{x} = \frac{a \sin \alpha}{\alpha}. \tag{10}$$

This can be written

$$\frac{\bar{x}}{a} = \frac{2a \sin \alpha}{2a\alpha}. \tag{11}$$

or $$\frac{OG}{OC} = \frac{\text{chord AB}}{\text{arc AB}}. \tag{12}$$

§ 139. Centre of Gravity of a Sector of a Circle.

Ex. Find the centre of gravity of a sector of a thin circular disc, of radius a and uniform thickness, the angle of the sector being 2α.

Let AB be the arc of the sector, C the mid-point of the arc, O the centre of the disc, OC the x-axis. Then G lies on OC, by symmetry (Fig. 84).

Dissect the sector into infinitely thin equal sectors, each of which can be regarded as an infinitely thin triangle, whose c.g. is at a distance $\frac{2}{3}a$ from O.

Let each thin sector be replaced by a particle of equal mass at its c.g. The whole sector is thereby replaced by a uniform circular arc of radius $\frac{2}{3}a$ and angle 2α. Hence, by (10),

$$\bar{x} = \tfrac{2}{3}a \cdot \frac{\sin \alpha}{\alpha}, \tag{13}$$

which can be written

$$\frac{OG}{OC} = \frac{2}{3}\frac{\text{chord AB}}{\text{arc AB}}. \tag{14}$$

§ 140. Centre of Gravity of an Arc of any Curve.

Ex. Find formulæ for the co-ordinates of the centre of gravity of the *arc* of any graph, when the line density is variable.

Let AB be the arc, P any point on it (Fig. 85).

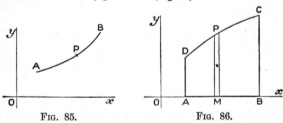

FIG. 85.   FIG. 86.

Let (x, y) be the co-ordinates of P, and let dm be the mass of an element of arc ds at P. Let $\lambda = $ the line density at P, and let $M = $ the mass of the whole arc.

Then $dm = \lambda\, ds$, and taking moments about the y and x axes in turn, we get

$$M\bar{x} = \int \lambda x\, ds, \quad M\bar{y} = \int \lambda y\, ds. \tag{15}$$

But
$$M = \int \lambda \, ds.$$

By division,
$$\bar{x} = \frac{\int \lambda x \, ds}{\int \lambda \, ds}, \quad \bar{y} = \frac{\int \lambda y \, ds}{\int \lambda \, ds}, \tag{16}$$

the integrals being *definite*.

§ 141. Centre of Gravity of the Area bounded by a Graph, the x-Axis, and two Ordinates.

—Assume that y is positive, and that the surface density σ is a function of x, so that σ is constant along any thin strip parallel to the y-axis (Fig. 86).

Dissect the area into infinitely thin strips parallel to the y-axis. Let dm be the mass of a typical strip MP, and let (x, y) be the co-ordinates of P. Then $dm = \sigma y \, dx$.

The co-ordinates of the centre of gravity of this strip are $(x, \frac{1}{2}y)$. Hence, taking moments about the y and x axes in turn, we get

$$M\bar{x} = \int \sigma x y \, dx, \quad M\bar{y} = \int \frac{1}{2}\sigma y^2 \, dx.$$

But
$$M = \int \sigma y \, dx.$$

By division,
$$\bar{x} = \frac{\int \sigma x y \, dx}{\int \sigma y \, dx}, \quad \bar{y} = \frac{\int \frac{1}{2}\sigma y^2 \, dx}{\int \sigma y \, dx}, \tag{17}$$

the integrals being *definite*.

Examples LXVI.

In Exs. 1-8 find the co-ordinates of the centres of gravity of the areas bounded by the given curves, the x-axis, and the given ordinates, assuming the surface density to be constant :—

1. $y = x^2$; $x = 0$, $x = 3$.
2. $y = 4 - x^2$; $x = -2$, $x = 2$.
3. $y = \sin x$; $x = 0$, $x = \pi$.
4. $y = \cos x$; $x = 0$, $x = \frac{1}{2}\pi$.
5. $y^2 = 4x$; $x = 0$, $x = 4$.
6. $y^2 = x^3$; $x = 1$, $x = 4$.
7. $y = \dfrac{4}{x^3}$; $x = 1$, $x = 2$.
8. $\dfrac{x^2}{a^2} + \dfrac{y^2}{b^2} = 1$; $x = 0$, $x = a$.

In Exs. 9-12 find the co-ordinates of the centres of gravity of the areas bounded by the given curves :—

9. $y^2 = 4x$, $y = x$.
10. $x^2 + y^2 = 25$, $y = 10 - 2x$.
11. $y = x^2$, $x = y^2$.
12. $y^2 = 4x$, $x + y = 3$.

13. Find by integration the distance of the centre of gravity of a triangle, of height h, from the base.

14. In a triangle, of height h, the surface density at any point is proportional to the square of the perpendicular distance of the point from the base. Find the distance of the c.g. from the base.

15. The parallel sides of a trapezium are 3 inches and 5 inches long, and the perpendicular distance between them is 12 inches. Find the distance of the c.g. from the shorter of the parallel sides.

16. Prove that the c.g. of a trapezium divides the line joining the middle points of the parallel sides in the ratio $(a + 2b) : (2a + b)$, where a, b are the lengths of the parallel sides.

17. Find the centre of gravity of a semi-circular disc, of radius a, dissecting it into strips parallel to the bounding diameter.

18. A circular disc of radius a is divided into two segments by a chord at distance $\frac{1}{2}a$ from the centre. Find the distance of the c.g. of the smaller segment from the centre of the disc.

19. Find the c.g. of a semicircular disc, of radius a, when the mass per unit area at any point is proportional to the perpendicular distance of the point from the bounding diameter.

Deduce the position of the c.g. of a *thin* wedge cut from a homogeneous solid sphere, of radius a, by two planes intersecting in a diameter.

20. Find the c.g. of a semicircular arc, of radius a, when the mass per unit length at any point is proportional to the perpendicular distance of the point from the diameter joining the ends of the arc.

Deduce the position of the c.g. of the curved surface of the wedge in Ex. 19.

21. A uniform rod, 2 ft. long, is bent into a circular arc subtending an angle 2θ at the centre of the circle. Find the distance of its c.g. from the centre of the circle.

22. A circular annulus, of inner radius a, outer radius b, is divided into two halves along a diameter. Find the distance of the c.g. of either half from the centre of the annulus.

23. A uniform wire is bent into the shape of the loop of the curve $9y^2 = x(3 - x)^2$. Find the distance of its c.g. from the origin.

24. Find the distance from the origin to the c.g. of the arc of the curve $4y^2 = x^3$, from $y = -\frac{1}{2}$ to $y = \frac{1}{2}$.

§ 142. Theorems of Pappus.

(1) When a plane curve revolves about an axis in its own plane, but not intersecting it, the area of the surface generated by the curve is equal to the product of its length and the circumference of the circle described by the centre of gravity of the arc of the curve.

Proof.—Let s be the length of the curve that revolves, ds an element at a distance y from the axis, $\bar{y}$ the distance of the c.g. of the curve from the axis, S the area of the surface generated (Fig. 87). Then

$$S = \int 2\pi y \, ds = 2\pi \int y \, ds.$$

But

$$\int y \, ds = s\bar{y},$$

$$\therefore S = 2\pi s\bar{y} = s \times 2\pi\bar{y}, \tag{18}$$

which proves the theorem.

(2) When a plane area revolves about an axis in its own plane, but not intersecting it, the volume generated by the area is equal to the product of the area and the circumference of the circle described by the centre of gravity of the area.

Proof.—Let A be the area that revolves, dA an element at a distance y from the axis, $\bar{y}$ the distance of the c.g. of the area from the axis, V the volume generated (Fig. 88). Then

$$V = \int 2\pi y\, dA = 2\pi \int y\, dA.$$

But
$$\int y\, dA = A\bar{y},$$
$$\therefore V = 2\pi A\bar{y} = A \times 2\pi\bar{y}, \tag{19}$$

which proves the theorem.

These theorems may be used to find S or V if $\bar{y}$ is known, or to find $\bar{y}$ if S or V is known.

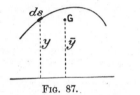

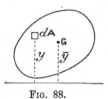

FIG. 87.   FIG. 88.

Ex. An anchor ring is generated by revolving a circle of radius a about an axis in its own plane at a distance b from the centre of the circle ($b > a$). Find the volume of the ring and the area of its curved surface.

By the second theorem, the volume is given by

$$V = \pi a^2 \times 2\pi b = 2\pi^2 a^2 b.$$

By the first theorem, the area of the curved surface is given by

$$S = 2\pi a \times 2\pi b = 4\pi^2 ab.$$

Examples LXVII.

1. In a right-angled triangle the lengths of the sides including the right angle are h and r. By supposing the triangle to revolve about the side h, find the volume of a cone.

2. A regular hexagon, of side a, revolves about one side. Find the volume generated and the area of its surface.

3. Find the centre of gravity of a semicircular arc, by applying Pappus's first theorem; and the centre of gravity of a semicircular disc, by applying Pappus's second theorem.

4. A line of length l has its ends at distances a and b from an axis. By supposing the line to revolve about the axis, find the area of the curved surface of a frustum of a cone.

5. The vertices of a triangle are the points $(0, 0)$, $(5, 2)$, $(2, 4)$. Find the volume generated when the triangle revolves about the x-axis.

6. The vertices of a triangle are the points $(1, 3)$, $(3, 8)$, $(5, 4)$. Find the volume generated when the triangle revolves about the y-axis.

7. Prove that the volume generated by the revolution of a triangle ABC about the side a is $4\pi S^2/3a$, where S = the area of the triangle.

8. The diagonals of a quadrilateral ABCD intersect in the point O. If the quadrilateral revolves about the side AB, prove that the volume generated is $4\pi Q(Q - S)/3a$, where a = AB, Q = area of quadrilateral, S = area of △COD.

MOMENTS OF INERTIA.

§ 143. The *moment of inertia* of a particle about an axis is defined to be the product of the mass of the particle and the square of its perpendicular distance from the axis.

The moment of inertia of a set of particles about an axis is defined to be the sum of their moments of inertia about the axis.

Let I be the moment of inertia about an axis of a set of particles of masses m_1, m_2, m_3, . . . at distances r_1, r_2, r_3, . . . respectively, from the axis. Then

$$I = m_1r_1^2 + m_2r_2^2 + m_3r_3^2 + \ldots = \Sigma mr^2. \qquad (1)$$

Let M be the total mass of the set of particles, and let k be the distance from the axis at which a particle of mass M would have the same moment of inertia as the set of particles. Then

$$Mk^2 = I = \Sigma mr^2, \qquad (2)$$

$$\therefore k^2 = \frac{I}{M} = \frac{\Sigma mr^2}{M}. \qquad (3)$$

The distance k is called the *radius of gyration* of the set of particles about the axis.

For continuous bodies, the summations must be replaced by definite integrals.

§ 144. A Theorem that applies to any Plane Body.—Let Ox, Oy be two rectangular axes in the plane of the body.

Let I_x = the moment of inertia about the x-axis,

I_y = the moment of inertia about the y-axis,

I_0 = the moment of inertia about an axis through O, perpendicular to the plane. Then we shall prove that

$$I_0 = I_x + I_y.$$

Proof.—Let dm be an element of mass at a point P, let (x, y) be the co-ordinates of P, and let r = OP (Fig. 89). Then

$$I_x = \int y^2\, dm, \qquad I_y = \int x^2\, dm,$$
$$\therefore I_x + I_y = \int (x^2 + y^2) dm = \int r^2\, dm = I_0,$$
$$\therefore I_0 = I_x + I_y. \tag{4}$$

Dividing by M, we have also
$$k_0{}^2 = k_x{}^2 + k_y{}^2, \tag{5}$$

where k_0, k_x, k_y are the corresponding radii of gyration.

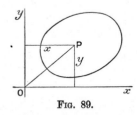

FIG. 89.   FIG. 90.

§ 145. **Radius of Gyration of a Uniform Rod.**—(1) *About a perpendicular axis through one end.* Let OA be the rod, l its length, λ its mass per unit length, I its moment of inertia and k its radius of gyration about an axis through O perpendicular to the rod (Fig. 90).

Let dm be the mass of an element dx at a distance x from O, and dI the moment of inertia of this element. Then

$$dI = dm \cdot x^2 = \lambda\, dx \cdot x^2 = \lambda x^2\, dx,$$
$$\therefore Mk^2 = I = \lambda \int_0^l x^2\, dx = \frac{\lambda l^3}{3}.$$

But $$M = \lambda l.$$

By division, $$k^2 = \frac{l^2}{3}. \tag{6}$$

(2) *About a perpendicular axis through the middle point.* In this case, the origin being at the middle point,

$$Mk^2 = \lambda \int_{-\frac{1}{2}l}^{\frac{1}{2}l} x^2\, dx = \frac{\lambda l^3}{12},$$
$$\therefore k^2 = \frac{l^2}{12}. \tag{7}$$

§ 146. **Radius of Gyration of a Uniform Circular Ring, Radius a.**—(1) *About the axis of the ring.* Let k_0 be the radius of gyration about an axis through the centre of the ring, perpendicular to its plane. Since every element of the ring is at a distance a from this axis,

$$\therefore k_0{}^2 = a^2. \tag{8}$$

(2) *About a diameter of the ring.* Let k_x, k_y be the radii of gyration about two perpendicular diameters. Then, by (5) and (8),

$$k_x{}^2 + k_y{}^2 = k_0{}^2 = a^2.$$

But $k_x = k_y$, by symmetry,

$$\therefore\ 2k_x{}^2 = a^2,$$

$$\therefore\ k_x{}^2 = \frac{a^2}{2}. \tag{9}$$

§ 147. Radius of Gyration of a Uniform Circular Disc, Radius a.

—(1) *About the axis of the disc.* Let k_0 be the radius of gyration about an axis through the centre of the disc, perpendicular to its plane.

Dissect the disc into infinitely thin concentric rings.

Let dm be the mass of a typical ring, of radius r and width dr, and let $\sigma =$ the mass per unit area.

The moment of inertia of this ring about the axis is

$$dm \cdot r^2 = \sigma \cdot 2\pi r\, dr \cdot r^2 = 2\pi\sigma r^3\, dr,$$

$$\therefore\ Mk_0{}^2 = 2\pi\sigma \int_0^a r^3\, dr = \frac{\pi\sigma a^4}{2}.$$

But $$M = \pi a^2 \sigma.$$

By division, $$k_0{}^2 = \frac{a^2}{2}. \tag{10}$$

(2) *About a diameter of the disc.*—Let k_x, k_y be the radii of gyration about two perpendicular diameters. Then, by (5) and (10),

$$k_x{}^2 + k_y{}^2 = k_0{}^2 = \tfrac{1}{2}a^2.$$

But $k_x = k_y$, by symmetry,

$$\therefore\ 2k_x{}^2 = \tfrac{1}{2}a^2,$$

$$\therefore\ k_x{}^2 = \frac{a^2}{4}. \tag{11}$$

§ 148. Radius of Gyration of a Homogeneous Solid Sphere, of Radius a, about a Diameter.

—Let the sphere be placed with its centre at the origin. Dissect it into infinitely thin discs, perpendicular to the x-axis, which we take to be the given diameter. Let dV be the volume of a typical disc, dm its mass, dI its moment of inertia about the x-axis. Let $\rho =$ the density ; then

$$dm = \rho\, dV = \rho \cdot \pi y^2\, dx = \pi\rho y^2\, dx,$$

and since the square of the radius of gyration of the disc is $\tfrac{1}{2}y^2$, by (10),

$$\therefore\ dI = dm \cdot \tfrac{1}{2}y^2 = \tfrac{1}{2}\pi\rho y^4\, dx = \tfrac{1}{2}\pi\rho(a^2 - x^2)^2\, dx,$$

$$\therefore\ Mk^2 = I = \tfrac{1}{2}\pi\rho \cdot 2 \int_0^a (a^2 - x^2)^2\, dx = \frac{8\pi\rho a^5}{15}.$$

But $$M = \frac{4\pi a^3 \rho}{3}.$$

By division, $$k^2 = \frac{2a^2}{5}. \tag{12}$$

The same kind of method could be applied to find the radius of gyration of any solid of revolution about its axis.

§ 149. Area Bounded by a Graph, the x-axis, and Two Ordinates.

—Let the radius of gyration be k_x about the x-axis, k_y about the y-axis.

Dissect the area into infinitely thin strips parallel to the y-axis. Let dm be the mass of a typical strip, and let the mass per unit area be unity. Then $dm = y\,dx$. Hence, since the square of the radius of gyration of the typical strip is, by (6), $\frac{1}{3}y^2$ about the x-axis, and x^2 about the y-axis,

$$\mathrm{M}k_x^2 = \int dm \cdot \tfrac{1}{3}y^2 = \int \tfrac{1}{3}y^3\,dx, \quad \mathrm{M}k_y^2 = \int dm \cdot x^2 = \int x^2 y\,dx.$$

But
$$\mathrm{M} = \int y\,dx. \tag{13}$$

By division,
$$k_x^2 = \frac{\int \tfrac{1}{3}y^3\,dx}{\int y\,dx}, \quad k_y^2 = \frac{\int x^2 y\,dx}{\int y\,dx}, \tag{14}$$

the integrals being *definite*.

Examples LXVIII.

In Exs. 1-17 find the squares of the radii of gyration of the given bodies about the given axes :—

1. A rectangle, of sides a and b ; (i) about a side of length b, (ii) about a side of length a, (iii) about an axis through a corner perpendicular to the plane of the rectangle.

2. A circular annulus, of inner radius a, outer radius b; (i) about an axis through the centre perpendicular to the plane of the annulus, (ii) about a diameter.

3. A triangular area, of altitude h ; (i) about an axis through the vertex parallel to the base, (ii) about the base.

4. A triangular area, of altitude h, in which the mass per unit area at any point is proportional to the square of the distance of the point from the base ; about the base.

5. A trapezoidal area, in which the lengths of the parallel sides are 3 ft. and 5 ft., and the distance between them is 4 ft. ; about the shorter of the parallel sides.

6. The area between the parabola $y^2 = 4ax$, the x-axis, and the ordinate $x = h$; about the x-axis.

7. The smaller segment cut from a solid sphere, of radius a, by a plane at a distance $\frac{1}{2}a$ from the centre ; about the axis of the segment.

8. A cone, of base-radius r ; about the axis of the cone.

9. A frustum of a cone, with end radii a and b ; about the axis of the frustum.

10. The solid generated by revolving the parabola $y^2 = 4ax$ from $x = 0$ to $x = h$ round the x-axis ; about the x-axis.

11. A uniform rod, of length l ; about an axis through one end, making an angle θ with the rod.

12. A uniform wire in the form of a triangle ABC ; about the side a.

13. The surface of the smaller spherical segment cut from a sphere, of radius a, by a plane at a distance c from the centre ; about the axis of the segment.

14. A solid anchor ring, generated by revolving a circle of radius a round an axis in its own plane at a distance b from the centre $(b > a)$; about the axis of the ring.

15. A thin spherical shell, of radius a ; about a diameter.

16. A hollow sphere, of inner radius a, outer radius b ; about a diameter.

17. A solid sphere, of radius a, in which the density at any point is inversely proportional to $r^{\frac{3}{2}}$, where $r =$ the distance of the point from the centre ; about a diameter.

18. Show that the radius of gyration of a set of equal particles, about any axis, is the root-mean-square of their distances from the axis.

§ **150. Moments of Inertia about Parallel Axes.**—Let AZ be any axis, and let G be the centre of gravity of any body, of mass M. We shall prove that:

The moment of inertia of the body about the axis AZ is equal to the sum of its moment of inertia about a parallel axis through G and the moment of inertia about AZ of a particle of mass M concentrated at G. That is, if K is the radius of gyration about the axis AZ, k the radius of gyration about a parallel axis through G, and h the perpendicular distance of G from AZ, then

$$MK^2 = Mk^2 + Mh^2, \tag{15}$$

or
$$K^2 = k^2 + h^2. \tag{16}$$

Proof.—Let GA be the perpendicular from G on AZ. Let the plane of the figure (Fig. 91) be the plane through G perpendicular to AZ. Let AG be the x-axis, G the origin, Gy the y-axis.

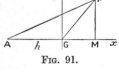

FIG. 91.

Dissect the body into infinitely thin rods parallel to AZ, and let dm be the mass of the rod which meets the plane of the figure in the point P.

Let $AP = R$, $GP = r$, $GM = x$, $MP = y$. Then, by geometry,

$$R^2 = r^2 + h^2 + 2hx.$$

Hence, since h is constant,

$$MK^2 = \int R^2\,dm = \int r^2\,dm + h^2 \int dm + 2h \int x\,dm$$
$$= Mk^2 + h^2 M + 2h M \bar{x}.$$

But $\bar{x} = 0$, since G is the origin,

$$\therefore MK^2 = Mk^2 + Mh^2.$$

§ 151. Ex. Find the square of the radius of gyration of a circular disc of radius a, (i) about an axis perpendicular to the disc and passing through a point on the circumference, (ii) about any axis parallel to a diameter and at a distance h from it.

(i) In the first case, by (10), $k^2 = \frac{1}{2}a^2$, and $h = a$,

$$\therefore \mathrm{K}^2 = \frac{1}{2}a^2 + a^2 = \frac{3a^2}{2}.$$

(ii) In the second case, by (11), $k^2 = \frac{1}{4}a^2$,

$$\therefore \mathrm{K}^2 = \frac{a^2}{4} + h^2.$$

§ 152. Moment of Inertia of a Solid of Revolution, about an Axis cutting the Axis of Revolution at Right Angles.—Let the solid be formed by the revolution of the area ABCD about the x-axis (Fig. 92), and let the y-axis be the axis about which the moment of inertia is required. Let I be this moment of inertia.

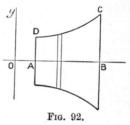

Fig. 92.

Dissect the solid into infinitely thin discs perpendicular to the x-axis. Let y be the radius of a typical disc at a distance x from O ; let dx be its thickness, dm its mass, and dI its moment of inertia about the y-axis. Let $\rho =$ the density. Then, by Ex. (ii), § 151,

$$dI = dm(\tfrac{1}{4}y^2 + x^2) = \rho\pi y^2\,dx(\tfrac{1}{4}y^2 + x^2),$$

$$\therefore\ I = \pi\rho \int_a^b (\tfrac{1}{4}y^2 + x^2)y^2\,dx. \tag{17}$$

Examples LXIX.

In Exs. 1-11 find the squares of the radii of gyration of the given bodies about the given axes :—

1. A circular disc, of radius a; about a tangent.

2. A solid sphere, of radius a; about a tangent line.

3. A triangle, of altitude h; about an axis through the centre of gravity parallel to the base.

4. A uniform wire bent into the shape of a rectangle of sides a and b; about an axis through one corner perpendicular to the plane of the rectangle.

5. A uniform solid cube, of edge a; about an edge.

6. An equilateral triangle, of side a; about an axis through its centre of gravity and perpendicular to its plane.

7. A regular tetrahedron, of edge a; about an axis through an apex and perpendicular to the opposite face.

8. A circular cylinder, of height h and radius r; about a diameter of one end.

9. A cone, of height h and base-radius r; (i) about an axis through the apex parallel to the base, (ii) about an axis through the centre of gravity parallel to the base, (iii) about a diameter of the base.

10. A solid hemisphere, of radius a; about an axis through the centre of gravity parallel to the base.

11. The solid generated by revolving the ellipse $\dfrac{x^2}{a^2} + \dfrac{y^2}{b^2} = 1$ round the x-axis; about the y-axis.

12. If A, B, C, D, . . . are any number of fixed points; and P is a variable point, in a plane, prove that the sum

$$AP^2 + BP^2 + CP^2 + DP^2 + \ldots$$

is least when P coincides with the centroid of A, B, C, D, . . .

FLUID PRESSURE.

§ 153. Hydrostatic Pressure on a Plane Area.—From Hydrostatics we know that, if dA is an element of area immersed in a liquid, at any inclination to the horizontal, and if z is the depth of dA below the surface of the liquid, the normal force exerted by the liquid on the element is $wzdA$, where w is the weight per unit volume of the liquid (atmospheric pressure being ignored).

We shall prove that: *the total thrust on a plane area, immersed in a liquid, is equal to the area multiplied by the pressure per unit area at the centre of gravity.*

Proof. Let A be the immersed area, P the total thrust on it, G its centre of gravity, $\bar{z}$ the depth of G.

Dissect the area A into infinitely small elements.

Let dA be a typical small element, dP the thrust on it, z its depth below the surface of the liquid. Then

$$dP = wzdA,$$
$$\therefore \; P = w\!\int\! zdA = w \, . \, A\bar{z} = A \, . \, w\bar{z}, \tag{1}$$

which proves the theorem, since $w\bar{z}$ is the pressure per unit area at G.

Corollary.—The average pressure per unit area is the pressure per unit area at the centre of gravity.

§ 154. Centre of Pressure.—The thrusts exerted by the liquid on the elements dA of the immersed area form a system of parallel forces which have a resultant. The point where this resultant meets the area is called the *centre of pressure*.

Let the y-axis be the line in which the plane of the immersed area meets the surface of the liquid, and let the x-axis be perpendicular to the y-axis and in the plane of the area.

Let h be the distance of the centre of gravity, and x_P the distance of the centre of pressure, from the y-axis. Also, let

K^2 be the square of the radius of gyration of the area about the y-axis. We shall prove that

$$x_P = \frac{K^2}{h}. \tag{2}$$

Proof.—Let the plane of the area be inclined at an angle θ to the horizontal, and let $\bar{z}$ be the depth of the centre of gravity. Then

$$\bar{z} = h \sin \theta. \tag{i}$$

Also, let dA be an element of the area, at a distance x from the y-axis, and at a depth z. Then

$$z = x \sin \theta. \tag{ii}$$

The moment of the whole thrust on the area about the y-axis is equal to the sum of the moments of the thrusts on the elements dA. Hence,

$$w\bar{z}A . x_P = \int wz \, dA . x,$$

that is, by (i) and (ii),

$$w(h \sin \theta) A x_P = \int wx^2 \sin \theta \, dA.$$

Hence, since $w \sin \theta$ is constant,

$$hAx_P = \int x^2 \, dA = AK^2,$$

$$\therefore \ x_P = \frac{K^2}{h}. \tag{2}$$

Corollary.—If k is the radius of gyration about an axis through the centre of gravity and parallel to the line in which the plane of the immersed area meets the surface,

$$x_P = \frac{k^2 + h^2}{h} = h + \frac{k^2}{h}. \tag{3}$$

Ex. 1. A rectangle, of sides a, b, is immersed with one of the sides b in the surface. Find the distance of the centre of pressure from that side.

In this case, $K^2 = \frac{1}{3}a^2$, $h = \frac{1}{2}a$. Hence, by (2),

$$x_P = \tfrac{2}{3}a.$$

Ex. 2. A circular disc, of radius a, is immersed vertically, with its centre at a depth h $(h > a)$. Find the depth of the centre of pressure.

By Ex. (ii), § 151, $K^2 = \frac{1}{4}a^2 + h^2$,

$$\therefore \ x_P = h + \frac{a^2}{4h}.$$

Examples LXX.

1. A rectangle is immersed in a liquid with one side in the surface. It is divided into two halves by a horizontal line. Find the ratio of the total thrusts on the two halves.

2. If the rectangle in Ex. 1 is vertical, and if each of the vertical sides is 12 ft. long, find the depth of the centre of pressure of each half.

3. Find the resultant horizontal thrust on a rectangular lockgate, 20 ft. wide, when the water stands at a depth of 8 ft. on one side, 4 ft. on the other. Also, find the moment of the resultant thrust about the bottom edge of the gate. [1 cub. ft. of water weighs $62\frac{1}{2}$ lbs.]

4. A triangle of altitude h is immersed vertically in a liquid. Find the depth of the centre of pressure (i) when the base is horizontal and the opposite vertex in the surface of the liquid, (ii) when the base is in the surface.

5. The lengths of the parallel sides of a trapezoidal plate are 3 ft. and 5 ft., and the distance between them is 4 ft. Find the depth of the centre of pressure when the plate is immersed vertically with the 3 ft. side in the surface.

6. A horizontal boiler, with flat circular ends of radius a, is half full of water. Find the depth of the centre of pressure of either end below the water surface.

7. The area bounded by the parabola $y = ax^2$ and the line $y = c$ is immersed vertically in liquid, with the line $y = c$ in the surface. Find the depth of the centre of pressure.

CHAPTER XII.

LOGARITHMIC AND EXPONENTIAL FUNCTIONS.

§ 155. **A Logarithmic Limit.**—Draw the graph of $\log_{10} x$ by means of a table of logarithms (Fig. 93). It crosses the x-axis at the point A where $x = 1$. Let μ be its gradient at this point. Then

$$\mu = \lim_{P \to A} \frac{NP}{AN}.$$

Let $AN = h$. Then

$ON = 1 + h$, $\quad NP = \log_{10}(1+h)$,

$$\therefore \mu = \lim_{h \to 0} \frac{\log_{10}(1+h)}{h}. \quad (1)$$

Now put $e = 10^{\mu}$. Then

$$\log_{10} e = \mu,$$

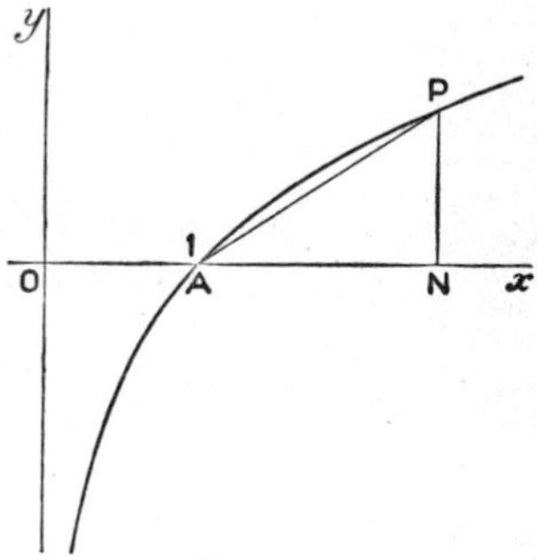

FIG. 93.

and

$$\log_{10}(1+h) = \log_{10} e \cdot \log_e(1+h) = \mu \cdot \log_e(1+h);$$

hence (1) can be written

$$\mu = \mu \cdot \lim_{h \to 0} \frac{\log_e(1+h)}{h}.$$

Dividing by μ, we get

$$\lim_{h \to 0} \frac{\log_e(1+h)}{h} = 1. \quad (2)$$

The value of the number e is $2 \cdot 718 \ldots$ to four figures (see § 165). A rough approximation can be found by giving h a small value in (1). Thus, if $h = \cdot 01$,

$$\mu \doteqdot \frac{\log_{10}(1 \cdot 01)}{0 \cdot 01} = \frac{\cdot 0043}{\cdot 01} = 0 \cdot 43 \ldots$$

and hence $\qquad e = 10^{\mu} \doteqdot 10^{\cdot 43} \doteqdot 2 \cdot 7 \ldots$

§ 156. **Differentiation of** $\log_e x$.—We can now prove that

$$\frac{d}{dx}(\log_e x) = \frac{1}{x}, \quad d(\log_e x) = \frac{dx}{x}. \tag{3}$$

Proof.—Put $y = \log_e x$. Then

$$y + \delta y = \log_e (x + \delta x), \quad y = \log_e x.$$

By subtraction,

$$\delta y = \log_e (x + \delta x) - \log_e x = \log_e \left(\frac{x + \delta x}{x}\right) = \log_e \left(1 + \frac{\delta x}{x}\right),$$

$$\therefore \frac{\delta y}{\delta x} = \frac{\log_e \left(1 + \dfrac{\delta x}{x}\right)}{\delta x} = \frac{\log_e \left(1 + \dfrac{\delta x}{x}\right)}{\dfrac{\delta x}{x}} \cdot \frac{1}{x}$$

$$\therefore \lim_{\delta x \to 0} \left(\frac{\delta y}{\delta x}\right) = 1 \times \frac{1}{x}, \text{ by (2)},$$

$$\therefore \frac{dy}{dx} = \frac{1}{x}.$$

Corollary.—If v is a function of x, we have, by (3), § 28,

$$\frac{d}{dx}(\log_e v) = \frac{1}{v}\frac{dv}{dx}, \quad d(\log_e v) = \frac{dv}{v}. \tag{4}$$

Henceforth, when the base of logarithms is omitted we shall understand it to be e.

Ex. 1. Differentiate (i) $\log (1 + x^2)$, (ii) $\log \dfrac{1 + x^2}{1 - x^2}$.

(i) By the Corollary,

$$\frac{d}{dx}\log (1 + x^2) = \frac{1}{1 + x^2}\frac{d}{dx}(1 + x^2) = \frac{2x}{1 + x^2}.$$

(ii) $$\log \frac{1 + x^2}{1 - x^2} = \log (1 + x^2) - \log (1 - x^2),$$

$$\therefore \frac{d}{dx}\log \frac{1 + x^2}{1 - x^2} = \frac{2x}{1 + x^2} - \frac{(-2x)}{1 - x^2} = \frac{4x}{1 - x^4}.$$

Ex. 2. Differentiate (i) $\log_a x$, (ii) $\log \{x + \sqrt{(x^2 + c)}\}$.

(i) $$\frac{d}{dx}(\log_a x) = \frac{d}{dx}\left(\frac{\log_e x}{\log_e a}\right) = \frac{1}{x \log_e a}. \tag{5}$$

(ii) Put $v = x + \sqrt{(x^2 + c)}$,

$$\therefore \frac{dv}{dx} = 1 + \frac{x}{\sqrt{(x^2 + c)}} = \frac{\sqrt{(x^2 + c)} + x}{\sqrt{(x^2 + c)}} = \frac{v}{\sqrt{(x^2 + c)}},$$

$$\therefore \frac{d}{dx}(\log v) = \frac{1}{v}\frac{dv}{dx} = \frac{1}{v} \cdot \frac{v}{\sqrt{(x^2 + c)}} = \frac{1}{\sqrt{(x^2 + c)}},$$

$$\therefore \frac{d}{dx}\log\{x + \sqrt{(x^2 + c)}\} = \frac{1}{\sqrt{(x^2 + c)}}. \tag{6}$$

Examples LXXI.

Differentiate the given functions with respect to x or θ :—

1. $\log(2x + 3)$.   **2.** $\log(ax + b)$.   **3.** $x^3 \log x$.

4. $\log(2x)$.   **5.** $\log(x^2)$.   **6.** $\log_{10} x$.   **7.** $\log_2 x$.

8. $\log(\log x)$.   **9.** $\log(\sin x)$.   **10.** $\sin(\log x)$.

11. $\log(\cos \theta)$.   **12.** $\log(\sec \theta)$.   **13.** $\log(\tan \tfrac{1}{2}\theta)$.

14. $\log\dfrac{a + x}{a - x}$.   **15.** $\log\dfrac{(x - a)^3}{(x - b)^2}$.   **16.** $\log\left(\dfrac{1 + x}{1 - x}\right)^{\frac{1}{2}}$.

17. $\log(\sec \theta + \tan \theta)$.   **18.** $x^n(1 - n \log x)$.

19. $\sqrt{x} - \log(1 + \sqrt{x})$.   **20.** $\tfrac{1}{2}\tan^2 \theta + \log(\cos \theta)$.

21. $\log\dfrac{1 + x + x^2}{1 - x + x^2}$.   **22.** $\log\tan\left(\dfrac{\pi}{4} + \dfrac{\theta}{2}\right)$.

23. $2x\tan^{-1} x - \log(1 + x^2)$.   **24.** $\log\sqrt{(\sin \theta \cos \theta)}$.

§ 157. Exponential Functions.—The symbol a^c is called a *power*, of which a is the *base*, and c is the *index* or *exponent*.

If x is a variable, the function a^x is a power in which *the exponent is variable* : it is called an *exponential function*. (Compare x^n, where the *base* is the variable.)

§ 158. Differentiation of e^x.—We shall prove that

$$\frac{d}{dx}(e^x) = e^x, \qquad d(e^x) = e^x\,dx. \tag{7}$$

Proof.—Put $y = e^x$. Then $x = \log_e y$,

$$\therefore \frac{dx}{dy} = \frac{1}{y}, \text{ by (3)},$$

$$\therefore \frac{dy}{dx} = y = e^x.$$

Corollary.—If v is a function of x, we have, by (3), § 28,

$$\frac{d}{dx}(e^v) = e^v\frac{dv}{dx}, \qquad d(e^v) = e^v\,dv. \tag{8}$$

§ 159. Direct Differentiation of e^x.—To differentiate e^x directly, from first principles, we first prove that

$$\lim_{x \to 0} \left(\frac{e^x - 1}{x} \right) = 1. \tag{9}$$

Proof.—Put $e^x - 1 = h$, $\therefore e^x = 1 + h$, $\therefore x = \log_e (1 + h)$,

$$\therefore \frac{e^x - 1}{x} = \frac{h}{\log_e (1 + h)}.$$

But $h \to 0$ when $x \to 0$,

$$\therefore \lim_{x \to 0} \left(\frac{e^x - 1}{x} \right) = \lim_{h \to 0} \frac{h}{\log_e (1 + h)} = 1,$$

by (2) ; which proves (9).

We can now differentiate e^x directly, as follows :—

$$y + \delta y = e^{x + \delta x}, \quad y = e^x,$$
$$\therefore \delta y = e^{x + \delta x} - e^x = e^x(e^{\delta x} - 1),$$
$$\therefore \frac{\delta y}{\delta x} = e^x \left(\frac{e^{\delta x} - 1}{\delta x} \right).$$

Hence, by (9), in the limit when $\delta x \to 0$,

$$\frac{dy}{dx} = e^x \times 1 = e^x.$$

Ex. 1. Differentiate (i) e^{cx}, (ii) $e^{ax} \cos bx$.

(i) By the Corollary, § 158,

$$\frac{d}{dx}(e^{cx}) = e^{cx}\frac{d}{dx}(cx) = e^{cx} \cdot c = ce^{cx}. \tag{10}$$

(ii) By the product rule,

$$\frac{d}{dx}(e^{ax} \cos bx) = ae^{ax}(\cos bx) + e^{ax}(- b \sin bx)$$
$$= e^{ax} (a \cos bx - b \sin bx).$$

Ex. 2. Differentiate a^x.

Since $a^x = (e^c)^x = e^{cx}$, where $c = \log_e a$,

$$\therefore \frac{d}{dx}(a^x) = ce^{cx} = e^{cx} \cdot c = a^x \log_e a. \tag{11}$$

Examples LXXII.

Differentiate the given functions :—

1. e^{-x}.
2. $(e^x)^3$.
3. $x^n e^{ax}$.
4. $e^{\tan x}$.
5. $x^2 e^{2x}$.
6. $e^x(x - 1)$.
7. $\sin^{-1}(e^x)$.
8. $\dfrac{x^2 + 2x}{e^x}$.
9. $\dfrac{e^x - e^{-x}}{e^x + e^{-x}}$.
10. $\log\left(\dfrac{e^x}{e^x + 1} \right)$.

§ 160. Logarithmic Differentiation.—When it is easier to differentiate $\log y$ than y, it is advantageous to take logarithms before differentiating. This method of differentiating is called *logarithmic differentiation.*

Ex. Differentiate (i) x^x, (ii) $\left(\dfrac{1+x}{1-x}\right)^{\frac{1}{2}}$.

(i) Put $y = x^x$. Taking logarithms, we have
$$\log y = x \log x.$$
Differentiating *both sides with respect to x*, we get
$$\frac{1}{y}\frac{dy}{dx} = x \cdot \frac{1}{x} + 1 \cdot \log x = 1 + \log x,$$
$$\therefore \frac{dy}{dx} = y(1 + \log x) = x^x (1 + \log x).$$

(ii) Put $y = \left(\dfrac{1+x}{1-x}\right)^{\frac{1}{2}}$. Then
$$\log y = \tfrac{1}{2} \log \frac{1+x}{1-x} = \tfrac{1}{2}\{\log(1+x) - \log(1-x)\},$$
$$\therefore \frac{1}{y}\frac{dy}{dx} = \tfrac{1}{2}\left(\frac{1}{1+x} + \frac{1}{1-x}\right) = \frac{1}{1-x^2},$$
$$\therefore \frac{dy}{dx} = \frac{y}{1-x^2} = \frac{1}{(1+x)^{\frac{1}{2}}(1-x)^{\frac{3}{2}}}.$$

§ 161. Proportional Errors.—Since
$$d(\log y) = \frac{dy}{y} \doteqdot \frac{\delta y}{y},$$
it is plain that logarithmic differentiation will be useful for finding proportional errors (see § 74).

Ex. Find the proportional error caused in y by a small error δx in x, when
$$y = \frac{2\pi x^{\frac{2}{3}}}{\sqrt{(1-x)}}.$$
Taking logarithms, we have
$$\log y = \log(2\pi) + \tfrac{2}{3}\log x - \tfrac{1}{2}\log(1-x),$$
$$\therefore \delta(\log y) \doteqdot \left\{0 + \frac{2}{3x} + \frac{1}{2(1-x)}\right\}\delta x,$$
$$\therefore \frac{\delta y}{y} \doteqdot \frac{(4-x)\delta x}{6x(1-x)}.$$
This is the proportional error in y.

Examples LXXIII.

In Exs. 1-13, differentiate the given functions :—

1. 10^x.   2. 2^x.   3. a^x.   4. xa^x.   5. $x^2 a^{-x}$.

6. $x^x e^{-x}$.   7. $x^{\log x}$.   8. $\sqrt[x]{(1+x)}$.   9. $(\sin x)^x$.

10. $x(x-4)\sqrt{(x+3)}$.   11. $(1+x)^{\frac{1}{3}}(5+2x)^{-\frac{1}{2}}$.

12. $\dfrac{(x-2)^2}{\sqrt{\{(x-1)^3(x-3)\}}}$.   13. $\dfrac{(x-a)^p(x-b)^q}{(x-c)^r}$.

14. Find the proportional change in y caused by a small change δx in x, when

$$\text{(i) } y = ax^n, \quad \text{(ii) } y = \frac{e^x}{x^2 + 1}, \quad \text{(iii) } y = \frac{\sin^m x}{\cos^n x}.$$

15. If $y = uvw$, where u, v, w are functions of x, prove that

$$\frac{1}{y}\frac{dy}{dx} = \frac{1}{u}\frac{du}{dx} + \frac{1}{v}\frac{dv}{dx} + \frac{1}{w}\frac{dw}{dx}.$$

16. If $y = \frac{u^a v^b}{w^c}$, prove that $\frac{\delta y}{y} \doteqdot \frac{a\delta u}{u} + \frac{b\delta v}{v} - \frac{c\delta w}{w}$.

17. If q is calculated from the formula $q = kr^2\sqrt{h}$, show that a small percentage error in r is four times as serious as the same percentage error in h.

18. What percentage error is made in calculating T from the formula $T = 2\pi\sqrt{(l/g)}$, if we put $g = 32$ instead of $32{\cdot}18$?

§ 162. The Number e as Base.—We have proved that

$$\frac{d}{dx}(e^x) = e^x, \qquad \frac{d}{dx}(\log_e x) = \frac{1}{x}, \tag{i}$$

$$\frac{d}{dx}(a^x) = a^x \log_e a, \qquad \frac{d}{dx}(\log_a x) = \frac{1}{x \log_e a}. \tag{ii}$$

From these formulæ we see that the number e forces itself upon us as the most convenient base for logarithms and exponential functions. For the use of e as base leads to the simple formulæ (i), whereas any other base a brings with it the inconvenient constant factors that appear in formulæ (ii).

Logarithms to base e are called *natural* logarithms.

§ 163. The Number e Expressed as a Limit.—By a property of logarithms, the limit (2), § 155, can be written

$$\lim_{h \to 0} \log_e (1 + h)^{\frac{1}{h}} = 1,$$

$$\therefore e = \lim_{h \to 0} (1 + h)^{\frac{1}{h}}. \tag{12}$$

Put $n = 1/h$. Then $n \to \infty$ when $h \to 0$, and we have also

$$e = \lim_{n \to \infty} \left(1 + \frac{1}{n}\right)^n. \tag{13}$$

§ 164. The Exponential Series.—It can be proved that the function e^x can be expanded in an infinite (unending) series of ascending powers of x, by the following method :—

Assume that

$$e^x = A_0 + A_1 x + A_2 x^2 + A_3 x^3 + A_4 x^4 + \ldots \text{ to } \infty, \tag{i}$$

where A_0, A_1, A_2, $\ldots$ are constants.

Differentiate (i) repeatedly with respect to x. We get

$$e^x = A_1 + 2A_2x + 3A_3x^2 + 4A_4x^3 + \ldots \tag{ii}$$
$$e^x = 1.2A_2 + 2.3A_3x + 3.4A_4x^2 + \ldots \tag{iii}$$
$$e^x = 1.2.3A_3 + 2.3.4A_4x + 3.4.5A_5x^2 + \ldots \tag{iv}$$
$$e^x = 1.2.3.4A_4 + 2.3.4.5A_5x + 3.4.5.6A_6x^2 + \ldots \tag{v}$$

and so on.

Next, put $x = 0$ in (i), (ii), (iii), (iv), (v), . . . Since $e^0 = 1$, each left-hand side $= 1$, when $x = 0$. Also, every term, except the first, on each right-hand side, is 0, when $x = 0$. Hence,

$$e^0 = 1 = A_0, \qquad \therefore A_0 = 1;$$
$$e^0 = 1 = A_1, \qquad \therefore A_1 = 1;$$
$$e^0 = 1 = 1.2A_2, \qquad \therefore A_2 = \frac{1}{1.2} = \frac{1}{2!};$$
$$e^0 = 1 = 1.2.3A_3, \qquad \therefore A_3 = \frac{1}{1.2.3} = \frac{1}{3!};$$
$$e^0 = 1 = 1.2.3.4A_4, \quad \therefore A_4 = \frac{1}{1.2.3.4} = \frac{1}{4!};$$

and so on. Substituting these values of A_0, A_1, A_2, . . . in (i), we get

$$e^x = 1 + \frac{x}{1!} + \frac{x^2}{2!} + \frac{x^3}{3!} + \frac{x^4}{4!} + \ldots \tag{14}$$

The series on the right is called the *exponential series*. It is valid for all values of x (see books on Algebra).

§ 165. **The Value of** e.—Putting $x = 1$ in (14), we get

$$e = 1 + \frac{1}{1!} + \frac{1}{2!} + \frac{1}{3!} + \frac{1}{4!} + \ldots \text{ to } \infty. \tag{15}$$

Let t_0, t_1, t_2, t_3, . . . denote the terms of the series on the right, in order. Then $t_1 = t_0$, $t_2 = \frac{1}{2}t_1$, $t_3 = \frac{1}{3}t_2$, . . . Hence

$$t_0 = 1\cdot$$
$$t_1 = 1\cdot$$
$$t_2 = \cdot5$$
$$t_3 = \cdot16666\ldots$$
$$t_4 = \cdot04166\ldots$$
$$t_5 = \cdot00833\ldots$$
$$t_6 = \cdot00138\ldots$$
$$t_7 = \cdot00019\ldots$$

$$\overline{2\cdot718\ldots}$$

Hence, to four figures,

$$e = 2\cdot718\ldots$$

The value of the number μ, introduced in § 155, is therefore given, to four figures, by

$$\mu = \log_{10} e = 0\cdot4343 \ldots$$

By using a few more terms of the series, we could show that, to eight figures,

$$e = 2\cdot7182818 \ldots$$

The value of μ to eight figures is given by

$$\mu = \log_{10} e = 0\cdot43429448 \ldots$$

§ 166. Taylor's and Maclaurin's Expansions.

The expansion of e^x is a particular case of *Taylor's expansion*, which is given by (1) in the following theorem :—

If $f(x)$ is a function of x that can be expanded in an infinite series of ascending powers of $(x - a)$, the expansion is given by

$$f(x) = f(a) + f'(a)\frac{(x - a)}{1!} + f''(a)\frac{(x - a)^2}{2!} + f'''(a)\frac{(x - a)^3}{3!} + \ldots \quad (1)$$

We get another form of Taylor's expansion by putting

$$x - a = h, \quad \therefore \ x = a + h,$$

which gives

$$f(a + h) = f(a) + f'(a)\frac{h}{1!} + f''(a)\frac{h^2}{2!} + f'''(a)\frac{h^3}{3!} + \ldots \quad (2)$$

Maclaurin's expansion is the expansion of $f(x)$ in ascending powers of x. It can be obtained from Taylor's expansion (1) by putting $a = 0$. This gives

$$f(x) = f(0) + f'(0)\frac{x}{1!} + f''(0)\frac{x^2}{2!} + f'''(0)\frac{x^3}{3!} + \ldots \quad (3)$$

The expansion of e^x can be obtained from Maclaurin's expansion, as a particular case, by putting $f(x) = e^x$.

To obtain Taylor's expansion (1), supposing the expansion to be possible, and without attempting here to justify the method used, we assume

$$f(x) = A_0 + A_1(x - a) + A_2(x - a)^2 + A_3(x - a)^3 + \ldots \quad \text{(i)}$$

where $A_0, A_1, A_2 \ldots$ are constants that have to be found.

Differentiating both sides repeatedly with respect to x,

$$f'(x) = A_1 + 2A_2(x - a) + 3A_3(x - a)^2 + 4A_4(x - a)^3 + \ldots \quad \text{(ii)}$$
$$f''(x) = 1 \cdot 2A_2 + 2 \cdot 3A_3(x - a) + 3 \cdot 4A_4(x - a)^2 + \ldots \quad \text{(iii)}$$
$$f'''(x) = 1 \cdot 2 \cdot 3A_3 + 2 \cdot 3 \cdot 4A_4(x - a) + \ldots \quad \text{(iv)}$$

and so on.   In (i), (ii), (iii), (iv), $\ldots$ put $x = a$.   Then we get

$$\begin{aligned} f(a) &= A_0, & \therefore \ A_0 &= f(a)\,; \\ f'(a) &= A_1, & \therefore \ A_1 &= f'(a)\,; \\ f''(a) &= 1 \cdot 2A_2, & \therefore \ A_2 &= f''(a)/2!\,; \\ f'''(a) &= 1 \cdot 2 \cdot 3A_3, & \therefore \ A_3 &= f'''(a)/3!\,; \end{aligned}$$

and so on. Substituting these values of A_0, A_1, A_2, . . . in (i), we find

$$f(x) = f(a) + f'(a)\frac{(x-a)}{1!} + f''(a)\frac{(x-a)^2}{2!} + f'''(a)\frac{(x-a)^3}{3!} + \cdots$$

Examples LXXIV.

In Exs. 1-12, derive the given expansions by the method of § 164, or as particular cases of Maclaurin's expansion :—

[The expansions in Exs. 1-6 are valid for all values of x. In Exs. 1-4, x is measured in radians.]

1. $\sin x = \dfrac{x}{1!} - \dfrac{x^3}{3!} + \dfrac{x^5}{5!} - \dfrac{x^7}{7!} + \dfrac{x^9}{9!} - \dfrac{x^{11}}{11!} + \cdots$

2. $\cos x = 1 - \dfrac{x^2}{2!} + \dfrac{x^4}{4!} - \dfrac{x^6}{6!} + \dfrac{x^8}{8!} - \dfrac{x^{10}}{10!} + \cdots$

3. $\sin(a+x) = \sin a + \dfrac{x\cos a}{1!} - \dfrac{x^2\sin a}{2!} - \dfrac{x^3\cos a}{3!} + \cdots$

4. $\cos(a+x) = \cos a - \dfrac{x\sin a}{1!} - \dfrac{x^2\cos a}{2!} + \dfrac{x^3\sin a}{3!} + \cdots$

5. $e^{cx} = 1 + \dfrac{cx}{1!} + \dfrac{c^2x^2}{2!} + \dfrac{c^3x^3}{3!} + \dfrac{c^4x^4}{4!} + \cdots$

6. $a^x = 1 + \dfrac{x\log a}{1!} + \dfrac{x^2(\log a)^2}{2!} + \dfrac{x^3(\log a)^3}{3!} + \cdots$

7. $\dfrac{1}{1-x} = 1 + x + x^2 + x^3 + x^4 + x^5 + \cdots$

[The Geometric Series ; valid if $x^2 < 1$.]

8. $\dfrac{1}{(1-x)^2} = 1 + 2x + 3x^2 + 4x^3 + 5x^4 + \cdots$ [$x^2 < 1$].

9. $\dfrac{1}{\sqrt{(1-x)}} = 1 + \dfrac{x}{2} + \dfrac{1.3}{2.4}x^2 + \dfrac{1.3.5}{2.4.6}x^3 + \cdots$ [$x^2 < 1$].

10. $(1+x)^n = 1 + nx + \dfrac{n(n-1)}{2!}x^2 + \dfrac{n(n-1)(n-2)}{3!}x^3 + \cdots$

[The Binomial Series ; valid if $x^2 < 1$.]

11. $\log_e(1+x) = \dfrac{x}{1} - \dfrac{x^2}{2} + \dfrac{x^3}{3} - \dfrac{x^4}{4} + \dfrac{x^5}{5} - \dfrac{x^6}{6} + \cdots$

[The Logarithmic Series ; valid if $x^2 < 1$].

12. $\log_{10}(a+x) = \log_{10} a + \mu\left(\dfrac{x}{a} - \dfrac{x^2}{2a^2} + \dfrac{x^3}{3a^3} - \dfrac{x^4}{4a^4} + \cdots\right)$,

where $\mu = \log_{10} e$. [Valid if $x^2 < a^2$.]

13. In Ex. 1 put x = the radian measure of $10°$. Hence calculate $\sin 10°$ to six decimal places. [Given $\pi = 3\cdot14159265$.]

14. In Ex. 3 put $a = 30°$, x = the radian measure of $1°$. Hence calculate $\sin 31°$ to six decimal places.

[Given $\pi = 3\cdot14159265$, $\sqrt{3} = 1\cdot7320508$.]

15. In Ex. 12 put $a = 100$, $x = 10$. Hence calculate $\log_{10} 110$ decimal places. [Given $\mu = 0\cdot4342945$

§ 167. Graphs of e^x, e^{-x}, $\log_e x$.—When we interchange x and y in the equation $y = e^x$, we get

$$x = e^y, \quad \text{or} \quad y = \log_e x.$$

It follows that the logarithmic function is the *inverse* of the exponential function, and that the graphs of e^x and $\log_e x$ are the reflections of each other in the line $y = x$ (§§ 49, 50). The graphs are shown in Fig. 94.

Again, since e^{-x} can be derived from e^x by changing the sign of x, the graph of e^{-x} is the reflection of the graph of e^x in the y-axis (Fig. 95).

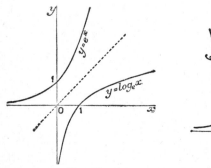

Fig. 94.

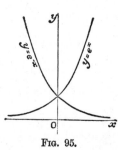

Fig. 95.

§ 168. Properties of e^x.—The following properties of e^x are important. The graph of e^x will help to keep them in mind :—

(i) $e^{+\infty} = +\infty$, $e^0 = 1$, $e^{-\infty} = 0$.

(ii) $e^x > 1$, if x is positive ; $e^x < 1$, if x is negative.

(iii) e^x is always positive, and steadily increases from 0 to $+\infty$, when x increases from $-\infty$ to $+\infty$.

(iv) The equation $e^x = y$, in which y is any given positive number, and x is the unknown, has only one real root. This root is $x = \log_e y$.

§ 169. Properties of $\log_e x$.

(i) $\log(+\infty) = +\infty$, $\log 1 = 0$, $\log(+0) = -\infty$.

(ii) $\log x$ is positive if $x > 1$, negative if $0 < x < 1$, and has no real value if x is negative.

(iii) $\log x$ steadily increases from $-\infty$ to $+\infty$, when x increases from 0 to $+\infty$.

(iv) The equation $\log_e x = y$, in which y is any given number, and x is the unknown, has only one root, which is positive. This root is $x = e^y$.

(v) $e^{\log_e x} = x$, by definition of a logarithm.

§ 170. **Limits of Two Indeterminate Forms.** — (1) When $x = +\infty$, $\dfrac{x}{e^x} = \dfrac{\infty}{\infty}$, which is indeterminate. We shall prove that

$$\frac{x}{e^x} \to 0, \text{ when } x \to \infty.$$

Proof.—From (14), § 164, we have

$$\frac{e^x}{x} = \frac{1}{x} + 1 + \frac{x}{2!} + \frac{x^2}{3!} + \cdots$$

$$\therefore \frac{e^x}{x} \to +\infty, \text{ when } x \to +\infty, \tag{1}$$

$$\therefore \frac{x}{e^x} \to 0, \text{ when } x \to +\infty. \tag{2}$$

We could also prove that, if n is any constant,

$$\frac{x^n}{e^x} \to 0, \text{ when } x \to +\infty. \tag{3}$$

(2) When $x = +0$, $x \log x = 0 \times (-\infty)$, which is indeterminate. We shall prove that

$$x \log x \to 0, \text{ when } x \to +0.$$

Proof.—Since $\log x$ is negative when $x < 1$, put $\log x = -y$. Then $x = e^{-y}$,

$$\therefore x \log x = e^{-y}(-y) = -\frac{y}{e^y},$$

which, by (2), approaches zero when $x \to +0$, since $y \to +\infty$;

$$\therefore x \log x \to 0, \text{ when } x \to +0. \tag{4}$$

We could also prove that, if n is any positive constant,

$$x^n \log x \to 0, \text{ when } x \to +0. \tag{5}$$

§ 171. **The Law of Organic Growth.**—Suppose the population of a country to increase by 10 per cent. every year. Let y_0 be the population at the beginning of some particular year, and let y be the population x years later. Then

$$y = y_0 (1 \cdot 1)^x.$$

Thus y is proportional to an exponential function a^x in which the base $a = 1 \cdot 1$. For reasons of this kind, an exponential function is sometimes said to vary according to the *law of organic growth*.

A *decrease* of 10 per cent. per year would give

$$y = y_0 \, (0 \cdot 9)^x$$

with $a = 0 \cdot 9$. Thus an exponential function with a base less than 1 would correspond to a law of organic *decay*.

§ 172. The Compound Interest Law.—Another way of describing how an exponential function varies is to say that it obeys the *compound interest law*.

Suppose, for simplicity, that interest is added to a sum of money every year at the rate of 100 per cent. per annum. Then, if the sum of money is £y_0 originally, at the end of x years it will be £y, where

$$y = y_0 \, . \, 2^x.$$

Thus y is proportional to an exponential function.

Any other rate of interest would lead to a similar result, the only difference being the base of the exponential function. In this connection a meaning can be given to the number e :—

Consider the value to which £1 would amount in one year, interest being at the rate of 100 per cent. per annum, but added at intervals during the year.

If interest were added every half-year, the amount at the end of the year would be $(1 + \frac{1}{2})^2$ pounds.

If interest were added every quarter, the amount at the end of the year would be $(1 + \frac{1}{4})^4$ pounds.

If interest were added every month, the amount at the end of the year would be $(1 + \frac{1}{12})^{12}$ pounds.

In general, if interest were added n times per year, at equal intervals, the amount at the end of the year would be, in pounds,

$$\left(1 + \frac{1}{n}\right)^n.$$

Now e is the limit of this expression when $n \to \infty$ (§ 163). Thus e is such a number that £1 would amount to £e after one year, interest being added continuously at the rate of 100 per cent. per annum.

§ 173. Damped Vibrations.—The graph in the next example, if we suppose t to denote time, illustrates a vibration with a diminishing amplitude. It shows how a vibration (e.g. of a pendulum) is damped out by resistances.

Ex. Draw the graph of $y = e^{-t} \sin t$, for positive values of t.

The graph of $y = e^{-t} \sin t$ lies between the graphs of $y = e^{-t}$ and $y = -e^{-t}$, touching each in turn (see § 48).

Maxima and minima occur alternately for values of t given by

$$\frac{dy}{dt} = -e^{-t} (\sin t - \cos t) = 0.$$

Now e^{-t} cannot be zero.   Hence $dy/dt = 0$ when

$$\sin t = \cos t, \quad \therefore \; \tan t = 1,$$

$$\therefore t = \frac{\pi}{4}, \; \frac{5\pi}{4}, \; \frac{9\pi}{4}, \; \frac{13\pi}{4}, \; \cdots$$

The graph is indicated in Fig. 96.

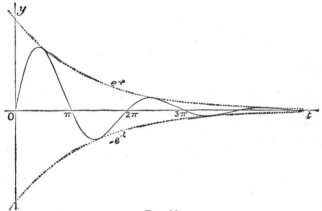

FIG. 96.

Examples LXXV.

1. Draw to scale the graph of $\log_{10} x$.   Measure the gradient of its tangent at the point where $x = 1$.

2. Draw to scale the graphs of e^x and e^{-x}, from $x = -2$ to $x = 2$.

3. Sketch the graphs of $\log_{10}(\sin x)$ and $\log_{10}(\tan x)$.

4. Calculate the difference for $3'$ in a four-figure table giving values of $\log_{10}(\sin \theta)$, when $\theta = 30°$.

5. Calculate the difference for $1'$ in a four-figure table giving values of $\log_{10}(\tan \theta)$, when $\theta = 45°$.

6. Prove that the tangent to the graph to $\log_e x$ at the point where $y = 1$ passes through the origin.

7. Prove that the subtangent to the curve $y = a^x$ is constant.

In Exs. 8-15 find the maximum or minimum values of the given functions, and the corresponding values of x :—

8. $x^2 e^{-x}$.   **9.** $x e^{-x}$.   **10.** $x^n e^{-x}$.   **11.** $x^3 e^x$.

12. $x \log x$.   **13.** $\dfrac{\log x}{x}$.   **14.** $x^2 \log \dfrac{1}{x}$.   **15.** $\dfrac{1}{e^{2x}} - \dfrac{2}{e^{3x}}$.

16. Sketch the graph of $y = e^{-x^2}$.   Find the co-ordinates of the points of inflexion.

6

17. If $y = e^{-x} (\sin x + \cos x)$, find the maximum and minimum values of y, for positive values of x. Sketch the graph.

18. Sketch the graph of $y = e^{-2x} \sin 3x$, for positive values of x. Find approximately the co-ordinates of the first maximum point on the graph.

19. Prove that the graph of $y = e^{-ax} \sin bx$ lies between the graphs of $y = e^{-ax}$, $y = - e^{-ax}$, touching each in turn; and that, if $a = b$, the points of contact are points of inflexion.

20. If $y = e^{-at} \sin bt$, where a and b are positive; and if $y_1, y_2, y_3, \ldots$ denote successive maximum values of y, prove that

$$\frac{y_1}{y_2} = \frac{y_2}{y_3} = \frac{y_3}{y_4} = \ldots = e^\delta, \text{ where } \delta = \frac{2\pi a}{b}.$$

The common value of these ratios is called the *decrement*, and its natural logarithm δ is called the *logarithmic decrement*.

Prove that the number of oscillations that occur before the amplitude is reduced to 1 per cent. of its initial value is approximately $4 \cdot 6 / \delta$.

§ **174. Integrals Associated with e^x and $\log x$.**—To the standard integrals in § 84 we now add the following :—

$$\int e^x \, dx = e^x, \qquad \int e^{ax} \, dx = \frac{e^{ax}}{a}. \tag{1}$$

$$\int \frac{dx}{x} = \log x, \qquad \int \frac{dx}{ax + b} = \frac{1}{a} \log (ax + b). \tag{2}$$

To prove these results we have only to verify that the differential coefficients of the right-hand sides are equal to the integrands on the left-hand sides.

The logarithms are natural logarithms (i.e. to base e).

Ex. Evaluate the indefinite integrals :

(i) $\int a^x \, dx$, (ii) $\int \frac{\log x}{x} dx$, (iii) $\int \frac{f'(x) \, dx}{f(x)}$, (iv) $\int \frac{x \, dx}{1 + x^2}$.

(i) Since $a^x = (e^c)^x = e^{cx}$, where $c = \log_e a$,

$$\therefore \int a^x \, dx = \int e^{cx} \, dx = \frac{e^{cx}}{c} = \frac{a^x}{\log_e a}. \tag{3}$$

(ii) Put $v = \log x$. Then $dv = dx/x$,

$$\therefore \int \frac{\log x}{x} \, dx = \int v \, dv = \frac{v^2}{2} = \frac{(\log x)^2}{2}.$$

(iii) Put $v = f(x)$. Then $dv = f'(x) \, dx$,

$$\therefore \int \frac{f'(x) \, dx}{f(x)} = \int \frac{dv}{v} = \log v = \log f(x),$$

$$\therefore \int \frac{f'(x) \, dx}{f(x)} = \log f(x). \tag{4}$$

(iv) $\int \frac{x \, dx}{1 + x^2} = \frac{1}{2} \int \frac{2x \, dx}{1 + x^2} = \frac{1}{2} \int \frac{d(1 + x^2)}{1 + x^2} = \frac{1}{2} \log (1 + x^2)$.

Examples LXXVI.

Evaluate the given indefinite integrals :—

1. $\int e^{2x} dx.$ 2. $\int e^{-x} dx.$ 3. $\int 10^x dx.$ 4. $\int 2^{3x} dx.$

5. $\int x e^{x^2} dx.$ 6. $\int e^{\sin x} \cos x\, dx.$ 7. $\int e^{\tan x} \sec^2 x\, dx.$

8. $\int \dfrac{6\, dx}{3x - 4}.$ 9. $\int \dfrac{(\log x)^2}{x}\, dx.$ 10. $\int \dfrac{ax^2 + bx + c}{x}\, dx.$

11. $\int \dfrac{dx}{a - bx}.$ 12. $\int \dfrac{(\log x)^n}{x}\, dx.$ 13. $\int \dfrac{\sin(\log x)}{x}\, dx.$

14. $\int \dfrac{\cos x\, dx}{\sin x}.$ 15. $\int \dfrac{\sec^2 x}{\tan x}\, dx.$ 16. $\int \dfrac{(2ax + b)\, dx}{ax^2 + bx + c}.$

17. $\int \dfrac{x\, dx}{x^2 - a^2}.$ 18. $\int \dfrac{e^x - e^{-x}}{e^x + e^{-x}}\, dx.$ 19. $\int \dfrac{dx}{(1 + x^2) \tan^{-1} x}.$

§ 175. Examples needing Integration by Parts (see § 93).

Ex. Evaluate (i) $\int \log x\, dx$, (ii) $\int e^{ax} \sin bx\, dx$.

(i) $\int \log x\, dx = \log x \cdot x - \int x\, d(\log x) = x \log x - \int x \cdot \dfrac{1}{x}\, dx,$

$$\therefore \int \log x\, dx = x (\log x - 1).$$

(ii) Put $z = \int e^{ax} \sin bx\, dx$. Then, since $d(e^{ax}) = a e^{ax}$, we have, multiplying by a and integrating by parts,

$$az = \int \sin bx \cdot d(e^{ax}) = \sin bx \cdot e^{ax} - \int e^{ax} d(\sin bx),$$

$$\therefore az = e^{ax} \sin bx - b \int e^{ax} \cos bx\, dx.$$

Multiplying by a and integrating by parts again, we get

$$a^2 z = a e^{ax} \sin bx - b \int \cos bx \cdot d(e^{ax})$$

$$= a e^{ax} \sin bx - b \{\cos bx \cdot e^{ax} - \int e^{ax} d(\cos bx)\}$$

$$= a e^{ax} \sin bx - b e^{ax} \cos bx - b^2 z,$$

$$\therefore (a^2 + b^2) z = e^{ax} (a \sin bx - b \cos bx),$$

$$\therefore z = \dfrac{e^{ax} (a \sin bx - b \cos bx)}{a^2 + b^2}.$$

Examples LXXVII.

Evaluate the given indefinite integrals :—

1. $\int x \log x\, dx.$ 2. $\int x^2 \log x\, dx.$ 3. $\int \dfrac{\log x\, dx}{x^2}.$

4. $\int x e^x\, dx.$ 5. $\int x^2 e^x\, dx.$ 6. $\int x^3 e^{ax}\, dx.$

7. $\int e^x \cos x\, dx.$ 8. $\int e^{-x} \sin 2x\, dx.$ 9. $\int e^{ax} \cos bx\, dx.$

10. Evaluate $\int x^n \log x\, dx$, considering $n = -1$ in particular.

Examples LXXVIII.

In Exs. 1-14, evaluate the given definite integrals :—

1. $\int_1^a \dfrac{dx}{x}.$ 2. $\int_1^4 \dfrac{dx}{1 + 2x}.$ 3. $\int_1^3 \dfrac{x\, dx}{1 + x^2}.$

4. $\int_0^\infty e^{-x}\, dx.$ 5. $\int_0^1 x e^x\, dx.$ 6. $\int_0^\infty x e^{-x}\, dx.$

7. $\int_0^1 x \log x \, dx.$ **8.** $\int_0^1 x^n \log x \, dx.$ **9.** $\int_1^\infty x^{-n} \log x \, dx.$

10. $\int_0^1 10^x \, dx.$ **11.** $\int_{-\infty}^0 a^x \, dx.$ **12.** $\int_0^{\frac{\pi}{2}} e^{-x} \cos x \, dx.$

13. $\int_0^1 \log \{x + \sqrt{(x^2 + 1)}\} \, dx.$ **14.** $\int_3^5 \log \{x + \sqrt{(x^2 - 9)}\} \, dx.$

15. Find the area in the first quadrant bounded by the graph of $y = be^{-\frac{x}{a}}$ and the co-ordinate axes.

16. Find the volume generated when the area in Ex. 15 revolves about the x-axis.

17. Find the area between the graph of $y = e^{-x} \sin x$ and the x-axis from $x = 0$ to $x = \pi$.

18. Find the volume generated when the area in Ex. 17 revolves about the x-axis.

19. If the pressure and volume of a gas are related by the equation $pv = $ C, find the work done by the gas while its volume expands from v_0 to nv_0; and deduce that the average value of p during the expansion is $\dfrac{p_0 \log n}{n - 1}$, where p_0 is the pressure when $v = v_0$.

20. At time t the velocity v of a moving point is given by $v = v_0 e^{-t}$. Show that v_0 is the velocity when $t = 0$. Find the time that elapses before the velocity is reduced to $\frac{1}{2}v_0$ and the average velocity during that time.

21. The pressure p, per unit area, at a point on a disc of unit radius is given by $p = Ae^{-kr}$, where r is the distance of the point from the centre. If $p = 100$ when $r = 0$, and $p = 10$ when $r = 1$, find the values of A and k.

Find the total pressure on the disc, and prove that the average pressure per unit area is about 25·3.

22. Given that $\dfrac{dy}{dx} = ay$, where a is a constant, and that $y = y_0$ when $x = 0$, prove that $y = y_0 e^{ax}$. [Invert both sides of the given equation.]

23. At every point of a certain graph the gradient is twice the ordinate, and $y = 3$ when $x = 0$. Find the equation of the graph.

24. At every point of a certain graph the gradient is equal to the ordinate and the graph passes through the point (3, 6). Find its equation.

25. If $\dfrac{dT}{d\theta} = \mu T$, where μ is a constant, and if $T = T_0$ when $\theta = 0$, express T in terms of θ.

26. If $\dfrac{dy}{dx} = ay + b$, where a and b are constants, and if $y = 0$ when $x = 0$, express y in terms of x.

27. If $L\dfrac{di}{dt} + Ri = E$, where L, R, E are constants, and if $i = 0$ when $t = 0$, express i in terms of t. Sketch the (t, i) graph.

28. If $\dfrac{d\theta}{dt} = -k(\theta - \theta_1)$, where k and θ_1 are constants, and if $\theta = \theta_0$ when $t = 0$, express θ in terms of t.

CHAPTER XIII.

INTEGRALS (*continued*).

§ 176. Standard Integrals.—We shall now give a longer list of standard integrals than we have used hitherto :—

$$\int x^n \, dx = \frac{x^{n+1}}{n+1}, \ (n \neq -1). \tag{1}$$

$$\int \frac{dx}{x} = \log_e x. \tag{2}$$

$$\int e^x \, dx = e^x. \tag{3}$$

$$\int \cos x \, dx = \sin x. \tag{4}$$

$$\int \sin x \, dx = -\cos x. \tag{5}$$

$$\int \sec^2 x \, dx = \int \frac{dx}{\cos^2 x} = \tan x \tag{6}$$

$$\int \mathrm{cosec}^2 x \, dx = \int \frac{dx}{\sin^2 x} = -\cot x. \tag{7}$$

$$\int \sec x \tan x \, dx = \int \frac{\sin x}{\cos^2 x} \, dx = \frac{1}{\cos x} = \sec x. \tag{8}$$

$$\int \mathrm{cosec}\, x \cot x \, dx = \int \frac{\cos x}{\sin^2 x} \, dx = \frac{-1}{\sin x} = -\mathrm{cosec}\, x. \tag{9}$$

$$\int \frac{dx}{\sqrt{(a^2 - x^2)}} = \sin^{-1}\frac{x}{a}, \quad \text{or} \quad -\cos^{-1}\frac{x}{a}. \tag{10}$$

$$\int \frac{dx}{a^2 + x^2} = \frac{1}{a}\tan^{-1}\frac{x}{a}, \quad \text{or} \quad -\frac{1}{a}\cot^{-1}\frac{x}{a}. \tag{11}$$

All these results follow at once from the fact that the differential coefficients of the right-hand sides are equal to the integrands on the left-hand sides.

The last two can also be readily proved by substitutions.

Ex. Evaluate (i) $\int \tan^2 \theta \, d\theta$, (ii) $\int \tan^4 \theta \, d\theta$, (iii) $\int \tan^{-1} x \, dx$.

(i) $\int \tan^2 \theta \, d\theta = \int (\sec^2 \theta - 1) d\theta = \tan \theta - \theta$.

(ii) $\int \tan^4 \theta \, d\theta = \int \tan^2 \theta \, (\sec^2 \theta - 1) d\theta$

$$= \int \tan^2 \theta \, d(\tan \theta) - \int \tan^2 \theta \, d\theta$$

$$= \tfrac{1}{3} \tan^3 \theta - \tan \theta + \theta, \text{ by (i)}.$$

(iii) Integrating by parts,

$$\int \tan^{-1} x \, dx = (\tan^{-1} x)x - \int x \, d(\tan^{-1} x)$$

$$= x \tan^{-1} x - \int \frac{x \, dx}{1 + x^2}$$

$$= x \tan^{-1} x - \tfrac{1}{2} \log(1 + x^2).$$

Examples LXXIX.

Evaluate the given integrals :—

1. $\int \sec^2 3\theta \, d\theta$.
2. $\int \tan \theta \sec^2 \theta \, d\theta$.
3. $\int \sec^3 \theta \tan \theta \, d\theta$.
4. $\int \sec^4 \theta \, d\theta$.
5. $\int \tan^n \theta \sec^2 \theta \, d\theta$.
6. $\int \sec^3 \theta \tan^3 \theta \, d\theta$.
7. $\int \sec^6 \theta \, d\theta$.
8. $\int \sec^n \theta \tan \theta \, d\theta$.
9. $\int \sec \tfrac{1}{2}\theta \tan \tfrac{1}{2}\theta \, d\theta$.
10. $\int \cot^2 \theta \, d\theta$.
11. $\int \cot^4 \theta \, d\theta$.
12. $\int \operatorname{cosec}^4 \theta \, d\theta$.
13. $\int \sin^{-1}x \, dx$.
14. $\int x \sin^{-1} x \, dx$.
15. $\int x \tan^{-1} x \, dx$.
16. $\int \dfrac{\sin^{-1} x \, dx}{\sqrt{(1 - x^2)}}$.
17. $\int \dfrac{\tan^{-1} x \, dx}{1 + x^2}$.
18. $\int \dfrac{1 + \sin \theta}{\cos^2 \theta} d\theta$.
19. $\int \dfrac{\cos x \, dx}{a + b \sin x}$.
20. $\int \dfrac{\sec^2 \theta \, d\theta}{4 + \tan^2 \theta}$.
21. $\int \dfrac{1 + \log x}{x} dx$.
22. $\int_0^1 \dfrac{dx}{\sqrt{(1 - x^2)}}$.
23. $\int_0^{\frac{1}{2}} \dfrac{dx}{\sqrt{(1 - 3x^2)}}$.
24. $\int_2^8 \dfrac{dx}{x \log x}$.
25. $\int_0^2 \dfrac{dx}{x^2 + 4}$.
26. $\int_0^\infty \dfrac{dx}{a^2 + x^2}$.
27. $\int_0^\infty \dfrac{e^{-x} \, dx}{1 + e^{-x}}$.
28. $\int_0^{\frac{\pi}{4}} \sec^2 \theta \, d\theta$.
29. $\int_0^{\frac{\pi}{4}} \sec^4 \theta \, d\theta$.
30. $\int_0^{\frac{\pi}{4}} \theta \sec^2 \theta \, d\theta$.

§ 177. Reduction Formulæ.

Ex. If $I_n = \int x^n e^x \, dx$, prove that $I_n = x^n e^x - nI_{n-1}$.

Proof.—Integrating by parts, we have

$$\int x^n e^x \, dx = \int x^n d(e^x) = x^n e^x - n\int x^{n-1} e^x \, dx,$$

that is, $\qquad I_n = x^n e^x - nI_{n-1}$.

If n is a positive integer we can, by repeated application of this formula, make I_n depend upon I_0; and since $I_0 = \int e^x \, dx = e^x$, we can therefore evaluate I_n.

Such a formula is called a *reduction formula*.

Examples LXXX.

1. If $I_n = \int (\log x)^n \, dx$, prove that $I_n = x(\log x)^n - nI_{n-1}$; and evaluate I_4.

2. If $I_n = \int x^m (\log x)^n \, dx$, prove that $I_n = \dfrac{x^{m+1}(\log x)^n}{m + 1} - \dfrac{nI_{n-1}}{m + 1}$; and evaluate I_3.

3. If $C_n = \int x^n \cos x \, dx$, $S_n = \int x^n \sin x \, dx$, prove that

(i) $C_n = x^n \sin x + nx^{n-1} \cos x - n(n-1)C_{n-2}$.

(ii) $S_n = -x^n \cos x + nx^{n-1} \sin x - n(n-1)S_{n-2}$.

4. If $C_n = \int \dfrac{\cos x \, dx}{x^n}$, $S_n = \int \dfrac{\sin x \, dx}{x^n}$, prove that

(i) $C_n = \dfrac{-\cos x}{(n-1)x^{n-1}} - \dfrac{S_{n-1}}{n-1}$, (ii) $S_n = \dfrac{-\sin x}{(n-1)x^{n-1}} + \dfrac{C_{n-1}}{n-1}$.

5. Prove that $\displaystyle\int_0^\infty x^n e^{-x} \, dx = n\,!$, if n is a positive integer.

Rational Integrands.

§ 178. Polynomials.—A *polynomial in x* is a function of the form

$$a_0 x^n + a_1 x^{n-1} + a_2 x^{n-2} + \ldots + a_n,$$

where a_0, a_1, a_2, . . . are constants, and n is a positive integer.

§ 179. Rational Functions.—A *rational fraction* is a fraction whose numerator and denominator are polynomials.

A *proper* rational fraction is one in which the degree of the numerator is less than that of the denominator.

An *improper* rational fraction is one in which the degree of the numerator is not less than that of the denominator.

A *rational function* is a function that can be reduced to a rational fraction.

§ 180. Rational Integrands.—*The chief general theorem in integration is that every integral whose integrand is a rational function of the variable of integration can be evaluated by elementary methods.*

General Method.—If the integrand is an improper fraction, divide the numerator by the denominator, and so express the integrand as the sum of a polynomial and a proper fraction. Then express the proper fraction in partial fractions by the rules of Algebra. The integration can then be performed (see § 184 for the general case).

Ex. Evaluate (i) $\displaystyle\int \dfrac{(3x+4)\, dx}{(x-2)(x+3)}$, (ii) $\displaystyle\int \dfrac{x^4 + 3x}{x^2 - 1}\, dx$.

(i) The integrand is a proper fraction, so we begin by expressing it in partial fractions, assuming the identity

$$\frac{3x+4}{(x-2)(x+3)} = \frac{A}{x-2} + \frac{B}{x+3},$$

where A and B are constants. Then

$$3x + 4 = A(x+3) + B(x-2),$$

and by the usual method of algebra, putting $x = 2$, we get
$$6 + 4 = 5A, \quad \therefore A = 2;$$
and putting $x = -3$,
$$-9 + 4 = -5B, \quad \therefore B = 1;$$
$$\therefore \int \frac{(3x + 4)\,dx}{(x - 2)(x + 3)} = \int \left(\frac{2}{x - 2} + \frac{1}{x - 3}\right) dx$$
$$= 2 \log (x - 2) + \log (x - 3)$$
$$= \log (x - 2)^2 + \log (x - 3)$$
$$= \log (x - 2)^2 (x - 3).$$

(ii) The integrand is an improper fraction. Accordingly, we begin by dividing the numerator by the denominator, obtaining the quotient $(x^2 + 1)$ and the remainder $(3x + 1)$, and hence
$$\frac{x^4 + 3x}{x^2 - 1} = x^2 + 1 + \frac{3x + 1}{x^2 - 1}.$$

The last fraction is a proper fraction, which we now express in partial fractions. Thence follows
$$\int \frac{x^4 + 3x}{x^2 - 1}\,dx = \int \left(x^2 + 1 + \frac{1}{x + 1} + \frac{2}{x - 1}\right) dx$$
$$= \tfrac{1}{3}x^3 + x + \log (x + 1) + 2 \log (x - 1).$$

Examples LXXXI.

Evaluate the given integrals :—

1. $\int \dfrac{2x + 3}{x + 2}\,dx.$ 2. $\int \dfrac{x\,dx}{x + 1}.$ 3. $\int \dfrac{x - 3}{1 - 2x}\,dx.$

4. $\int \dfrac{\alpha x + \beta}{\gamma x + \delta}\,dx.$ 5. $\int \dfrac{x^3\,dx}{x - 1}.$ 6. $\int \dfrac{dx}{9x^2 - 4}.$

7. $\int \dfrac{x + 5}{(x + 2)(x + 3)}\,dx.$ 8. $\int \dfrac{x + 3}{x(2x + 3)}\,dx.$

9. $\int \dfrac{x^2 - 2x + 4}{2x^2 - 5x - 3}\,dx.$ 10. $\int \dfrac{(x - 1)(x - 4)}{(x - 2)(x - 3)}\,dx.$

11. $\int \dfrac{x\,dx}{(x^2 + 1)(x^2 + 2)}.$ 12. $\int \dfrac{3x^3 - 7x - 2}{x(x^2 - 1)}\,dx.$

13. $\int \dfrac{\cos x\,dx}{\sin x(1 + \sin x)}.$ 14. $\int \dfrac{(x^2 - 3x + 3)\,dx}{(x - 1)(x - 2)(x - 3)}.$

15. $\int \dfrac{dx}{(\alpha x + \beta)(\gamma x + \delta)}.$ 16. $\int \dfrac{x\,dx}{(x - a)(x - b)(x - c)}.$

17. $\int_0^1 \dfrac{dx}{(x + 1)(x + 2)}.$ 18. $\int_1^2 \dfrac{5 + 12x + 5x^2}{x(x + 1)(x + 2)}\,dx.$

19. $\int_0^\infty \dfrac{5\,dx}{(3x + 1)(x + 2)}.$ 20. $\int_2^\infty \dfrac{dx}{x(x + 1)(x + 2)}$

§ 181. Quadratic Denominators.

We first note the standard integrals :—

$$\int \frac{dx}{a^2 + x^2} = \frac{1}{a} \tan^{-1} \frac{x}{a}. \tag{1}$$

$$\int \frac{dx}{a^2 - x^2} = \frac{1}{2a} \log \frac{a + x}{a - x}, \quad (x^2 < a^2). \tag{2}$$

$$\int \frac{dx}{x^2 - a^2} = \frac{1}{2a} \log \frac{x - a}{x + a}, \quad (x^2 > a^2). \tag{3}$$

The first of these has been given before. The second can be proved by expressing the integrand in partial fractions ; we find

$$\frac{1}{a^2 - x^2} = \frac{1}{2a}\left(\frac{1}{a + x} + \frac{1}{a - x}\right),$$

$$\therefore \int \frac{dx}{a^2 - x^2} = \frac{1}{2a}\{\log (a + x) - \log (a - x)\} = \frac{1}{2a} \log \frac{a + x}{a - x}.$$

The third can be proved similarly.

§ 182. The Integral $\displaystyle\int \frac{dx}{ax^2 + bx + c}$.

Put $\displaystyle z = \int \frac{dx}{ax^2 + bx + c} = \frac{1}{a} \int \frac{dx}{\left(x + \dfrac{b}{2a}\right)^2 - \dfrac{b^2 - 4ac}{4a^2}}.$

Case I.—If $b^2 > 4ac$, put $u = x + \dfrac{b}{2a}$, $\kappa^2 = \dfrac{b^2 - 4ac}{4a^2}$. Then

$$z = \frac{1}{a}\int \frac{du}{u^2 - \kappa^2} = \frac{1}{2a\kappa} \log \frac{u - \kappa}{u + \kappa}, \text{ by (3).}$$

Case II.—If $b^2 < 4ac$, put $u = x + \dfrac{b}{2a}$, $\kappa^2 = \dfrac{4ac - b^2}{4a^2}$. Then

$$z = \frac{1}{a}\int \frac{du}{u^2 + \kappa^2} = \frac{1}{a\kappa} \tan^{-1} \frac{u}{\kappa}, \text{ by (1).}$$

Note.—If $b^2 > 4ac$, that is, if the denominator has real factors, it may be better to use partial fractions.

Ex. Evaluate (i) $\displaystyle\int \frac{dx}{x^2 + 4x + 2}$, (ii) $\displaystyle\int \frac{dx}{2x^2 + 6x + 5}$.

(i) Put $\displaystyle z = \int \frac{dx}{x^2 + 4x + 2} = \int \frac{dx}{(x + 2)^2 - (\sqrt{2})^2}.$

$$\therefore z = \frac{1}{2\sqrt{2}} \log \frac{x + 2 - \sqrt{2}}{x + 2 + \sqrt{2}}.$$

6 *

(ii) **Put**
$$z = \int \frac{dx}{2x^2 + 6x + 5} = \frac{1}{2}\int \frac{dx}{(x + \frac{3}{2})^2 + \frac{1}{4}},$$
$$\therefore z = \frac{1}{2} \cdot \frac{1}{\frac{1}{2}} \tan^{-1} \frac{x + \frac{3}{2}}{\frac{1}{2}} = \tan^{-1}(2x + 3).$$

§ 183. The Integral $\int \dfrac{Ax + B}{ax^2 + bx + c}\, dx.$

Method.—Express the numerator $(Ax + B)$ in the form
$$L(\text{diff. coeff. of denom.}) + M,$$
where L and M are constants. The integral then becomes the sum of two integrals, both of which can be evaluated.

Note, however, that if the denominator has real factors it may be better to use partial fractions.

Ex. Evaluate $\int \dfrac{3x - 1}{x^2 - 4x + 7}\, dx,\ = z$, say.

Put
$$3x - 1 = L(2x - 4) + M,$$
$$\therefore 3x - 1 = 2Lx - 4L + M.$$

By equating coefficients, we find $L = \frac{3}{2}$, $M = 5$,
$$\therefore z = \int \frac{\frac{3}{2}(2x - 4) + 5}{x^2 - 4x + 7}\, dx$$
$$= \frac{3}{2}\int \frac{dv}{v} + 5\int \frac{du}{u^2 + (\sqrt{3})^2}$$
$$= \frac{3}{2}\log v + \frac{5}{\sqrt{3}}\tan^{-1}\frac{u}{\sqrt{3}},$$

where $v = x^2 - 4x + 7$, $u = x - 2$. Hence
$$z = \frac{3}{2}\log(x^2 - 4x + 7) + \frac{5}{\sqrt{3}}\tan^{-1}\frac{x - 2}{\sqrt{3}}.$$

Examples LXXXII.

Evaluate the given integrals :—

1. $\int \dfrac{1}{x^2 + 4}\, dx.$ 2. $\int \dfrac{x}{x^2 + 4}\, dx.$ 3. $\int \dfrac{x^2}{x^2 + 4}\, dx.$

4. $\int \dfrac{2x + 3}{x^2 + 4}\, dx.$ 5. $\int \dfrac{1 - 3x}{x^2 + 9}\, dx.$ 6. $\int \dfrac{1}{x^2 - 3}\, dx.$

7. $\int \dfrac{dx}{x^2 + 4x + 8}.$ 8. $\int \dfrac{x\, dx}{x^2 + 4x + 8}.$ 9. $\int \dfrac{x^2\, dx}{x^2 + 4x + 8}.$

10. $\int \dfrac{x^3\, dx}{x^2 - 2x + 2}.$ 11. $\int \dfrac{(3x + 2)dx}{9x^2 + 6x + 5}.$ 12. $\int \dfrac{dx}{3x^2 + 4x + 5}.$

13. $\int \dfrac{dx}{x^2 + 4x - 3}.$ 14. $\int \dfrac{(3x - 1)\, dx}{3x^2 + 2x + 1}.$ 15. $\int \dfrac{x\, dx}{2x^2 + 3x - 4}.$

16. $\int_0^1 \dfrac{(x + 1)dx}{x^2 + x + 1}.$ 17. $\int_1^2 \dfrac{dx}{x^2 + x - 1}.$ 18. $\int_5^\infty \dfrac{dx}{x^2 - 4x + 13}.$

19. $\int_0^1 \dfrac{x\,dx}{x^4 + 1}$. **20.** $\int_{-1}^1 \dfrac{x\,dx}{x^2 + 2x + 5}$. **21.** $\int_0^1 \dfrac{(4x^2 + 3)\,dx}{8x^2 + 4x + 5}$.

22. $\int_0^1 \dfrac{\tan^{-1} x\,dx}{1 + x^2}$. **23.** $\int_2^\infty \dfrac{x\,dx}{x^4 - 1}$. **24.** $\int_0^\infty \dfrac{x\,dx}{x^4 + x^2 + 1}$.

25. $\int_0^1 \log(1 + x^2)dx$. **26.** $\int_0^1 x^2 \tan^{-1} x\,dx$. **27.** $\int_0^1 x^3 \tan^{-1} x\,dx$.

§ **184. Rational Integrands : General Case.**—It is a theorem in Algebra that every polynomial can be factorised into linear or quadratic factors, all real. Consequently, in the denominator of the most general rational integrand, there will occur linear factors, repeated linear factors, quadratic factors, and repeated quadratic factors.

We shall assume that any quadratic factor that occurs cannot be factorised into real linear factors, and that the integrand is a proper fraction. The integrand can then be expressed in partial fractions as follows :—

If a linear factor $(x - a)$ occurs in the denominator, and if it occurs only once, we assume one fraction of the type

$$\frac{\text{A}}{x - a}$$

as the corresponding part of the set of partial fractions.

If a linear factor $(x - a)$ occurs r times, i.e. if $(x - a)^r$ is a factor of the denominator, we assume r fractions of the type

$$\frac{\text{A}_1}{x - a} + \frac{\text{A}_2}{(x - a)^2} + \ldots + \frac{\text{A}_r}{(x - a)^r}$$

as the corresponding part of the set of partial fractions.

If a quadratic factor $(x^2 + px + q)$ occurs in the denominator, and if it occurs only once, we assume one fraction of the type

$$\frac{\text{A}x + \text{B}}{x^2 + px + q}$$

as the corresponding part of the set of partial fractions.

If a quadratic factor $(x^2 + px + q)$ occurs r times, i.e. if $(x^2 + px + q)^r$ is a factor, we assume r fractions of the type

$$\frac{\text{A}_1 x + \text{B}_1}{x^2 + px + q} + \frac{\text{A}_2 x + \text{B}_2}{(x^2 + px + q)^2} + \ldots + \frac{\text{A}_r x + \text{B}_r}{(x^2 + px + q)^r}$$

as the corresponding part of the set of partial fractions.

We have already considered integrals of the types

$$\int \frac{dx}{x - a}, \qquad \int \frac{dx}{(x - a)^r}, \qquad \int \frac{\text{A}x + \text{B}}{x^2 + px + q}\,dx\,;$$

it remains to prove that every integral of the type

$$\int \frac{Ax + B}{(x^2 + px + q)^r} \, dx \tag{i}$$

can be evaluated. We shall then have proved the chief general theorem of Integration (§ 180).

Proof.—After replacing x by $(x + \frac{1}{2}p - \frac{1}{2}p)$ in the numerator $(Ax + B)$, and expressing the integral (i) as the sum of two integrals, we find

$$\int \frac{Ax + B}{(x^2 + px + q)^r} \, dx = \frac{1}{2}A \int \frac{dv}{v^r} + (B - \frac{1}{2}pA) \int \frac{du}{(u^2 + a^2)^r},$$

where $v = x^2 + px + q$, $u = x + \frac{1}{2}p$, $a = \sqrt{(q - \frac{1}{4}p^2)}$.

The first integral on the right can be evaluated at once.

To evaluate the second, put $u = a \tan \theta$; then we find

$$\int \frac{du}{(u^2 + a^2)^r} = \frac{1}{a^{2r-1}} \int \cos^{2r-2} \theta \, d\theta,$$

which can be evaluated by the reduction formula (13), § 187.

Ex. 1. Evaluate $\int \dfrac{dx}{(x-3)^2(x-1)}$,

Since the factor $(x - 3)$ occurs twice, and the factor $(x - 1)$ occurs once, we assume

$$\frac{1}{(x-3)^2(x-1)} = \frac{A}{x-3} + \frac{B}{(x-3)^2} + \frac{C}{x-1},$$

$$\therefore \quad 1 = A(x-3)(x-1) + B(x-1) + C(x-3)^2, \tag{i}$$

$$\therefore \quad 1 = (A + C)x^2 + (-4A + B - 6C)x + 3A - B + 9C.$$

Equating coefficients of like powers of x,

$$A + C = 0, \quad -4A + B - 6C = 0, \quad 3A - B + 9C = 1.$$

Solving these three simultaneous equations,

$$A = -\tfrac{1}{4}, \quad B = \tfrac{1}{2}, \quad C = \tfrac{1}{4}.$$

$$\therefore \int \frac{dx}{(x-3)^2(x-1)} = \int \left(\frac{-\frac{1}{4}}{x-3} + \frac{\frac{1}{2}}{(x-3)^2} + \frac{\frac{1}{4}}{x-1} \right) dx$$

$$= -\tfrac{1}{4} \log (x-3) - \tfrac{1}{2} \frac{1}{x-3} + \tfrac{1}{4} \log (x-1)$$

$$= -\frac{1}{2(x-3)} + \tfrac{1}{4} \log \frac{x-1}{x-3}.$$

The coefficients B and C could be found by putting $x = 3$ and $x = 1$ in (i). It would then only remain to find A.

Ex. 2. Evaluate (i) $\int \dfrac{2dx}{(x-1)(x^2+1)}$, (ii) $\int \dfrac{dx}{(1+x^2)^2}$.

(i) Assume $\dfrac{2}{(x-1)(x^2+1)} = \dfrac{A}{x-1} + \dfrac{Bx+C}{x^2+1}$,

$\therefore 2 = A(x^2+1) + (Bx+C)(x-1)$,

$\therefore 2 = (A+B)x^2 + (-B+C)x + A - C$.

Equating coefficients of like powers of x,

$$A+B=0, \quad -B+C=0, \quad A-C=2.$$

Solving these three simultaneous equations,

$$A=1, \quad B=-1, \quad C=-1.$$

$\therefore \int \dfrac{2dx}{(x-1)(x^2+1)} = \int \left(\dfrac{1}{x-1} - \dfrac{x+1}{x^2+1} \right) dx$

$\qquad = \log(x-1) - \tfrac{1}{2}\log(x^2+1) - \tan^{-1} x$.

(ii) Put $x = \tan\theta$, $dx = \sec^2\theta\, d\theta$, $1+x^2 = \sec^2\theta$,

$\therefore \int \dfrac{dx}{(1+x^2)^2} = \int \dfrac{\sec^2\theta\, d\theta}{\sec^4\theta} = \int \cos^2\theta\, d\theta = \tfrac{1}{2}(\theta + \tfrac{1}{2}\sin 2\theta)$,

$\therefore \int \dfrac{dx}{(1+x^2)^2} = \dfrac{1}{2}\left(\tan^{-1} x + \dfrac{x}{1+x^2} \right)$.

Examples LXXXIII.

Evaluate the given integrals :—

1. $\int \dfrac{x\, dx}{(x-a)^2}$.

2. $\int \dfrac{(x-1)dx}{x(x+1)^2}$.

3. $\int \dfrac{dx}{(x-2)^2(x-3)}$.

4. $\int \dfrac{x^2\, dx}{(x-a)^2}$.

5. $\int \dfrac{dx}{x^2(1-x)^2}$.

6. $\int \dfrac{x^2+1}{x^3(x+1)}\, dx$.

7. $\int \dfrac{x^3\, dx}{(x-a)^2}$.

8. $\int \dfrac{4x^2\, dx}{(1-x^2)^2}$.

9. $\int \dfrac{3dx}{x^3-3x+2}$.

10. $\int \dfrac{3x+5}{(x+1)(x+2)^3}\, dx$.

11. $\int \dfrac{x^3+3x^2+6x+6}{x^3(x+1)^2}\, dx$.

12. $\int_{2}^{\infty} \dfrac{dx}{x^2(x-1)}$.

13. $\int_{3}^{\infty} \dfrac{4\, dx}{(x^2-1)^2}$.

14. $\int_{3}^{\infty} \dfrac{dx}{x^3-x^2-x+1}$.

15. $\int \dfrac{(3x+2)\, dx}{(x^2+4)(1-x)}$.

16. $\int \dfrac{dx}{x^4-3x^2-4}$.

17. $\int \dfrac{x^3\, dx}{x^2+a^2}$.

18. $\int \dfrac{dx}{x(x^2-2x+2)}$.

19. $\int \dfrac{dx}{x^4+5x^2+4}$.

20. $\int \dfrac{dx}{x^3-1}$.

21. $\int \dfrac{x^3\, dx}{(x+1)(x^2+1)}$.

22. $\int \dfrac{dx}{x^3(1+x^2)}$.

23. $\int_{0}^{\infty} \dfrac{dx}{x^4+4}$.

24. $\int \dfrac{(2x+1)dx}{(x-2)(x^2+1)^2}$.

25. $\int \left(\dfrac{x^2-1}{x^2+1} \right)^2 dx$.

26. $\int \dfrac{dx}{x^4+1}$.

27. $\int_{0}^{1} \dfrac{x^2+4x+1}{(x^2+1)(x+1)}\, dx$.

28. $\int \dfrac{(x^2+1)\, dx}{x^4+x^2+1}$.

29. $\int \dfrac{x^5\, dx}{(x^3+1)^2}$.

30. $\int_{1}^{\infty} \dfrac{x^2+2}{x^4(x^2+1)}\, dx$.

31. $\int_{0}^{\infty} \dfrac{(x+4)dx}{(x^2+4)^2}$.

32. $\int_{2}^{\infty} \dfrac{dx}{x^4-1}$.

33. $\int_{0}^{\infty} \dfrac{(5x+1)dx}{(x+2)(x^2+x+1)}$.

34. $\int_{2}^{4} \dfrac{6x^3+3x}{(x^3-1)(x-1)}\, dx$.

Trigonometric Integrands.

§ 185. Standard Trigonometric Integrals.

$$\int \cos \theta \, d\theta = \sin \theta. \tag{1}$$
$$\int \sin \theta \, d\theta = - \cos \theta. \tag{2}$$
$$\int \cot \theta \, d\theta = \log (\sin \theta). \tag{3}$$
$$\int \tan \theta \, d\theta = - \log (\cos \theta) = \log (\sec \theta). \tag{4}$$

$$\int \operatorname{cosec} \theta \, d\theta = \int \frac{d\theta}{\sin \theta} = \log \left(\tan \frac{\theta}{2} \right). \tag{5}$$

$$\int \sec \theta \, d\theta = \int \frac{d\theta}{\cos \theta} = \log \tan \left(\frac{\pi}{4} + \frac{\theta}{2} \right), \tag{6a}$$

$$= \log (\sec \theta + \tan \theta), \tag{6b}$$

$$= \tfrac{1}{2} \log \frac{1 + \sin \theta}{1 - \sin \theta}. \tag{6c}$$

The following six are added for the sake of reference :—

$$\int \cos^2 \theta \, d\theta = \tfrac{1}{2}(\theta + \sin \theta \cos \theta). \tag{7}$$
$$\int \sin^2 \theta \, d\theta = \tfrac{1}{2}(\theta - \sin \theta \cos \theta). \tag{8}$$
$$\int \sec^2 \theta \, d\theta = \tan \theta. \tag{9}$$
$$\int \tan^2 \theta \, d\theta = \tan \theta - \theta. \tag{10}$$
$$\int \operatorname{cosec}^2 \theta \, d\theta = - \cot \theta. \tag{11}$$
$$\int \cot^2 \theta \, d\theta = - \cot \theta - \theta. \tag{12}$$

§ 186. *Proof of* (3).

$$\int \cot \theta \, d\theta = \int \frac{\cos \theta \, d\theta}{\sin \theta} = \int \frac{d(\sin \theta)}{\sin \theta} = \log (\sin \theta).$$

The proof of (4) is similar.
Proof of (5).

$$\int \frac{d\theta}{\sin \theta} = \int \frac{d\theta}{2 \sin \tfrac{1}{2}\theta \cos \tfrac{1}{2}\theta} = \int \frac{\tfrac{1}{2} \sec^2 \tfrac{1}{2}\theta \, d\theta}{\tan \tfrac{1}{2}\theta}$$

$$= \int \frac{d(\tan \tfrac{1}{2}\theta)}{\tan \tfrac{1}{2}\theta} = \log (\tan \tfrac{1}{2}\theta).$$

Proof of (6a).

$$\int \frac{d\theta}{\cos \theta} = \int \frac{d\theta}{\sin (\tfrac{1}{2}\pi + \theta)} = \log \tan \left(\frac{\pi}{4} + \frac{\theta}{2} \right), \text{ by (5).}$$

Proof of (6b).

$$\int \sec \theta \, d\theta = \int \frac{\sec \theta (\sec \theta + \tan \theta) \, d\theta}{\sec \theta + \tan \theta}$$

$$= \int \frac{d(\sec \theta + \tan \theta)}{\sec \theta + \tan \theta} = \log (\sec \theta + \tan \theta).$$

Proof of (6c).

$$\int \frac{d\theta}{\cos \theta} = \int \frac{\cos \theta \, d\theta}{\cos^2 \theta} = \int \frac{d(\sin \theta)}{1 - \sin^2 \theta} = \tfrac{1}{2} \log \frac{1 + \sin \theta}{1 - \sin \theta}, \text{ by (2), § 181.}$$

Proofs of (7)-(12).

For (7) and (8), see Ex. 2, § 88.   For (10), see Ex. § 176.

Integrals (9) and (11) are standard, and (12) is derived from (11) in the same way as (10) from (9).

Ex. Evaluate (i) $\int \sec^3 \theta \, d\theta$, (ii) $\int \sec^4 \theta \, d\theta$.

(i) Put $z = \int \sec^3 \theta \, d\theta = \int \sec \theta \sec^2 \theta \, d\theta = \int \sec \theta \, d(\tan \theta)$.

Integrating by parts, we get

$$z = \sec \theta \tan \theta - \int \tan \theta \, . \, \sec \theta \tan \theta \, d\theta$$
$$= \sec \theta \tan \theta - \int \sec \theta \, (\sec^2 \theta - 1) \, d\theta$$
$$= \sec \theta \tan \theta - z + \int \sec \theta \, d\theta,$$
$$\therefore \, 2z = \sec \theta \tan \theta + \log \, (\sec \theta + \tan \theta),$$
$$\therefore \, z = \tfrac{1}{2} \{ \sec \theta \tan \theta + \log(\sec \theta + \tan \theta) \}.$$

(ii) The same method could be used.   Alternatively, put

$$z = \int \sec^4 \theta \, d\theta = \int \sec^2 \theta \, . \, \sec^2 \theta \, d\theta = \int (1 + \tan^2 \theta) \, d(\tan \theta),$$
$$\therefore \, z = \tan \theta + \tfrac{1}{3} \tan^3 \theta.$$

§ 187. Trigonometric Reduction Formulæ.

The following formulæ are mainly of theoretical interest.   In practice the rules of § 88 are often more convenient.   Formulæ (13), (14), (19), (20), however, lead to the useful rules given in § 188.

$$\int \cos^n \theta \, d\theta = \frac{\sin \theta \cos^{n-1} \theta}{n} + \frac{n-1}{n} \int \cos^{n-2} \theta \, d\theta. \tag{13}$$

$$\int \sin^n \theta \, d\theta = \frac{- \cos \theta \sin^{n-1} \theta}{n} + \frac{n-1}{n} \int \sin^{n-2} \theta \, d\theta. \tag{14}$$

$$\int \tan^n \theta \, d\theta = \frac{\tan^{n-1} \theta}{n-1} - \int \tan^{n-2} \theta \, d\theta. \tag{15}$$

$$\int \cot^n \theta \, d\theta = \frac{- \cot^{n-1} \theta}{n-1} - \int \cot^{n-2} \theta \, d\theta. \tag{16}$$

$$\int \sec^n \theta \, d\theta = \frac{\sin \theta}{(n-1) \cos^{n-1} \theta} + \frac{n-2}{n-1} \int \sec^{n-2} \theta \, d\theta. \tag{17}$$

$$\int \operatorname{cosec}^n \theta \, d\theta = \frac{- \cos \theta}{(n-1) \sin^{n-1} \theta} + \frac{n-2}{n-1} \int \operatorname{cosec}^{n-2} \theta \, d\theta. \tag{18}$$

For brevity, we put $s = \sin \theta$, $c = \cos \theta$ in the next two :—

$$\int s^m c^n \, d\theta = \frac{s^{m+1} c^{n-1}}{m+n} + \frac{n-1}{m+n} \int s^m c^{n-2} \, d\theta. \tag{19}$$

$$\int s^m c^n \, d\theta = - \frac{s^{m-1} c^{n+1}}{m+n} + \frac{m-1}{m+n} \int s^{m-2} c^n \, d\theta. \tag{20}$$

Proof of (13).   Put
$$I_n = \int \cos^n \theta \, d\theta = \int \cos^{n-1} \theta \cos \theta \, d\theta = \int \cos^{n-1} \theta \, d(\sin \theta).$$
Integrating by parts, we get
$$I_n = \cos^{n-1} \theta \, (\sin \theta) - \int \sin \theta \, d(\cos^{n-1} \theta)$$
$$= \sin \theta \cos^{n-1} \theta + (n-1) \int \cos^{n-2} \theta \sin^2 \theta \, d\theta$$
$$= \sin \theta \cos^{n-1} \theta + (n-1) \int \cos^{n-2} \theta \, (1 - \cos^2 \theta) d\theta,$$
$$\therefore \ I_n = \sin \theta \cos^{n-1} \theta + (n-1)(I_{n-2} - I_n),$$
$$\therefore \ nI_n = \sin \theta \cos^{n-1} \theta + (n-1)I_{n-2},$$
from which (13) follows, on dividing by n.

The proof of (14) is similar.

Proof of (15).   Put
$$I_n = \int \tan^n \theta \, d\theta = \int \tan^{n-2} (\sec^2 \theta - 1) d\theta,$$
$$\therefore \ I_n = \int \tan^{n-2} \theta \, d(\tan \theta) - \int \tan^{n-2} \theta \, d\theta,$$
$$\therefore \ I_n = \frac{\tan^{n-1} \theta}{n-1} - I_{n-2}.$$

The proof of (16) is similar.

Proof of (17).   Put
$$I_n = \int \sec^n \theta \, d\theta = \int \sec^{n-2} \theta \, d(\tan \theta).$$
Integrating by parts, we get
$$I_n = \sec^{n-2} \theta \tan \theta - \int \tan \theta \, d(\sec^{n-2} \theta)$$
$$= \sec^{n-2} \theta \tan \theta - (n-2) \int \sec^{n-2} \theta \tan^2 \theta \, d\theta$$
$$= \sec^{n-2} \theta \tan \theta - (n-2) \int \sec^{n-2} \theta \, (\sec^2 \theta - 1) d\theta$$
$$= \sec^{n-2} \theta \tan \theta - (n-2)(I_n - I_{n-2}),$$
$$\therefore \ (n-1)I_n = \sec^{n-2} \theta \tan \theta + (n-2) \, I_{n-2},$$
from which (17) follows, on dividing by $(n-1)$.

The proof of (18) is similar.

Proof of (19).

Put $I_{m,\,n} = \int s^m c^n \, d\theta$.   Then, multiplying by $(m+1)$,
$$(m+1)I_{m,\,n} = \int c^{n-1} \cdot (m+1)s^m c \, d\theta = \int c^{n-1} d(s^{m+1}).$$
Integrating by parts,
$$(m+1)I_{m,\,n} = c^{n-1}s^{m+1} - \int s^{m+1} d(c^{n-1})$$
$$= s^{m+1}c^{n-1} + (n-1)\int s^{m+2}c^{n-2} \, d\theta$$
$$= s^{m+1}c^{n-1} + (n-1)\int s^m(1 - c^2)c^{n-2} \, d\theta,$$
$$\therefore \ (m+1)I_{m,\,n} = s^{m+1}c^{n-1} + (n-1)(I_{m,\,n-2} - I_{m,\,n}),$$
$$\therefore \ (m+n)I_{m,\,n} = s^{m+1}c^{n-1} + (n-1)I_{m,\,n-2}$$
from which (19) follows, on dividing by $(m+n)$.

The proof of (20) is similar.

Examples LXXXIV.

In Exs. 1-18 evaluate the given integrals :—

1. $\int \cot 2\theta \, d\theta$.

2. $\int \sec \tfrac{1}{2}\theta \, d\theta$.

3. $\int \tan (ax + b) dx$.

4. $\int \dfrac{d\theta}{\sin 3\theta}$.

5. $\int \dfrac{d\theta}{\cos n\theta}$.

6. $\int \dfrac{1 - \sin \theta}{\cos \theta} \, d\theta$.

7. $\int \cos^3 \theta \, d\theta$.   **8.** $\int \cos^4 \theta \, d\theta$.   **9.** $\int \cos^5 \theta \, d\theta$.

10. $\int \tan^3 \theta \, d\theta$.   **11.** $\int \tan^4 \theta \, d\theta$.   **12.** $\int_0^{\frac{\pi}{4}} \tan^5 \theta \, d\theta$.

13. $\int \dfrac{d\theta}{\sin^3 \theta}$.   **14.** $\int \dfrac{d\theta}{\sin^4 \theta}$.   **15.** $\int_0^{\frac{\pi}{4}} \dfrac{\sin^2 \theta}{\cos \theta} \, d\theta$.

16. $\int \dfrac{\cos^3 \theta}{\sin \theta} \, d\theta$.   **17.** $\int \dfrac{\sin^4 \theta}{\cos \theta} \, d\theta$.   **18.** $\int_0^{\frac{\pi}{4}} \dfrac{\sin^2 \theta}{\cos^3 \theta} \, d\theta$.

In Exs. 19-24, apply the Rule: To evaluate $\int \sin^m \theta \cos^n \theta \, d\theta$ when the sum of the indices is an even *negative* integer, make the substitution $x = \tan \theta$, $dx = \sec^2 \theta \, d\theta$:—

19. $\int \dfrac{\sin \theta}{\cos^3 \theta} \, d\theta$.   **20.** $\int \dfrac{\sin^n \theta \, d\theta}{\cos^{n+2} \theta}$.   **21.** $\int \dfrac{d\theta}{\sin^2 \theta \cos^2 \theta}$.

22. $\int \dfrac{\sin^2 \theta}{\cos^6 \theta} \, d\theta$.   **23.** $\int \dfrac{\sin^n \theta \, d\theta}{\cos^{n+4} \theta}$.   **24.** $\int \dfrac{d\theta}{\sqrt{(\sin^3 \theta \cos^5 \theta)}}$.

§ **188. The Definite Integral** $\displaystyle\int_0^{\frac{\pi}{2}} \sin^m \theta \cos^n \theta \, d\theta$.—From (13), (14), (19), (20), follow the useful formulæ :—

$$\int_0^{\frac{\pi}{2}} \cos^n \theta \, d\theta = \frac{n-1}{n} \int_0^{\frac{\pi}{2}} \cos^{n-2} \theta \, d\theta. \tag{21}$$

$$\int_0^{\frac{\pi}{2}} \sin^n \theta \, d\theta = \frac{n-1}{n} \int_0^{\frac{\pi}{2}} \sin^{n-2} \theta \, d\theta. \tag{22}$$

$$\int_0^{\frac{\pi}{2}} \sin^m \theta \cos^n \theta \, d\theta = \frac{n-1}{m+n} \int_0^{\frac{\pi}{2}} \sin^m \theta \cos^{n-2} \theta \, d\theta. \tag{23}$$

$$\int_0^{\frac{\pi}{2}} \sin^m \theta \cos^n \theta \, d\theta = \frac{m-1}{m+n} \int_0^{\frac{\pi}{2}} \sin^{m-2} \theta \cos^n \theta \, d\theta. \tag{24}$$

Proof of (21). From (13) we have

$$\int_0^{\frac{\pi}{2}} \cos^n \theta \, d\theta = \left[\frac{\sin \theta \cos^{n-1} \theta}{n} \right]_0^{\frac{\pi}{2}} + \frac{n-1}{n} \int_0^{\frac{\pi}{2}} \cos^{n-2} \theta \, d\theta.$$

Now $\cos \theta = 0$ when $\theta = \frac{1}{2}\pi$, and $\sin \theta = 0$ when $\theta = 0$. Hence, the first term on the right is zero, and (21) follows.

Similarly, (22), (23), (24) follow from (14), (19), (20).

Note.—The same kind of proof would show that formulæ (21)-(24) remain true if both limits of integration are *any whole multiples of* $\frac{1}{2}\pi$.

Ex. Evaluate (i) $\int_0^\pi \cos^6 \theta \, d\theta$, (ii) $\int_0^{\frac{\pi}{2}} \sin^5 \theta \cos^5 \theta \, d\theta$.

(i) Put $I_n = \int_0^\pi \cos^n \theta \, d\theta$. Then, applying formula (21) repeatedly, but with π as the upper limit (see Note above), we have

$$I_6 = \frac{5}{6} I_4 = \frac{5}{6}\frac{3}{4} I_2 = \frac{5}{6}\frac{3}{4}\frac{1}{2} I_0 = \frac{5}{16}\int_0^\pi d\theta,$$

$$\therefore \int_0^\pi \cos^6 \theta \, d\theta = \frac{5\pi}{16}.$$

(ii) Put $I_{m,\,n} = \int_0^{\frac{\pi}{2}} \sin^m \theta \cos^n \theta \, d\theta$. Then, applying (23), we have

$$I_{5,\,5} = \frac{4}{10} I_{5,\,3} = \frac{4}{10}\frac{2}{8} I_{5,\,1} = \frac{1}{10}\int_0^{\frac{\pi}{2}} \sin^5 \theta \cos \theta \, d\theta,$$

$$\therefore \int_0^{\frac{\pi}{2}} \sin^5 \theta \cos^5 \theta \, d\theta = \frac{1}{10}\left[\frac{\sin^6 \theta}{6}\right]_0^{\frac{\pi}{2}} = \frac{1}{60}.$$

Examples LXXXV.

In Exs. 1-6 evaluate the given definite integrals :—

1. $\int_0^{\frac{\pi}{2}} \sin^2 \theta \, d\theta.$　　　　**2.** $\int_0^{\frac{\pi}{2}} \sin^4 \theta \, d\theta.$　　　　**3.** $\int_0^\pi \sin^4 \theta \cos^4 \theta \, d\theta.$

4. $\int_0^\pi \cos^7 \theta \, d\theta.$　　　　**5.** $\int_0^\pi \cos^8 \theta \, d\theta.$　　　　**6.** $\int_{-\pi}^\pi \sin^6 \theta \cos^5 \theta \, d\theta.$

7. By means of the substitution $x = \sin \theta$, evaluate

$$\text{(i) } \int_0^1 x^3(1 - x^2)^4 \, dx, \qquad \text{(ii) } \int_0^1 \frac{x^4 \, dx}{\sqrt{(1 - x^2)}}.$$

8. By means of the substitution $x = \sin^2 \theta$, evaluate

$$\text{(i) } \int_0^1 x^{\frac{3}{2}}(1 - x)^{\frac{3}{2}} \, dx, \qquad \text{(ii) } \int_0^1 x\sqrt{(x - x^2)} \, dx.$$

9. Find the average values between $\theta = 0$ and $\theta = \pi$, of

(i) $\sin^3 \theta$,　　(ii) $\sin^4 \theta$,　　(iii) $\sin^{2n} \theta$,　　(iv) $\sin^{2n+1} \theta$.

§ 189. The Integral $\int \dfrac{d\theta}{a \sin^2 \theta + b \sin \theta \cos \theta + c \cos^2 \theta}$, $= z$, say.

Note that the denominator is homogeneous, and of the second degree, in $\sin \theta$ and $\cos \theta$.

Method.—Divide numerator and denominator by $\cos^2 \theta$, and then make the substitution $x = \tan \theta$, $dx = \sec^2 \theta \, d\theta$. Thus

$$z = \int \frac{\sec^2 \theta \, d\theta}{a \tan^2 \theta + b \tan \theta + c} = \int \frac{dx}{ax^2 + bx + c},$$

which can now be evaluated as in § 182.

Ex. Evaluate $\displaystyle\int \frac{d\theta}{1 + 3 \cos^2 \theta}, = z$, say.

Here the denominator is not homogeneous, but it can at once be made so, by using the identity $\cos^2 \theta + \sin^2 \theta = 1$. Thus

$$z = \int \frac{d\theta}{(\cos^2 \theta + \sin^2 \theta) + 3 \cos^2 \theta} = \int \frac{d\theta}{4 \cos^2 \theta + \sin^2 \theta},$$

$$\therefore z = \int \frac{\sec^2 \theta \, d\theta}{4 + \tan^2 \theta} = \int \frac{dx}{4 + x^2} = \tfrac{1}{2} \tan^{-1}\left(\frac{x}{2}\right), \text{ where } x = \tan \theta \,;$$

$$\therefore z = \tfrac{1}{2} \tan^{-1}\left(\tfrac{1}{2} \tan \theta\right).$$

Examples LXXXVI.

Evaluate the given integrals :—

1. $\displaystyle\int \frac{d\theta}{\sin \theta \cos \theta}.$ 2. $\displaystyle\int \frac{d\theta}{1 + \cos^2 \theta}.$ 3. $\displaystyle\int \frac{d\theta}{4 \cos^2 \theta - \sin^2 \theta}.$

4. $\displaystyle\int \frac{d\theta}{1 + 3 \cos^2 2\theta}.$ 5. $\displaystyle\int \frac{d\theta}{2 \cos 2\theta + 3 \sin \theta \cos \theta}.$

6. $\displaystyle\int_0^{\frac{\pi}{4}} \frac{d\theta}{1 + \sin \theta \cos \theta}.$ 7. $\displaystyle\int \frac{d\theta}{(a \cos \theta + b \sin \theta)^2}.$

8. $\displaystyle\int_0^{\pi} \frac{d\theta}{\cos^2 \theta + 4 \sin^2 \theta}.$ 9. $\displaystyle\int \frac{d\theta}{\cos \theta \, (a \cos \theta + b \sin \theta)}.$

10. $\displaystyle\int_0^{2\pi} \frac{d\theta}{a^2 \cos^2 \theta + b^2 \sin^2 \theta}.$ 11. $\displaystyle\int \frac{d\theta}{4 - 4 \cos \theta \sin \theta - 7 \sin^2 \theta}.$

§ 190. Rational Trigonometric Functions.—By trigonometry,

$$\sin \theta = 2 \sin \frac{\theta}{2} \cos \frac{\theta}{2} = \frac{2 \sin \tfrac{1}{2}\theta \cos \tfrac{1}{2}\theta}{\cos^2 \tfrac{1}{2}\theta + \sin^2 \tfrac{1}{2}\theta},$$

$$\cos \theta = \cos^2 \frac{\theta}{2} - \sin^2 \frac{\theta}{2} = \frac{\cos^2 \tfrac{1}{2}\theta - \sin^2 \tfrac{1}{2}\theta}{\cos^2 \tfrac{1}{2}\theta + \sin^2 \tfrac{1}{2}\theta}.$$

Hence, dividing numerators and denominators by $\cos^2 \tfrac{1}{2}\theta$, and putting $t = \tan \tfrac{1}{2}\theta$, we have

$$\sin \theta = \frac{2t}{1 + t^2}, \qquad \cos \theta = \frac{1 - t^2}{1 + t^2}.$$

Thus, $\sin \theta$ and $\cos \theta$ are *rational* functions of t.

Any *rational trigonometric function* is a function that becomes a rational function of t when we make the substitution $t = \tan \tfrac{1}{2}\theta$.

§ 191. Rational Trigonometric Integrands.—*Every integral whose integrand is a rational trigonometric function of the variable of integration can be evaluated :*—

Proof.—Let $\int f(\theta)d\theta$ be any integral in which the integrand $f(\theta)$ is a rational trigonometric function of θ.

Make the substitution

$$t = \tan\frac{\theta}{2}, \quad \therefore \; \theta = 2\tan^{-1} t, \quad \therefore \; d\theta = \frac{2\,dt}{1 + t^2}, \text{ by (3), § 54.}$$

Then the integral is transformed into

$$\int \frac{2\,f(\theta)}{1 + t^2}\,dt,$$

where $f(\theta)$, in terms of t, is a rational function of t.

Thus, the new integral is one in which the integrand is a *rational* function of the variable of integration, and can therefore always be evaluated (§ 180). Hence the following general method :—

General Method.—When the integrand is a rational trigonometric function of θ, where θ is the variable of integration, we can make the substitution

$$t = \tan\tfrac{1}{2}\theta,$$

$$\sin\theta = \frac{2t}{1 + t^2}, \quad \cos\theta = \frac{1 - t^2}{1 + t^2}, \quad d\theta = \frac{2\,dt}{1 + t^2}.$$

Note.—Although this method could be applied *in all cases*, it is not usually the simplest in practice.

Ex. Evaluate $\displaystyle\int \frac{d\theta}{5 + 3\cos\theta}$.

Making the above substitution, we get

$$\int \frac{d\theta}{5 + 3\cos\theta} = \int \frac{\dfrac{2\,dt}{1 + t^2}}{5 + \dfrac{3(1 - t^2)}{1 + t^2}} = \int \frac{dt}{4 + t^2},$$

$$\therefore \; \int \frac{d\theta}{5 + 3\cos\theta} = \tfrac{1}{2}\tan^{-1}\left(\frac{t}{2}\right) = \tfrac{1}{2}\tan^{-1}\left(\tfrac{1}{2}\tan\frac{\theta}{2}\right).$$

Examples LXXXVII.

In Exs. 1-14 evaluate the given integrals :—

1. $\displaystyle\int \frac{d\theta}{\sin\theta}$.   2. $\displaystyle\int \frac{d\theta}{3 + 5\cos\theta}$.   3. $\displaystyle\int_0^\pi \frac{d\theta}{1 + \sin\theta}$.

4. $\displaystyle\int \frac{d\theta}{\cos\theta}$.   5. $\displaystyle\int \frac{d\theta}{5 - 3\cos\theta}$.   6. $\displaystyle\int_0^{\frac{\pi}{2}} \frac{d\theta}{\sin\theta + \cos\theta}$.

7. $\displaystyle\int \frac{d\theta}{4\cos\theta + 3\sin\theta}$.   8. $\displaystyle\int \frac{d\theta}{\cos\theta + 2(1 - \sin\theta)}$.

9. $\displaystyle\int \frac{d\theta}{1 + \cos\theta + \sin\theta}$.   10. $\displaystyle\int \frac{d\theta}{13 + 12\sin\theta + 5\cos\theta}$.

11 $\int_0^\pi \dfrac{d\theta}{2 + \cos\theta}$.   **12** $\int_0^{\frac{\pi}{2}} \dfrac{d\theta}{1 + 2\cos\theta}$.   **13** $\int_0^\pi \dfrac{d\theta}{(5 + 3\cos\theta)^2}$.

14 $\int \dfrac{d\theta}{a + b\cos\theta}$, when $a > b > 0$, and when $b > a > 0$.

15 Show how the integral $\int \dfrac{A\cos\theta + B\sin\theta + C}{a\cos\theta + b\sin\theta + c}\,d\theta$ can be evaluated after the numerator of the integrand has been expressed in the form

L (denom.) + M (diff. coeff. of denom.) + N,

where L, M, N are constants.

In Exs. 16-20 evaluate the given integrals, using the method indicated in Ex. 15 :—

16 $\int \dfrac{\sin\theta\,d\theta}{4\cos\theta + 3\sin\theta}$.   **17** $\int \dfrac{d\theta}{1 + \tan\theta}$.   **18** $\int \dfrac{1 - \tan\theta}{1 + \tan\theta}\,d\theta$.

19 $\int \dfrac{5\sin\theta + 2}{\cos\theta + 2\sin\theta + 3}\,d\theta$.   **20** $\int_0^{\frac{\pi}{2}} \dfrac{2 + 7\sin\theta - \cos\theta}{5 + 3\cos\theta + 4\sin\theta}\,d\theta$.

IRRATIONAL INTEGRANDS.

§ 192. The commonest kind of irrationality that occurs in integrals is the square-root of a linear or quadratic function.

Square-Root of a Linear Function in the Integrand.—We repeat the rule of § 91 :—

Rule.—When the square-root of a *linear* function, $\sqrt{(ax + b)}$, occurs in the integrand, make the substitution

$$\sqrt{(ax + b)} = v,\ \therefore\ ax + b = v^2,\ x = \frac{v^2 - b}{a},\ dx = \frac{2v\,dv}{a}.$$

If there is no other kind of irrationality in the integrand, this substitution will transform the integral into one in which the integrand is a *rational* function of v. It can then be evaluated (§ 180). For an example, see § 91.

Examples LXXXVIII.

In Exs. 1-13, evaluate the given integrals :—

1. $\int \dfrac{x}{1 + \sqrt{x}}\,dx$.   **2.** $\int \dfrac{dx}{2 - x - \sqrt{x}}$.   **3.** $\int_8^{15} \dfrac{dx}{(x - 3)\sqrt{(x + 1)}}$.

4. $\int_0^1 \dfrac{1 - \sqrt{x}}{1 + \sqrt{x}}\,dx$.   **5.** $\int \dfrac{dx}{x + \sqrt{(x - 1)}}$.   **6.** $\int_x^\infty \dfrac{dx}{(2 + x)\sqrt{(1 + x)}}$.

7. $\int_3^8 \dfrac{\sqrt{(x + 1)}}{x}\,dx$.   **8.** $\int_1^\infty \dfrac{\sqrt{(2x - 1)}}{x^2}\,dx$.   **9.** $\int \dfrac{dx}{(x + c)\sqrt{(x - a)}}$.

10. $\int_1^2 \dfrac{dx}{(x^2 - x + 1)\sqrt{(x - 1)}}$.   **11.** $\int \dfrac{dx}{\sqrt{(x + a)} - \sqrt{(x + b)}}$.

12. $\int_5^8 \dfrac{dx}{\sqrt{(x+4)} - \sqrt{(x-4)}}.$ **13.** $\int_1^5 \dfrac{dx}{\sqrt{(3x+1)} + \sqrt{(x+3)}}.$

In Exs. 14-18, apply the rule: when fractional powers of one linear function, $ax + b$, occur in the integrand, make the substitution

$$(ax + b)^{\frac{1}{n}} = v, \quad \therefore \ ax + b = v^n, \quad x = \frac{v^n - b}{a}, \quad dx = \frac{nv^{n-1}\,dv}{a},$$

where n is the L.C.M. of the denominators of the fractional indices :—

14. $\int \dfrac{x\,dx}{\sqrt[5]{(x+1)}}.$ **15.** $\int \dfrac{x\,dx}{(x-1)^{\frac{1}{2}} + (x-1)^{\frac{5}{6}}}.$

16. $\int_0^1 \dfrac{dx}{x^{\frac{1}{2}} + x^{\frac{2}{3}}}.$ **17.** $\int_0^1 \dfrac{x\,dx}{(1-x)^{\frac{1}{3}}}.$ **18.** $\int_0^1 \dfrac{x^{\frac{1}{3}} - 1}{x^{\frac{2}{3}} + 1}\,dx.$

§ 193. Square-Root of a Quadratic Function in the Integrand.
—Note first the two standard integrals :—

$$\int \frac{dx}{\sqrt{(c - x^2)}} = \sin^{-1} \frac{x}{\sqrt{c}}. \tag{1}$$

$$\int \frac{dx}{\sqrt{(x^2 + c)}} = \log\{x + \sqrt{(x^2 + c)}\}. \tag{2}$$

The first is already known in a slightly different form (p. 165).

The second follows from the fact that the derivative of the right-hand side is equal to the integrand on the left [see (ii), Ex. 2, § 156].

In (1), c is necessarily positive for the integral to be real. In (2), c may be positive or negative.

§ 194. The Integrals (i) $\int \dfrac{dx}{\sqrt{(x^2 + px + q)}}$, (ii) $\int \dfrac{dx}{\sqrt{(q + px - x^2)}}.$

(i) Put $z = \int \dfrac{dx}{\sqrt{(x^2 + px + q)}} = \int \dfrac{dx}{\sqrt{\{(x + \frac{1}{2}p)^2 + q - \frac{1}{4}p^2\}}},$

$\therefore z = \int \dfrac{du}{\sqrt{(u^2 + c)}} = \log\{u + \sqrt{(u^2 + c)}\}$, by (2),

where $u = x + \frac{1}{2}p$, $c = q - \frac{1}{4}p^2$. Hence

$$\int \frac{dx}{\sqrt{(x^2 + px + q)}} = \log\{x + \tfrac{1}{2}p + \sqrt{(x^2 + px + q)}\}. \tag{3}$$

(ii) Put $z = \int \dfrac{dx}{\sqrt{(q + px - x^2)}} = \int \dfrac{dx}{\sqrt{\{q + \frac{1}{4}p^2 - (x - \frac{1}{2}p)^2\}}},$

$\therefore z = \int \dfrac{du}{\sqrt{(c - u^2)}} = \sin^{-1} \dfrac{u}{\sqrt{c}}$, by (1), where $u = x - \frac{1}{2}p$, $c = q + \frac{1}{4}p^2$.   Hence

$$\int \frac{dx}{\sqrt{(q + px - x^2)}} = \sin^{-1} \frac{2x - p}{\sqrt{(4q + p^2)}}. \tag{4}$$

Ex. Evaluate (i) $\int \dfrac{dx}{\sqrt{(x^2 + x + 1)}}$, (ii) $\int \dfrac{dx}{\sqrt{(1 - 2x - 3x^2)}}$.

(i) Put $\quad z = \int \dfrac{dx}{\sqrt{(x^2 + x + 1)}} = \int \dfrac{dx}{\sqrt{\{(x + \frac{1}{2})^2 + \frac{3}{4}\}}}$,

$$\therefore z = \log \{x + \tfrac{1}{2} + \sqrt{(x^2 + x + 1)}\}.$$

(ii) Put $\quad z = \int \dfrac{dx}{\sqrt{(1 - 2x - 3x^2)}} = \dfrac{1}{\sqrt{3}} \int \dfrac{dx}{\sqrt{(\frac{1}{3} - \frac{2}{3}x - x^2)}}$,

$$\therefore z = \frac{1}{\sqrt{3}} \int \frac{dx}{\sqrt{\{\frac{4}{9} - (x + \frac{1}{3})^2\}}} = \frac{1}{\sqrt{3}} \sin^{-1} \left(\frac{x + \frac{1}{3}}{\frac{2}{3}} \right),$$

$$\therefore z = \frac{1}{\sqrt{3}} \sin^{-1} \left(\frac{3x + 1}{2} \right).$$

§ 195. The Integral $\int \dfrac{Ax + B}{\sqrt{(ax^2 + bx + c)}}\, dx$.

Method.—Begin by expressing the numerator $(Ax + B)$ in the form

$$L(\text{diff. coeff. of } ax^2 + bx + c) + M,$$

where L and M are constants.   The integral then becomes the sum of two integrals, both of which can be evaluated.

Ex. Evaluate $\int \dfrac{3x + 1}{\sqrt{(x^2 + 3x + 4)}}\, dx$, $= z$, say.

Put
$$3x + 1 = L(2x + 3) + M,$$
$$\therefore 3x + 1 = 2Lx + 3L + M.$$

Hence, by equating coefficients, $L = \frac{3}{2}$, $M = -\frac{7}{2}$;

$$\therefore z = \int \frac{\frac{3}{2}(2x + 3) - \frac{7}{2}}{\sqrt{(x^2 + 3x + 4)}}\, dx$$

$$= \frac{3}{2} \int \frac{dv}{\sqrt{v}} - \frac{7}{2} \int \frac{dx}{\sqrt{(x^2 + 3x + 4)}},$$

where $v = x^2 + 3x + 4$.   The first integral $= 3\sqrt{v}$, and the second is a particular case of (3), § 194,

$$\therefore z = 3\sqrt{(x^2 + 3x + 4)} - \tfrac{7}{2} \log \{x + \tfrac{3}{2} + \sqrt{(x^2 + 3x + 4)}\}.$$

Examples LXXXIX.

Evaluate the given integrals:—

1. $\int \dfrac{dx}{\sqrt{(x^2 + 3)}}$.

2. $\int \dfrac{dx}{\sqrt{(3 - x^2)}}$.

3. $\int \dfrac{dx}{\sqrt{(x^2 - 6x + 12)}}$.

4. $\int \dfrac{dx}{\sqrt{(3 - 2x^2)}}$.

5. $\int \dfrac{dx}{\sqrt{(3x^2 - 1)}}$.

6. $\int \dfrac{dx}{\sqrt{(4x^2 - 4x + 1)}}$.

7. $\int \dfrac{dx}{\sqrt{(x^2 - 2bx)}}$.

8. $\int \dfrac{dx}{\sqrt{(x - x^2)}}$.

9. $\int \dfrac{dx}{\sqrt{(3x^2 + 4x + 5)}}$.

10. $\int_0^a \dfrac{dx}{\sqrt{(2ax-x^2)}}.$　　**11.** $\int_0^4 \dfrac{dx}{\sqrt{(x^2+9)}}.$　　**12.** $\int_1^2 \dfrac{dx}{\sqrt{(x^2+x-2)}}.$

13. $\int_1^2 \dfrac{dx}{\sqrt{(x^2-1)}}.$　　**14.** $\int_4^5 \dfrac{dx}{\sqrt{(x^2-16)}}.$　　**15.** $\int_2^5 \dfrac{dx}{\sqrt{(11x-5-2x^2)}}.$

16. $\int \dfrac{2x+1}{\sqrt{(1-x^2)}}\,dx.$　　**17.** $\int \dfrac{3x-1}{\sqrt{(x^2+5)}}\,dx.$　　**18.** $\int \left(\dfrac{1+x}{1-x}\right)^{\frac{1}{2}} dx.$

19. $\int \dfrac{x\,dx}{\sqrt{(x^2-ax)}}.$　　**20.** $\int \dfrac{(4x-1)\,dx}{\sqrt{(x^2+x-1)}}.$　　**21.** $\int \dfrac{(2x+3)\,dx}{\sqrt{(3x^2-6x+4)}}.$

22. $\int \dfrac{x+a}{\sqrt{(x^2+c)}}\,dx.$　　**23.** $\int \dfrac{(x+1)\,dx}{\sqrt{(6x-x^2)}}.$　　**24.** $\int \dfrac{x\,dx}{\sqrt{(2-3x-2x^2)}}.$

§ 196. Next, consider the integrals :—

$$\int \sqrt{(c-x^2)}\,dx = \tfrac{1}{2}x\sqrt{(c-x^2)} + \tfrac{1}{2}c\sin^{-1}\frac{x}{\sqrt{c}}. \qquad (5)$$

$$\int \sqrt{(x^2+c)}\,dx = \tfrac{1}{2}x\sqrt{(x^2+c)} + \tfrac{1}{2}c\log\{x+\sqrt{(x^2+c)}\}. \qquad (6)$$

We shall first prove (6) :—

Put $z = \int \sqrt{(x^2+c)}\,dx$. Then, integrating by parts,

$$z = \sqrt{(x^2+c)}\,.\,x - \int xd\sqrt{(x^2+c)}$$

$$= x\sqrt{(x^2+c)} - \int \frac{x^2}{\sqrt{(x^2+c)}}\,dx.$$

Now put $x^2 = (x^2+c) - c$ in the numerator of the integrand on the right. Then

$$z = x\sqrt{(x^2+c)} - \int \frac{(x^2+c)-c}{\sqrt{(x^2+c)}}\,dx$$

$$= x\sqrt{(x^2+c)} - z + c\int \frac{dx}{\sqrt{(x^2+c)}},$$

$$\therefore\ 2z = x\sqrt{(x^2+c)} + c\log\{x+\sqrt{(x^2+c)}\},$$

from which (6) follows.

We could prove (5) in the same way.

Both (5) and (6) can also be proved by substitutions, (5) by a trigonometric substitution, as in § 92, and (6) by trigonometric or hyperbolic substitutions (see § 253).

Examples XC.

Evaluate the given integrals :—

1. $\int \sqrt{(a^2-x^2)}\,dx.$　　**2.** $\int \sqrt{(x^2+a^2)}\,dx.$　　**3.** $\int \sqrt{(x^2-a^2)}\,dx.$

4. $\int_0^1 \sqrt{(x^2+1)}\,dx.$　　**5.** $\int_1^2 \sqrt{(x^2-1)}\,dx.$　　**6.** $\int_3^5 \sqrt{(x^2-9)}\,dx.$

7. $\int \sqrt{(x^2-6x+6)}\,dx.$　　　　**8.** $\int \sqrt{(7+6x-3x^2)}\,dx.$

9. $\int \dfrac{x^2+x+1}{\sqrt{(x^2+2x+3)}}\,dx.$　　**10.** $\int \dfrac{x^2\,dx}{\sqrt{(x^2-4x+8)}}.$

11. $\int_0^1 \dfrac{x-x^2}{\sqrt{(1-x^2)}}\,dx.$　　**12.** $\int_0^1 \dfrac{4x^2+4x+3}{\sqrt{(2x^2+4x+3)}}\,dx.$

§ 197. The integral $\int \dfrac{dx}{(x - a)\sqrt{(ax^2 + bx + c)}}$.

Method.—Begin by making the substitution

$$x - a = \frac{1}{v}, \qquad x = \frac{1}{v} + a, \qquad \dot{x} = -\frac{dv}{v^2}.$$

The integral is thereby transformed into a known type.

Ex. Evaluate $\int \dfrac{dx}{x\sqrt{(x^2 + 1)}}, = z$, say.

Put $\qquad\qquad x = \dfrac{1}{v}, \qquad dx = -\dfrac{dv}{v^2},$

$$\therefore z = \int \frac{-dv}{v^2 \cdot \frac{1}{v}\left(\frac{1}{v^2} + 1\right)^{\frac12}} = \int \frac{-dv}{(v^2 + 1)^{\frac12}} = -\log\{v + \sqrt{(v^2 + 1)}\},$$

$$\therefore z = -\log\frac{1 + \sqrt{(x^2 + 1)}}{x} = \log\frac{x}{1 + \sqrt{(x^2 + 1)}}.$$

Examples XCI.

Evaluate the given integrals :—

1. $\displaystyle\int \frac{dx}{x\sqrt{(x^2 - 1)}}$.

2. $\displaystyle\int \frac{dx}{x\sqrt{(4 - x^2)}}$.

3. $\displaystyle\int \frac{dx}{x\sqrt{(2x^2 + 3x + 1)}}$.

4. $\displaystyle\int \frac{dx}{x\sqrt{(x^2 - a^2)}}$.

5. $\displaystyle\int \frac{(x - 1)dx}{x\sqrt{(x^2 - 9)}}$.

6. $\displaystyle\int \frac{(x^2 + 1)dx}{x\sqrt{(4x^2 + 1)}}$.

7. $\displaystyle\int \frac{dx}{x^2\sqrt{(2x^2 - 1)}}$.

8. $\displaystyle\int \frac{\sqrt{(x^2 + 1)}}{x}\,dx$.

9. $\displaystyle\int \frac{1}{x}\left(\frac{x - 1}{x + 1}\right)^{\frac12}dx$.

10. $\displaystyle\int_{1}^{\infty} \frac{dx}{x\sqrt{(x^2 + 1)}}$.

11. $\displaystyle\int_{1}^{\infty} \frac{dx}{x^2\sqrt{(x^2 - 1)}}$.

12. $\displaystyle\int_{1}^{2} \frac{\sqrt{(x^2 - 1)}}{x^3}\,dx$.

13. $\displaystyle\int_{-1}^{0} \frac{dx}{(1 + x)^{\frac12}(1 - x)^{\frac32}}$.

14. $\displaystyle\int_{1}^{\infty} \frac{dx}{(2x - 1)\sqrt{(x^2 - x + 1)}}$.

15. $\displaystyle\int_{1}^{\infty} \frac{dx}{(3x - 1)\sqrt{(9x^2 - 6x)}}$.

16. $\displaystyle\int_{2}^{\infty} \frac{dx}{(x - 1)^2\sqrt{(x^2 - 3x + 3)}}$.

§ 198. Trigonometric Substitutions.—Trigonometric substitutions are often useful when the square-root of a quadratic function occurs in the integrand, especially for definite integrals. The object of these substitutions is primarily to transform a given integral into one with a rational trigonometric integrand, because such an integral can always be evaluated (§ 191).

Note, however, that trigonometric substitutions are not always the best. Hyperbolic substitutions are sometimes preferable (see § 253).

§ 199. A few typical substitutions are given below. The square-root of the quadratic function is placed on the left, and is followed by the appropriate substitution :—

$\sqrt{(a^2 - x^2)}$; $x = a \sin \theta$, $dx = a \cos \theta \, d\theta$, $\sqrt{(a^2 - x^2)} = a \cos \theta$.

$\sqrt{(x^2 + a^2)}$; $x = a \tan \theta$, $dx = a \sec^2 \theta \, d\theta$, $\sqrt{(x^2 + a^2)} = a \sec \theta$.

$\sqrt{(x^2 - a^2)}$; $x = a \sec \theta$, $dx = a \sec \theta \tan \theta \, d\theta$, $\sqrt{(x^2 - a^2)} = a \tan \theta$.

$\sqrt{\{(x - a)^2 + b^2\}}$; $x - a = b \tan \theta$, $dx = b \sec^2 \theta \, d\theta$.

$\sqrt{\{x(a - x)\}}$; $x = a \sin^2 \theta$, $dx = 2a \sin \theta \cos \theta \, d\theta$.

$\sqrt{\{(x - a)(b - x)\}}$; $x = a \cos^2 \theta + b \sin^2 \theta$, $dx = 2(b - a) \sin \theta \cos \theta \, d\theta$.

Ex. Evaluate (i) $\displaystyle\int_0^\infty \frac{dx}{(x^2 + a^2)^{\frac{3}{2}}}$; (ii) $\displaystyle\int_0^4 \frac{x^{\frac{3}{2}} \, dx}{\sqrt{(4 - x)}}$.

(i) Put

$$x = a \tan \theta, \quad dx = a \sec^2 \theta \, d\theta, \quad \sqrt{(x^2 + a^2)} = a \sec \theta.$$

When $x = 0$, $\theta = 0$; when $x = \infty$, $\theta = \frac{1}{2}\pi$.

$$\therefore \int_0^\infty \frac{dx}{(x^2 + a^2)^{\frac{3}{2}}} = \int_0^{\frac{\pi}{2}} \frac{a \sec^2 \theta \, d\theta}{a^3 \sec^3 \theta} = \frac{1}{a^2}\int_0^{\frac{\pi}{2}} \cos \theta \, d\theta = \frac{1}{a^2}.$$

(ii) Put

$$x = 4 \sin^2 \theta, \quad dx = 8 \sin \theta \cos \theta \, d\theta.$$

When $x = 0$, $\theta = 0$; when $x = 4$, $\theta = \frac{1}{2}\pi$.

$$\therefore \int_0^4 \frac{x^{\frac{3}{2}} \, dx}{\sqrt{(4 - x)}} = \int_0^{\frac{\pi}{2}} \frac{(4 \sin^2 \theta)^{\frac{3}{2}} \cdot 8 \sin \theta \cos \theta \, d\theta}{\sqrt{(4 \cos^2 \theta)}}$$

$$= 32 \int_0^{\frac{\pi}{2}} \sin^4 \theta \, d\theta = 6\pi.$$

Examples XCII.

Evaluate the given integrals :—

1. $\displaystyle\int \frac{x^2 \, dx}{\sqrt{(1 - x^2)}}$.

2. $\displaystyle\int \frac{dx}{x\sqrt{(x^2 - 1)}}$.

3. $\displaystyle\int \frac{\sqrt{(x^2 - 1)}}{x^3} \, dx$.

4. $\displaystyle\int \frac{dx}{(a^2 - x^2)^{\frac{3}{2}}}$.

5. $\displaystyle\int \frac{dx}{(x^2 + a^2)^{\frac{3}{2}}}$.

6. $\displaystyle\int \frac{dx}{(x^2 - a^2)^{\frac{3}{2}}}$.

7. $\displaystyle\int \sqrt{(4 - x^2)} \, dx$.

8. $\displaystyle\int \sqrt{(x^2 + 1)} \, dx$.

9. $\displaystyle\int (1 - x^2)^{\frac{3}{2}} \, dx$.

10. $\displaystyle\int_{\frac{1}{2}}^1 \frac{\sqrt{(1 - x^2)}}{x^2} \, dx$.

11. $\displaystyle\int_0^a \frac{x^{\frac{5}{2}} \, dx}{\sqrt{(a - x)}}$.

12. $\displaystyle\int_0^a x\left(\frac{a - x}{a + x}\right)^{\frac{1}{2}} dx$.

13. $\displaystyle\int_0^1 x^6 \sqrt{(1 - x^2)} \, dx$.

14. $\displaystyle\int_0^{2a} x^2 \sqrt{(2ax - x^2)} \, dx$.

15. $\displaystyle\int_0^1 \frac{dx}{(x^2 + x + 1)^{\frac{3}{2}}}$.

16. $\displaystyle\int_0^{\frac{1}{2}} \frac{dx}{(1 - 2x^2)^2 \sqrt{(1 - x^2)}}$.

17. $\displaystyle\int_0^1 \frac{dx}{(1 + x^2)\sqrt{(1 - x^2)}}$.

18. $\displaystyle\int_2^\infty \frac{dx}{(x^2 + 1)\sqrt{(x^2 - 3)}}$.

19. $\int_a^b \dfrac{dx}{\sqrt{\{(x-a)(b-x)\}}}.$ 20. $\int_a^b \dfrac{x\,dx}{\sqrt{\{(x-a)(b-x)\}}}.$

21. $\int_a^b \sqrt{\{(x-a)(b-x)\}}dx.$ 22. $\int_a^b x(x-a)^{\frac{1}{2}}(b-x)^{\frac{3}{2}}\,dx.$

Examples XCIII.

In Exs. 1-13, find the areas bounded by the x-axis and the given curves between the given values of x:—

1. $y = x^{-1}$; $x = a, x = b.$ **2.** $y = \tan x$; $x = 0, x = \tfrac{1}{4}\pi.$

3. $y = \log x$; $x = 1, x = a.$ **4.** $y = \sec x$; $x = 0, x = \tfrac{1}{4}\pi.$

5. $y = x \log x$; $x = 0, x = 1.$ **6.** $y = x^2 e^{-x}$; $x = 0, x = \infty.$

7. $y = \dfrac{1}{\sqrt{(2-x^2)}}$; $x = 0, x = 1.$ **8.** $y = \dfrac{1}{\sqrt{(x^2+7)}}$; $x = 0, x = 3.$

9. $y = \dfrac{1}{x^2-1}$; $x = 2, x = \infty.$ **10.** $y = \dfrac{1}{4-x^2}$; $x = 0, x = 1.$

11. $y = \dfrac{1}{x^2 - 6x + 10}$; $x = 2, x = 4.$

12. $y = \dfrac{a^2 b}{(x-a)^2 + b^2}$; $x = -\infty, x = +\infty.$

13. $y = \dfrac{x^2 + x + 1}{x^2 + 1}$; the values of x at the turning points.

14. Find the area of one loop of the curve $y^2 = x^4(4 - x^2).$

15. Find the area enclosed by the curve $a^4 y^2 = x^5(2a - x).$

16. Find the area of the loop of the curve $y^2 = \dfrac{x^2(a-x)}{a+x}.$

In Exs. 17-20 find the volumes generated when the areas bounded by the x-axis and the given curves revolve about the x-axis:—

17. $y = \sin^2 x$; $x = 0, x = \pi.$ **18.** $y = 1 - \cos^3 x$; $x = 0, x = 2\pi.$

19. $y = \log x$; $x = 0, x = 1.$ **20.** $y = \dfrac{a^2 b}{a^2 + x^2}$; $x = -\infty, x = \infty.$

In Exs. 21-26 find the lengths of the given curves between the points where x has the given values:—

21. $y = \tfrac{1}{4}x^2 - \tfrac{1}{2}\log x$; $x = 2, x = 4.$ **22.** $y = 2\sec x$; $x = 0, x = \tfrac{1}{4}\pi.$

23. $y = \log(\sec x)$; $x = 0, x = \tfrac{1}{4}\pi.$ **24.** $y = x^2$; $x = 0, x = 1.$

25. $y = 3\log(x^2 - 9)$; $x = 6, x = 9.$ **26.** $y = \log x$; $x = 1, x = 2.$

In Exs. 27-32 find the areas of the surfaces generated when the given curves, between the given values of x, revolve about the x-axis:—

27. $y = \sin x$; $x = 0, x = \pi.$ **28.** $y = 2\sec x$; $x = 0, x = \tfrac{1}{4}\pi.$

29. $xy = 3$; $x = 1, x = 2.$ **30.** $y = \tfrac{1}{4}x^2 - \tfrac{1}{2}\log x$; $x = 1, x = 2.$

31. $y = x^2$; $x = 0, x = \tfrac{2}{8}.$ **32.** $4x^2 + 3y^2 = 12$; $x = 0, x = \sqrt{3}.$

33. Find the area of the surface generated when the ellipse

$$\frac{x^2}{a^2} + \frac{y^2}{b^2} = 1, \ (a > b),$$

revolves (i) about the x-axis, (ii) about the y axis.

CHAPTER XIV.

IMPLICIT FUNCTIONS. PARTIAL DERIVATIVES.

§ 200. Implicit Functions.—When two variables are connected by an equation which does not express either of them explicitly in terms of the other, each is said to be an *implicit* function of the other. The general equation connecting x and y implicitly may be denoted by $f(x, y) = 0$.

We can sometimes solve such an equation so as to express one of the variables in terms of the other, but this is not always possible, and it is not necessary for the purpose of differentiation. For example, let the equation be

$$x^2 + y^2 = 4. \tag{i}$$

In this case, when x varies, the terms x^2 and y^2 both vary, but their sum remains constant. Hence the rate of change of their sum is zero; thus

$$\frac{d}{dx}(x^2 + y^2) = \frac{d}{dx}(4) = 0,$$

$$\therefore 2x + 2y\frac{dy}{dx} = 0, \tag{ii}$$

$$\therefore \frac{dy}{dx} = -\frac{x}{y}. \tag{iii}$$

Thus dy/dx is found, in terms of x and y.

By differentiating (ii) or (iii) we can find d^2y/dx^2. Thus, if we divide (ii) by 2 and differentiate again, using the product rule to differentiate the second term, we get

$$1 + \frac{dy}{dx} \cdot \frac{dy}{dx} + y\frac{d^2y}{dx^2} = 0, \tag{iv}$$

$$\therefore \frac{d^2y}{dx^2} = -\frac{1 + \left(\dfrac{dy}{dx}\right)^2}{y}. \tag{v}$$

This can be simplified. Using (iii) and (i), we find

$$\frac{d^2y}{dx^2} = -\frac{4}{y^3}. \tag{vi}$$

By differentiating again we could find d^3y/dx^3, d^4y/dx^4, . . .

Rule.—To find dy/dx, differentiate the equation throughout with respect to x, regarding y as a function of x.

To find d^2y/dx^2, differentiate throughout again; and so on.

Ex. Verify that the curve $x^3 - 3xy + y^3 = 3$ passes through the point (2, 1), and at this point find (i) the gradient, (ii) the equation of the tangent, (iii) the radius of curvature.

Let A be the point (2, 1). When we put $x = 2$, $y = 1$, the given equation is satisfied; hence the point A lies on the curve.

(i) Differentiating the equation with respect to x, we get

$$3x^2 - 3\left(y + x\frac{dy}{dx} \right) + 3y^2 \frac{dy}{dx} = \frac{d}{dx}(3) = 0,$$

$$\therefore (x - y^2)\frac{dy}{dx} = x^2 - y, \tag{1}$$

$$\therefore \frac{dy}{dx} = \frac{x^2 - y}{x - y^2}.$$

Putting $x = 2$, $y = 1$, we find at the point A

$$\frac{dy}{dx} = \frac{2^2 - 1}{2 - 1^2} = 3.$$

(ii) By § 26, the equation of the tangent at A is

$$y - 1 = 3(x - 2),$$
$$\therefore y = 3x - 5.$$

(iii) Differentiating equation (1) throughout, we get

$$\left(1 - 2y\frac{dy}{dx} \right)\frac{dy}{dx} + (x - y^2)\frac{d^2y}{dx^2} = 2x - \frac{dy}{dx},$$

$$\therefore \frac{d^2y}{dx^2} = \frac{2\left\{ x - \frac{dy}{dx} + y\left(\frac{dy}{dx}\right)^2 \right\}}{x - y^2}.$$

Putting $x = 2$, $y = 1$, $dy/dx = 3$, we find at the point A

$$\frac{d^2y}{dx^2} = 16,$$

and by § 73 it follows that at the point A

$$\rho = \frac{(1 + 3^2)^{\frac{3}{2}}}{16} = \frac{10\sqrt{10}}{16} = \frac{5\sqrt{10}}{8}.$$

Examples XCIV.

In Exs. 1-11 express dy/dx in terms of x and y, taking logarithms in Exs. 9-11 before differentiating :—

1. $4x^2 - y^2 = 1.$

2. $3x^3 + 2xy^2 = 2y + 3.$

3. $2x^2 + 6xy + y^2 = 1.$

4. $(x - 2)^2 + (y - 3)^2 = 4.$

5. $y = \sin(2x + 3y).$

6. $y = a + xe^y.$

7. $xy = C.$

8. $x^2 \sin y = C.$

9. $x^m y^n = C.$

10. $\sin^m x \cos^n y = C.$

11. $(3x + 2y)^3 = C(2x + y)^4.$

12. If $6x = (1 - y^2)(1 + 2y)$, find the values of y when $x = 0$, and the corresponding values of dy/dx. Sketch the graph.

13. If $x^2 + 2xy + 3y^2 = 1$, prove that $\dfrac{d^2y}{dx^2} = \dfrac{-2}{(x + 3y)^3}$.

14. If $\dfrac{x^2}{a^2} + \dfrac{y^2}{b^2} = 1$, prove that $\dfrac{d^2y}{dx^2} = -\dfrac{b^4}{a^2y^3}$, $\dfrac{d^3y}{dx^3} = -\dfrac{3b^6x}{a^4y^5}$.

15. If $\theta = \alpha + x \sin \theta$, find the values of θ, $d\theta/dx$, and $d^2\theta/dx^2$, when $x = 0$.

16. If $ax^2 + 2hxy + by^2 = 0$, verify that $d^2y/dx^2 = 0$.

In Exs. 17-22 find the gradient and the equation of the tangent at the point whose co-ordinates are given :—

17. $x^2 + y^2 = 10y$; $(4, 2)$.   **18.** $x^3 + 3xy = y^3 + 37$; $(3, 2)$.

19. $y^2(x - 3) = 2x$; $(6, 2)$.   **20.** $y^2(2a - x) = x^3$; (a, a).

21. $y^2 = \dfrac{2x^2}{4 - x}$; $(2, 2)$.   **22.** $\dfrac{1}{x} + \dfrac{1}{y} = \dfrac{1}{2}$; $(3, 6)$.

23. Find the equations of the tangents to the curve
$$2x^2 - 3xy + y^2 = 5$$
at the points where it is cut by the line $3y = 2x + 1$.

24. Find the angle of intersection of the curves
$$y = x^2, \quad 3x^2 + y^2 = 4.$$

25. The tangent to the curve $y^2 = x(2 - x)^2$ at the point $(1, 1)$ cuts the curve at P. Find the equation of the tangent at P.

26. The tangent to the curve $x^3 + y^3 = 9$ at the point $(2, 1)$ cuts the curve at P. Find the co-ordinates of P.

In Exs. 27-35 find the radii of curvature at the points whose co-ordinates are given :—

27. $2x^2 + y^2 = 17$; $(2, 3)$.   **28.** $x^2 + 2xy + 2y^2 = 10$; $(2, 1)$.

29. $x^3 + 3xy + y^3 = 5$; $(1, 1)$.   **30.** $y^2(a^2 - x^2) = a^3x$; $(0, 0)$.

31. $y = mx + ax^2 + bxy + cy^2$; $(0, 0)$.

32. $x^4 + y^3 + x^2 + y^2 = 2a(x + y)$; $(0, 0)$.

33. $ay^2 = x(x - b)(x - c)$; $(0, 0)$, $(b, 0)$ and $(c, 0)$.

34. $\sqrt{x} + \sqrt{y} = \sqrt{a}$; (x, y).

35. $8a^2y^2 = x^2(a^2 - x^2)$; (x, y).

36. Prove that y is a maximum at the point $(0, 1)$, and at the point $(1, 2)$, on the curve
$$x^3 + y^3 - 9xy + 3x^2 + 9x - 2y + 1 = 0.$$

37. Find the radius of curvature, and the co-ordinates of the centre of curvature, at the point $(3, 3)$ on the curve
$$x^3 + y^3 = 6xy.$$

38. Find the co-ordinates of the points of inflexion on the curve
$$x^2y^2 = a^2(a^2 - x^2).$$
[Divide both sides by x^2 before differentiating.]

39. Find the value of x at the points of inflexion on the curve
$$y^2 = \dfrac{x}{1 - x^2}.$$
[Invert both sides before differentiating.]

§ 201. Rates of Change.—When x and y are connected by an equation, explicitly or implicitly, the two sides of the equation remain equal when x and y vary. Consequently, both sides must change at the same rate :—

Rule.—To compare the rates of change of two variables, construct the equation that connects them, and equate the rate of change of the left side to the rate of change of the right side, i.e. *differentiate the equation throughout with respect to the time t.*

Ex. A rod AB, 20 ins. long, slides with its ends on two guides intersecting at right angles in the point O. Find the velocity of the end B when OB = 16 ins. and the velocity of the end A is 8 ins. per sec. (Fig. 97).

Let $x = $ OA, $y = $ OB. Since $OA^2 + OB^2 = AB^2$,
$$\therefore x^2 + y^2 = 20^2. \qquad (i)$$
The rate of change of x is given, and the rate of change of y is to be found.

Differentiating both sides of (i) with respect to t, we get

$$2x\frac{dx}{dt} + 2y\frac{dy}{dt} = 0,$$
$$\therefore \frac{dy}{dt} = -\frac{x}{y}\frac{dx}{dt}.$$

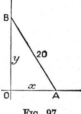

FIG. 97.

When OB $= y = 16$, we have $x = \sqrt{(20^2 - 16^2)} = 12$, and therefore, since $dx/dt = 8$ ins./sec.,
$$\frac{dy}{dt} = -\frac{12}{16} \times 8 = -6 \text{ ins./sec.}$$

§ 202. Differentials.—If x and y are connected by an equation, since the two sides of the equation are always equal to one another, their *differentials* with respect to the same independent variable must be equal. Hence :—

Rule.—To compare the differentials dx and dy, equate the *differential of the left side to that of the right side.*

Ex. P is a variable point on a circle of radius a, centre O ; and C is a fixed point at a distance c from O (Fig. 98). If $\angle$ COP $= \theta$, $\angle$ OCP $= \phi$, express $d\phi$ in terms of $d\theta$.

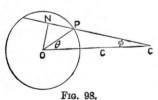

FIG. 98.

First find the equation that connects θ and ϕ. If ON is the perpendicular from O on CP, we have
ON = OC sin OCP = OP sin OPN.
But $\angle$OPN $= \theta + \phi$,
$$\therefore c \sin \phi = a \sin (\theta + \phi).$$
Equating the differentials of both sides, we get
$$c \cos \phi \, d\phi = a \cos (\theta + \phi).(d\theta + d\phi),$$

$$\therefore \; \{c \cos \phi - a \cos (\theta + \phi)\} \, d\phi = a \cos (\theta + \phi) d\theta,$$

$$\therefore \; d\phi = \frac{a \cos (\theta + \phi)}{c \cos \phi - a \cos (\theta + \phi)} \, d\theta.$$

This can be written in the simple form

$$d\phi = \frac{\text{PN}}{\text{CP}} \, d\theta.$$

Examples XCV.

1. The shape of a cone is changing, but so that its volume remains constant. Show that, when the height and diameter of the base are equal, the former is changing twice as fast as the latter.

2. A battleship, steaming due north at 20 knots, is firing at a fixed target which bears 60° E. of N. If the range is 10 nautical miles, at what rate is the range changing in yards per minute ? [One nautical mile=2000 yds., approx.]

3. A point P moves on the circle $x^2 + y^2 = a^2$, so that the x-component of its velocity is constant and equal to u. Find the y-component of its velocity, and the angular velocity of the radius OP, when the co-ordinates of P are (x, y). Also, find the acceleration of the point P.

4. A rod AB slides with its ends on two guides that intersect at 60° in the point O. If AB = 7 ft., find the velocity of A at the instant when OB = 5 ft. and the velocity of B = 22 ft./sec.

5. In the last example find the angular velocity of the rod at the same instant.

6. A point P moves round a circular track of radius 80 ft., centre O, the angular velocity of the radius OP being ω. If A is a point distant 50 ft. from O, and $\angle$ AOP = θ, find the angular velocity of the line AP when $\theta = 0°$, 60°, 180°.

7. A rod AB, of length b, moves with the end B on a circle of radius a, centre C, and the end A on a straight line passing through C (connecting-rod motion). If the radius CB revolves at a constant rate, and if D is the point where AB meets the radius perpendicular to CA, prove that the velocity of the end A is proportional to CD.

8. If $x = r \cos \theta$, and $y = r \sin \theta$, and if r and θ are functions of t, prove that

$$\dot{x} = \dot{r} \cos \theta - r\dot{\theta} \sin \theta, \qquad \dot{y} = \dot{r} \sin \theta + r\dot{\theta} \cos \theta.$$

Also, if $r^2 = x^2 + y^2$, and $\tan \theta = y/x$, and if x and y are functions of t, prove that

$$r\dot{r} = x\dot{x} + y\dot{y}, \qquad r^2\dot{\theta} = x\dot{y} - \dot{x}y.$$

[Dots denote differentiation with respect to t.]

9. A ladder AB, $32\frac{1}{2}$ ft. long, rests with the end A on the ground, and the end B against a wall. If the end A is $12\frac{1}{2}$ ft. from the wall, how far (approximately) does B rise up the wall when A is pushed 1 ft. nearer the wall ?

10. In a triangle ABC, AB = 5, AC = 8. Prove that, when the angle

BAC increases from $\frac{1}{3}\pi$ to $(\frac{1}{3}\pi + \delta\theta)$, the increase in the side BC is $\frac{20\sqrt{3}}{7}\,\delta\theta$, approximately.

11. In a triangle ABC, the side CA changes from b to $(b + \delta b)$, while c and A remain constant. Prove that

$$\delta a \doteqdot \delta b \cos C, \qquad \delta B \doteqdot \delta b \sin C/a, \qquad \delta C \doteqdot -\,\delta b \sin C/a.$$

12. In Fig. 99, P is a variable point on the circle, C is a fixed point, and PN is perpendicular to OA.

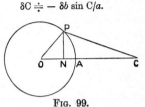

If $\angle AOP = \theta$, arc $AP = s$, $OA = a$, $OC = c$, $ON = x$, $NP = y$, $CP = r$; and if dx, ds, dr denote differentials with respect to θ, prove that

$$-\,a\,dx = y\,ds = \frac{ar\,dr}{c}.$$

Fig. 99.

§ 203. Maxima and Minima.

We sometimes need to find a maximum or minimum value of a function of two variables when these are connected implicitly by an equation that cannot easily be solved to express one variable in terms of the other. We can then proceed as in the following example :—

Ex. If $z = x^2 + y^2$, find the stationary values of z when x and y are connected by the equation

$$5x^2 + 5y^2 - 6xy = 8. \tag{i}$$

The equation (i) defines y implicitly as a function of x. We may therefore regard z as a function of x,

$$\therefore \frac{dz}{dx} = 2\left(x + y\,\frac{dy}{dx}\right). \tag{ii}$$

It follows that, when z is stationary,

$$x + y\,\frac{dy}{dx} = 0. \tag{iii}$$

Again, differentiating (i), we have

$$10x + 10y\,\frac{dy}{dx} - 6\left(y + x\,\frac{dy}{dx}\right) = 0,$$

$$\therefore 5x - 3y + (5y - 3x)\,\frac{dy}{dx} = 0. \tag{iv}$$

This equation holds good always. Hence, both (iii) and (iv) hold good when z is stationary. Eliminating dy/dx from them, we find that, when z is stationary,

$$y^2 = x^2,$$
$$\therefore y = x, \tag{v}$$
$$\text{or } y = -x. \tag{vi}$$

From (v) and (i) we find

$$x^2 = 2, \qquad y^2 = 2,$$
$$\therefore z = 4.$$

From (vi) and (i), we find

$$x^2 = \tfrac{1}{2}, \qquad y^2 = \tfrac{1}{2},$$
$$\therefore z = 1.$$

Hence the stationary values of z are 4 and 1.

Examples XCVI.

1. If $z = x^2 + y^2$, find the stationary values of z when x and y are connected by the equation

$$14x^2 - 4xy + 11y^2 = 60.$$

2. If x and y are connected by the equation

$$\sqrt{(x^2 + 16)} + \sqrt{(y^2 + 36)} = 15,$$

and if $z = 3x + 4y$, verify that z is a maximum when $x = 3$, $y = 8$.

3. If $z = x + y$, and if $\dfrac{1}{x} + \dfrac{1}{y} = \dfrac{1}{f}$, where f is a positive constant, prove that z is a minimum when $x = y = 2f$.

4. If $\tan \phi = 3 \tan \theta$, and if $z = \phi - \theta$, prove that z is a maximum when $\theta = 30°$, $\phi = 60°$.

5. If the total surface area of a circular cylinder is constant, prove that its volume is a maximum when the height and diameter are equal.

6. If the sum of the areas of the surfaces of a cube and a sphere is constant, prove that the sum of their volumes is least when an edge of the cube is equal to the diameter of the sphere.

7. Find the area of the greatest piece of ground, in the form of a right-angled triangle, that can be enclosed by a mile of fencing.

8. The sides of a quadrilateral are given. Prove that the area is a maximum when the quadrilateral is cyclic.

[Express the area in terms of two opposite angles.]

§ 204. Functions of Two or More Independent Variables.—A variable may be a function of two or more independent variables. For example, if S is the area of a triangle ABC, we have $S = \tfrac{1}{2}bc \sin A$, so that S may be regarded as a function of b, c, and A, each of which may be varied independently of the others.

Again, the pressure p of a gas may be regarded as a function of the volume v and the temperature t, either of which may be varied independently of the other.

§ 205. Partial Derivatives.—If z is a function of other independent variables besides x, the derivative of z with respect to x is called the *partial derivative* of z with respect to x. Interpreted as a rate of change, it is the rate at which z changes with respect to x while the other independent variables remain constant.

Let z be a function of two independent variables x and y, denoted by $z = f(x, y)$.   Then z has a partial derivative with respect to x and one with respect to y.   The notation for these partial derivatives is

$$\frac{\partial z}{\partial x}, \frac{\partial z}{\partial y}; \quad \left(\frac{dz}{dx}\right)_y, \left(\frac{dz}{dy}\right)_x; \quad \frac{\partial f}{\partial x}, \frac{\partial f}{\partial y}; \quad \text{or} \quad f_x', f_y'.$$

Ex. If
$$z = y \sin (xy),$$
$$\frac{\partial z}{\partial x} = y^2 \cos (xy), \qquad \frac{\partial z}{\partial y} = \sin (xy) + xy \cos (xy).$$

If u is a function of three independent variables x, y, z, denoted by $u = f(x, y, z)$, then u has a partial derivative with respect to each independent variable.   The notation for the three partial derivatives is usually

$$\frac{\partial u}{\partial x}, \frac{\partial u}{\partial y}, \frac{\partial u}{\partial z}; \quad \frac{\partial f}{\partial x}, \frac{\partial f}{\partial y}, \frac{\partial f}{\partial z}; \quad \text{or} \quad f_x', f_y', f_z'.$$

Examples XCVII.

In Exs. 1-9 find $\dfrac{\partial z}{\partial x}$ and $\dfrac{\partial z}{\partial y}$:—

1. $z = xy$.

2. $z = x^2 y^3$.

3. $z = \sin (ax + by)$.

4. $z = \dfrac{y}{x}$.

5. $z = \tan \dfrac{y}{x}$.

6. $z = \tan^{-1} \dfrac{y}{x}$.

7. $z = \dfrac{x}{x - y}$.

8. $z = \dfrac{x^2 - y^2}{x^2 + y^2}$.

9. $z = \dfrac{1}{(x^2 + y^2)^n}$.

10. If $u = e^{-ax} \cos (pt - bx)$, find $\dfrac{\partial u}{\partial x}$ and $\dfrac{\partial u}{\partial t}$.

11. If $v = \dfrac{1}{r}$, and $r = \sqrt{(x^2 + y^2 + z^2)}$, find $\dfrac{\partial v}{\partial x}, \dfrac{\partial v}{\partial y}, \dfrac{\partial v}{\partial z}$.

12. If $z = f(x + ay)$, prove that $\dfrac{\partial z}{\partial y} = a \dfrac{\partial z}{\partial x}$.

13. If $z = \dfrac{1}{x^2 + xy + y^2}$, prove that $x \dfrac{\partial z}{\partial x} + y \dfrac{\partial z}{\partial y} = -2z$.

14. If $z = x^n f\left(\dfrac{y}{x}\right)$, prove that $x \dfrac{\partial z}{\partial x} + y \dfrac{\partial z}{\partial y} = nz$.

15. If $r^2 = x^2 + y^2$, and $\tan \theta = y/x$, prove that

$$\frac{\partial r}{\partial x} = \frac{x}{r}, \quad \frac{\partial r}{\partial y} = \frac{y}{r}, \quad \frac{\partial \theta}{\partial x} = -\frac{y}{r^2}, \quad \frac{\partial \theta}{\partial y} = \frac{x}{r^2}.$$

16. If $\theta = t^n e^{-v}$, where $v = r^2/4t$, prove that

$$\frac{1}{r^2} \frac{\partial}{\partial r}\left(r^2 \frac{\partial \theta}{\partial r}\right) = \frac{\partial \theta}{\partial t},$$

provided the constant n has a certain value.   Find it.

§ 206. **Geometrical Meaning of Partial Derivatives.**—Let OX,

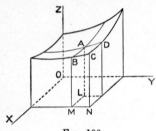

OY be two rectangular axes in a horizontal plane ; let A be any point on a surface, and AL the perpendicular from A on the horizontal plane.

Let (x, y) be the co-ordinates of L, and let $z = AL$ (Fig. 100).

Then z is a function of x and y, and the partial derivatives $\dfrac{\partial z}{\partial x}, \dfrac{\partial z}{\partial y}$ are the gradients of the sections AB, AD of the surface,

Fig. 100.

made by planes parallel to the planes XOZ, YOZ, respectively.

Thus, if OX points due east, and OY due north, and if the surface is the surface of a hill, the partial derivatives are the gradients of the hill in the easterly and northerly directions, respectively.

§ 207. **Total Differential of a Function of Two Variables.**—Let z be a function of two independent variables x and y, and let δz be the change in z caused by *small* independent changes δx and δy in x and y. To prove geometrically that

$$\delta z \doteqdot \frac{\partial z}{\partial x}\delta x + \frac{\partial z}{\partial y}\delta y. \tag{1}$$

Proof.—In Fig. 100, let the co-ordinates of L, M, N be

$$(x, y), \quad (x + \delta x, y), \quad (x + \delta x, y + \delta y)$$

respectively, and let $z_A = AL$, $z_B = BM$, $z_C = CN$. Also, let the letter A or B, used as a suffix to a gradient, indicate that the gradient refers to the point A or B, respectively.

Now $(z_B - z_A) = $ the change in z from A to B. Hence, by (1), § 75,

$$z_B - z_A \doteqdot \left(\frac{\partial z}{\partial x}\right)_A \delta x.$$

Again, $(z_C - z_B) = $ the change in z from B to C. Hence,

$$z_C - z_B \doteqdot \left(\frac{\partial z}{\partial y}\right)_B \delta y.$$

By addition,

$$z_C - z_A \doteqdot \left(\frac{\partial z}{\partial x}\right)_A \delta x + \left(\frac{\partial z}{\partial y}\right)_B \delta y.$$

But $\delta z = z_{\text{C}} - z_{\text{A}}$; and $\left(\dfrac{\partial z}{\partial y}\right)_{\text{B}} \doteqdot \left(\dfrac{\partial z}{\partial y}\right)_{\text{A}}$ since δx is small,

$$\therefore\ \delta z \doteqdot \left(\frac{\partial z}{\partial x}\right)_{\text{A}} \delta x + \left(\frac{\partial z}{\partial y}\right)_{\text{A}} \delta y.$$

This is the desired result when we leave out the suffix A, which is no longer needed.

As δx and δy get smaller and smaller, the approximation (1) becomes more and more accurate, in the sense that the ratio of the left side to the right side approaches unity. The ultimate form of (1) when δx, δy, and δz are all "infinitely small" is written

$$dz = \frac{\partial z}{\partial x}dx + \frac{\partial z}{\partial y}dy. \tag{2}$$

In this form, dx, dy, dz are called *differentials* and dz is called the *total* or *exact differential* of z (compare § 77).

The above theorem can be generalised. Thus, if u is a function of three independent variables x, y, z, and if δu is the change in u caused by small independent changes δx, δy, δz in x, y, z, we have

$$\delta u \doteqdot \frac{\partial u}{\partial x}\delta x + \frac{\partial u}{\partial y}\delta y + \frac{\partial u}{\partial z}\delta z. \tag{3}$$

§ 208. Application to Small Errors.

Ex. 1.   If a, b are the sides, and c the hypotenuse. of a right-angled triangle, find the approximate error in c due to small errors δa, δb in a, b respectively.

Since
$$c^2 = a^2 + b^2,$$
$$\therefore\ \delta(c^2) \doteqdot \frac{\partial(c^2)}{\partial a}\delta a + \frac{\partial(c^2)}{\partial b}\delta b,$$
$$\therefore\ 2c\delta c \doteqdot 2a\delta a + 2b\delta b,$$
$$\therefore\ \delta c \doteqdot \frac{a\delta a + b\delta b}{c}.$$

Ex. 2.   If T is calculated from the formula $\mathrm{T} = 2\pi\sqrt{(l/g)}$, find the proportional error in T due to small errors δl in l, and δg in g.

Taking logarithms, we have

$$\log \mathrm{T} = \log (2\pi) + \tfrac{1}{2}\log l - \tfrac{1}{2}\log g,$$
$$\therefore\ \delta(\log \mathrm{T}) \doteqdot \tfrac{1}{2}\frac{\delta l}{l} - \tfrac{1}{2}\frac{\delta g}{g},$$
$$\therefore\ \frac{\delta \mathrm{T}}{\mathrm{T}} \doteqdot \tfrac{1}{2}\left(\frac{\delta l}{l} - \frac{\delta g}{g}\right).$$

Examples XCVIII.

In Exs. 1-10 find the total differential of z :—

1. $z = xy$.

2. $z = ax + by$.

3. $z = x^3 + 2xy^2$.

4. $z = r \cos \theta$.

5. $z = e^{ax + by}$.

6. $z = x \log (3x + y)$.

7. $z = \dfrac{y}{x}$.

8. $z = \dfrac{1}{xy}$.

9. $z = \dfrac{\cos \theta}{r}$.

10. $z = \dfrac{xy}{x + y}$.

11. If $z = \sin^m x \cos^n y$, prove that $dz = z(m \cot x \, dx - n \tan y \, dy)$.

12. If $z = \dfrac{\tan^2 \theta}{\tan^2 \phi}$, prove that $\dfrac{dz}{z} = 4\left(\dfrac{d\theta}{\sin 2\theta} - \dfrac{d\phi}{\sin 2\phi} \right)$.

13. The formula $A = \frac{1}{2}r^2\theta$ is used to calculate the area of a sector of a circle. Find the error δA in A due to small errors δr, $\delta \theta$ in r, θ respectively. Illustrate geometrically.

14. If small errors δa, δh are made in measuring the base and altitude of a triangle, prove that the proportional error in the calculated area S is given by

$$\frac{\delta S}{S} \doteq \frac{\delta a}{a} + \frac{\delta h}{h}.$$

15. The diameter, D ins., of a pipe needed to give a discharge of G gallons of water per hour is given by

$$D = \frac{1}{15}\left(\frac{G^2 L}{H} \right)^{\frac{1}{5}},$$

where L = length of pipe in yards, H = head of water in feet.

If G is increased by 12 per cent., and H decreased by 6 per cent., find the approximate percentage increase in D.

16. If $Q = \frac{2}{3}(5b - h)h^{\frac{3}{2}}$, and if δQ is the error in Q due to small errors δb in b and δh in h, prove that

$$\frac{\delta Q}{Q} \doteq \frac{5\{2h\delta b + (3b - h)\delta h\}}{2h(5b - h)}.$$

17. The formula $S = \frac{1}{2}bc \sin A$ gives the area of a triangle ABC in terms of b, c, A. Find the partial derivatives of S with respect to b, c, A, regarding these as independent variables, and verify your results geometrically.

Also, prove that, if δb, δc, δA are small errors in b, c, A, the proportional error in S is given by

$$\frac{\delta S}{S} = \frac{\delta b}{b} + \frac{\delta c}{c} + \cot A \delta A.$$

18. If δb, δc, δA are small errors in two of the sides and the included angle of a triangle, prove that the consequent error in the third side a is given by

$$\delta a \doteq \delta b \cos C + \delta c \cos B + \frac{bc}{a} \sin A \delta A.$$

19. If small changes δa, δb, δc occur in the sides of a triangle, and if δA, δB, δC are the consequent changes in the angles, prove that

$$2S\delta A \doteq a(\delta a - \delta b \cos C - \delta c \cos B),$$

where S = the area. Also, verify that $\delta A + \delta B + \delta C = 0$.

20. Express the area S of a triangle ABC in terms of a, B, and C, and prove that

$$\frac{\delta S}{S} \div \frac{2\delta a}{a} + \frac{c\delta B}{a \sin B} + \frac{b\delta C}{a \sin C}.$$

§ 209. Differentiation of a Function of Functions.

—Let z be a function of x and y, and let x and y be functions of t. Then z is a function of t through x and y.

Let δx, δy, δz be the changes in x, y, z respectively, caused by a change δt in t. Then, dividing (1) by δt, we get

$$\frac{\delta z}{\delta t} \div \frac{\partial z}{\partial x}\frac{\delta x}{\delta t} + \frac{\partial z}{\partial y}\frac{\delta y}{\delta t}, \tag{4}$$

and in the limit, when $\delta t \to 0$,

$$\frac{dz}{dt} = \frac{\partial z}{\partial x}\frac{dx}{dt} + \frac{\partial z}{\partial y}\frac{dy}{dt}. \tag{5}$$

In particular, if $z = f(x, y)$ and y is a function of x, we find, by putting $t = x$ in (5),

$$\frac{dz}{dx} = \frac{\partial f}{\partial x} + \frac{\partial f}{\partial y}\frac{dy}{dx}. \tag{6}$$

We can apply (6) to find dy/dx from an equation of the form

$$f(x, y) = \text{Const.}$$

For, differentiating with respect to x, we get

$$\frac{\partial f}{\partial x} + \frac{\partial f}{\partial y}\frac{dy}{dx} = 0,$$

$$\therefore \frac{dy}{dx} = - \frac{\dfrac{\partial f}{\partial x}}{\dfrac{\partial f}{\partial y}}. \tag{7}$$

Ex. If $x^3 - 3xy + y^3 = 3$, find dy/dx. (See also Ex. § 200.)

Put $\qquad f(x, y) = x^3 - 3xy + y^3.$

Then $\qquad \dfrac{\partial f}{\partial x} = 3x^2 - 3y, \quad \dfrac{\partial f}{\partial y} = -3x + 3y^2,$

$$\therefore \frac{dy}{dx} = - \frac{3x^2 - 3y}{-3x + 3y^2} = \frac{x^2 - y}{x - y^2}.$$

§ 210. Tangent and Normal to a Curve at any Point.

—Let P be any point on a curve. Let (x, y) be the (temporarily fixed) co-ordinates of P; and let (X, Y) be the current co-ordinates of a point on the tangent at P.

Then, by § 26, the equation of this tangent is

$$Y - y = \frac{dy}{dx}(X - x). \tag{8}$$

The equation of the normal at P is

$$Y - y = -\frac{dx}{dy}(X - x). \tag{9}$$

If the equation of the curve is given in the form

$$f(x, y) = \text{Const.}$$

by means of (7) we can write the equation of the tangent in the form

$$(X - x)\frac{\partial f}{\partial x} + (Y - y)\frac{\partial f}{\partial y} = 0, \tag{10}$$

and the equation of the normal in the form

$$\frac{X - x}{\dfrac{\partial f}{\partial x}} = \frac{Y - y}{\dfrac{\partial f}{\partial y}}. \tag{11}$$

Ex. Find the equations of the tangent and normal to the curve

$$x^3 + y^3 = a^3. \tag{i}$$

at the point (x, y). Also find the length of the perpendicular from the origin on the tangent.

By (10), the equation of the tangent is

$$(X - x)3x^2 + (Y - y)3y^2 = 0,$$

or

$$x^2X + y^2Y = x^3 + y^3,$$

or, by (i),

$$x^2X + y^2Y = a^3.$$

The length of the perpendicular from the origin on the tangent is therefore

$$\frac{a^3}{\sqrt{(x^4 + y^4)}}.$$

The equation of the normal is

$$\frac{X - x}{x^2} = \frac{Y - y}{y^2}.$$

Examples XCIX.

In Exs. 1-6, find dy/dx by applying formula (7) :—

1. $ax^2 + 2hxy + by^2 + 2gx + 2fy + c = 0.$
2. $(x + 2y)^3 = 3axy.$ 3. $(x^2 + y^2)^2 = a^2(x^2 - y^2).$
4. $y = \cos(x + y).$ 5. $\cos x = x \cos y.$ 6. $ax^y = by^x.$
7. If $z = \log(x + y)$, and $y^2 = x^2 + c$, find dz/dx.

In Exs. 8-13, find the equations of the tangents and normals to the given curves at the point (x, y) :—

    8. $y^2 = 4ax.$ **9.** $ay^2 = x^3.$ **10.** $x^3 - 3axy + y^3 = 0.$

    11. $x^m y^n = c.$ **12.** $ax^2 + by^2 = 1.$ **13.** $x^n + y^n = a^n.$

    14. Any tangent to the curve $x^{\frac{2}{3}} + y^{\frac{2}{3}} = a^{\frac{2}{3}}$ cuts the co-ordinate axes in A and B. Prove that $OA^2 + OB^2 = $ constant.

    15. The tangent to the curve $b^2 y^2 = x^2(a^2 - x^2)$ at the point (x, y) cuts the y-axis in the point B. Prove that $OB = x^4/b^2 y.$

    16. Prove that the tangent to the curve $(x + y)^4 = ax^3$ at any point (x, y) passes through the point $\left(-\dfrac{x}{3}, \dfrac{x}{3} \right).$

    17. In the conic $ax^2 + by^2 = 1$, prove that the subnormal is proportional to x, and the subtangent to $y^2/x.$

    18. In the curve $x^m y^n = c$, prove that the ratio of the subtangent to the abscissa is $n : m.$ Hence give a geometrical construction for drawing the tangent at any point.

    19. In the curve $4x = 1 - y^2 + 2 \log y$, prove that the sum of the tangent and subtangent is constant, when $y < 1.$

    20. The normal to the curve $x^3 + y^3 = a^3$ at any point P meets the co-ordinate axes in A and B. Prove that the area of the triangle OAB is equal to the square of the perpendicular from P on the line $y = x.$

    21. If the two curves $f(x, y) = 0$, $\phi(x, y) = 0$ intersect orthogonally, prove that the co-ordinates of the points of intersection satisfy the equation

$$\frac{\partial f}{\partial x} \frac{\partial \phi}{\partial x} + \frac{\partial f}{\partial y} \frac{\partial \phi}{\partial y} = 0.$$

Prove that the two curves

$$x^3 - 3xy^2 = a^3, \quad 3x^2 y - y^3 = b^3$$

intersect orthogonally.

    22. Prove that the two parabolas

$$y^2 = 4a(a + x), \quad y^2 = 4b(b - x)$$

intersect orthogonally.

    23. If x, y, z are three variables connected by an equation $f(x, y, z) = 0$, prove that

$$\left(\frac{\partial y}{\partial z} \right)_x \times \left(\frac{\partial z}{\partial x} \right)_y \times \left(\frac{\partial x}{\partial y} \right)_z = -1.$$

    24. The z-axis being vertical, prove that the gradient, at any point (x, y, z), of the section of the surface $z = f(x, y)$ made by a vertical plane inclined at an angle ϕ to the zx plane, is

$$\frac{\partial z}{\partial x} \cos \phi + \frac{\partial z}{\partial y} \sin \phi.$$

Deduce that the maximum gradient at that point is

$$\left\{ \left(\frac{\partial z}{\partial x} \right)^2 + \left(\frac{\partial z}{\partial y} \right)^2 \right\}^{\frac{1}{2}}.$$

Find the gradient of the " line of greatest slope " at the point $(2, 1, 11)$ on the surface $z = 2x^2 + 3y^2.$

CHAPTER XV.

PARAMETRIC EQUATIONS.

§ 211. Parametric Equations.—When x and y are both expressed in terms of a third variable t (say), this third variable is called a *parameter*. The equations that express x and y in terms of the parameter are called *parametric equations*.

The equation connecting x and y can be obtained by eliminating t from the parametric equations.

The point on the (x, y) graph that corresponds to the value t of the parameter is called " the point t."

Ex. The equations $x = at^2$, $y = 2at$ are parametric equations of the parabola $y^2 = 4\,ax$.

The equations $x = a \cos \theta$, $y = a \sin \theta$ are parametric equations of the circle $x^2 + y^2 = a^2$.

§ 212. When x and y are given as functions of t, we can regard y as a function of x through t. The first differential coefficient dy/dx is given by

$$\frac{dy}{dx} = \frac{dy}{dt}\frac{dt}{dx} = \frac{dy}{dt} \bigg/ \frac{dx}{dt} = \frac{\dot{y}}{\dot{x}}. \tag{1}$$

The " dot " notation is often used to indicate differentiation with respect to any parameter.

For the second differential coefficient, we have

$$\frac{d^2y}{dx^2} = \frac{d}{dx}\left(\frac{\dot{y}}{\dot{x}}\right) = \frac{d}{dt}\left(\frac{\dot{y}}{\dot{x}}\right) \times \frac{dt}{dx} = \frac{\dot{x}\ddot{y} - \ddot{x}\dot{y}}{\dot{x}^2} \times \frac{1}{\dot{x}},$$

$$\therefore \frac{d^2y}{dx^2} = \frac{\dot{x}\ddot{y} - \ddot{x}\dot{y}}{\dot{x}^3}. \tag{2}$$

From § 73 it follows that the *radius of curvature* of the (x, y) graph at the point t is given by

$$\frac{1}{\rho} = \frac{\dot{x}\ddot{y} - \ddot{x}\dot{y}}{\dot{x}^3}\left\{1 + \left(\frac{\dot{y}}{\dot{x}}\right)^2\right\}^{\frac{3}{2}},$$

$$\therefore \frac{1}{\rho} = \frac{\dot{x}\ddot{y} - \ddot{x}\dot{y}}{(\dot{x}^2 + \dot{y}^2)^{\frac{3}{2}}}. \tag{3}$$

Further, at a point of inflexion, $\rho = \infty$,

$$\therefore \; \dot{x}\ddot{y} - \ddot{x}\dot{y} = 0. \qquad (4)$$

Ex. 1. Find the equations of the tangent and normal to the curve $x = t^2$, $y = 3t$, at the point $t = 1$.

We have
$$\frac{dy}{dx} = \frac{\dot{y}}{\dot{x}} = \frac{3}{2t}.$$

Hence, at the point $t = 1$, $x = 1$, $y = 3$, $dy/dx = \frac{3}{2}$. The equation of the tangent at this point is therefore

$$y - 3 = \tfrac{3}{2}(x - 1),$$
that is, $\qquad\qquad 3x - 2y + 3 = 0.$

The equation of the normal is

$$y - 3 = -\tfrac{2}{3}(x - 1),$$
that is, $\qquad\qquad 2x + 3y - 11 = 0.$

Ex. 2. Find the radius of curvature of the ellipse
$$x = a \cos \phi, \qquad y = b \sin \phi,$$

at the point ϕ, and in particular at the points $\phi = 0$, $\phi = \frac{1}{2}\pi$.
Using dots to indicate differentiation with respect to ϕ,

$$\dot{x} = -a \sin \phi, \qquad \dot{y} = b \cos \phi,$$
$$\ddot{x} = -a \cos \phi, \qquad \ddot{y} = -b \sin \phi,$$
$$\therefore \; \dot{x}^2 + \dot{y}^2 = a^2 \sin^2 \phi + b^2 \cos^2 \phi,$$
$$\dot{x}\ddot{y} - \ddot{x}\dot{y} = ab(\sin^2 \phi + \cos^2 \phi) = ab,$$
$$\therefore \; \rho = \frac{(a^2 \sin^2 \phi + b^2 \cos^2 \phi)^{\frac{3}{2}}}{ab}.$$

Hence, when $\phi = 0$, $\rho = b^2/a$; when $\phi = \frac{1}{2}\pi$, $\rho = a^2/b$.

Examples C.

In Exs. 1-8, find dy/dx in terms of the parameter. Also, find the equation connecting x and y :—

1. $x = 2t - 3$, $y = 4t$.
2. $x = 1 - t^2$, $y = t(1 - t^2)$.
3. $x = t^2 + 1$, $y = t^3 + 2$.
4. $x = 2t + 1$, $y = 4t(t - 1)$.
5. $x = a \sec \theta$, $y = b \tan \theta$.
6. $x = a \cos^3 \theta$, $y = a \sin^3 \theta$.
7. $x = \dfrac{3t}{1 + t^3}$, $y = \dfrac{3t^2}{1 + t^3}$.
8. $x = c \log t$, $y = \dfrac{c}{2}\left(t + \dfrac{1}{t}\right)$.

In Exs. 9-12, find the equations of the tangent and normal at the point where the parameter has the given value :—

9. $x = 3t$, $y = 4t^{-1}$; $(t = 2)$.
10. $x = 4t^2 + t + 2$, $y = t^2 - 2t + 3$; $(t = 0)$.
11. $x = 2 \sin \theta$, $y = \cos 2\theta$; $(\theta = \frac{1}{6}\pi)$.
12. $x = \dfrac{3at}{1 + t^3}$, $y = \dfrac{3at^2}{1 + t^3}$; $(t = 2)$.

In Exs. 13-17, find the radius of curvature at the given point :—

13. $x = 3t$, $y = 5t^{-1}$; $(t = 2)$.

14. $x = (\lambda + 1)^2$, $y = \lambda^2 - \lambda + 1$; $(\lambda = 5)$.

15. $x = t^2$, $y = t - \frac{1}{3}t^3$; at the point t.

16. $x = 4e^u$, $y = e^{2u} - 2u$; at the point u.

17. $x = \theta + \sin \theta \cos \theta$, $y = 4 \cos \theta$; at the point θ.

18. In the parabola $x = at^2$, $y = 2at$, if the normal at P meets the x-axis in G, prove that the radius of curvature at P is proportional to PG³.

19. In the ellipse $x = a \cos \phi$, $y = b \sin \phi$, if C is the centre, P the point ϕ, D the point $(\phi + \frac{1}{2}\pi)$, ρ the radius of curvature at P, and if the normal at P meets the x-axis in G, prove that

$$\rho = \frac{CD^3}{ab} = \frac{a^2 PG^3}{b^4}.$$

20. In the curve $x = 2a(t - \frac{1}{3}t^3)$, $y = 2at^2$, prove that $t = \tan \frac{1}{2}\psi$, and $\rho = a \sec^4 \frac{1}{2}\psi$, where ψ is the angle made by the tangent at the point t with the x-axis, and ρ is the radius of curvature at the same point.

21. In the trochoid $x = a\theta - c \sin \theta$, $y = a - c \cos \theta$, show that the points of inflexion occur at $\theta = \cos^{-1}(c/a)$. [See § 215.]

22. Prove that the co-ordinates of the points of inflexion on the curve $x = 2a \sec \theta$, $y = 2a \sec \theta \tan \theta$ are $x = \pm a\sqrt{6}$, $y = \pm a\sqrt{3}$.

23. If $x = a (\cos \theta + \theta \sin \theta)$, $y = a (\sin \theta - \theta \cos \theta)$, prove that

$$\frac{dy}{dx} = \tan \theta, \quad \frac{dx}{dy} = \cot \theta.$$

$$\frac{d^2y}{dx^2} = \frac{1}{a\theta \cos^3 \theta}, \quad \frac{d^2x}{dy^2} = - \frac{1}{a\theta \sin^3 \theta}.$$

24. If $x = 2a \cos \theta - b \cos 2\theta$, $y = 2a \sin \theta - b \sin 2\theta$, prove that

$$\frac{d^2y}{dx^2} = \frac{a^2 + 2b^2 - 3ab \cos \theta}{2(- a \sin \theta + b \sin 2\theta)^3}, \quad \frac{d^2x}{dy^2} = \frac{a^2 + 2b^2 - 3ab \cos \theta}{2(- a \cos \theta + b \cos 2\theta)^3}.$$

25. The co-ordinates of a moving point are given in terms of the time t by the equations $x = a(1 - \cos t) \cos t$, $y = a(1 - \cos t) \sin t$.

Prove that, at time t, its resultant velocity is $2a \sin \dfrac{t}{2}$, and its resultant acceleration $a\sqrt{(5 - 4 \cos t)}$.

26. The co-ordinates of a moving point P are given in terms of the time t by the equations $x = r \cos nt$, $y = r \sin nt$, where r is a function of t, and n a constant.

Prove that the angular velocity of the radius vector OP is constant, the resultant velocity of the point P at time t is $\sqrt{(\dot{r}^2 + n^2 r^2)}$, and the resultant acceleration is $\sqrt{\{(\ddot{r} - n^2 r)^2 + 4n^2 \dot{r}^2\}}$.

§ 213. The Tangent and Normal at any Point.

—Let the co-ordinates (x, y) of any point on a curve be given as functions of a parameter t ; and let (X, Y) be the co-ordinates of any point on the tangent at the point t. Then the equation of this tangent is, by § 26,

$$Y - y = \frac{\dot{y}}{\dot{x}}(X - x),$$

or $\qquad\qquad \dot{y}(X - x) = \dot{x}(Y - y).$ $\qquad\qquad$ (5)

The equation of the normal at the same point is

$$\dot{x}(X - x) + \dot{y}(Y - y) = 0. \qquad\qquad (6)$$

Ex. Find the equation of the tangent at the point t on the curve given by $x = t^2$, $y = t^3$. Also, find the value of the parameter at the point where this tangent cuts the curve again.

By (5), the equation of the tangent at the point t is

$$3t^2(X - t^2) = 2t(Y - t^3),$$

or $\qquad\qquad 2(Y - t^3) - 3t(X - t^2) = 0.$ $\qquad\qquad$ (i)

Let u be the value of the parameter at any point where this tangent meets the curve. Then the co-ordinates of this point are (u^2, u^3), and since it lies on (i),

$$\therefore\; 2(u^3 - t^3) - 3t(u^2 - t^2) = 0.$$

This is a cubic equation in u. Two of its roots are known to be equal to t, because the tangent (i) meets the curve in two coincident points at the point t. Let the third root be α. Then

$$\text{sum of roots} = \alpha + 2t = -\frac{\text{coeff. of } u^2}{\text{coeff. of } u^3} = \frac{3t}{2},$$

$$\therefore\; \alpha = -\tfrac{1}{2}t.$$

This is the value of the parameter where the tangent at the point t meets the curve again.

Examples CI.

In Exs. 1-4 find the equations of the tangent and normal to the given curves :—

1. $x = at^2$, $y = 2at$; at the point t.
2. $x = a\cos\phi$, $y = b\sin\phi$; at the point ϕ.
3. $x = a\sec\theta$, $y = b\tan\theta$; at the point θ.
4. $x = a\cos^3\theta$, $y = a\sin^3\theta$; at the point θ.
5. The normal to the parabola $x = at^2$, $y = 2at$ at the point t meets the curve again at P. Find the value of the parameter at P.
6. The normal to the curve $x^3 = ay^2$ at the point (at^2, at^3) meets the curve again in points where the values of the parameter are u and v. Prove that $u^{-1} + v^{-1} + t^{-1} = 0$.
7. Find the equation of a straight line which is both a tangent and a normal to the curve $y^2 = x^3$. [Put $x = t^2$, $y = t^3$.]
8. The tangent at the point λ to the curve

$$x = \frac{3a}{\lambda^3 + 1}, \qquad y = \frac{3a\lambda}{\lambda^3 + 1},$$

meets the curve again at P. Find the value of the parameter at P.

9. If OA, OB are the intercepts made on the co-ordinate axes by a tangent to the curve

$$x = \frac{2a}{1 + t^2}, \quad y = \frac{2at^3}{1 + t^2},$$

find the maximum area of the triangle OAB.

10. If p, q are the perpendiculars from the origin on the tangent and normal to the curve $x^{\frac{2}{3}} + y^{\frac{2}{3}} = a^{\frac{2}{3}}$ at any point, prove that $4p^2 + q^2 = a^2$. [Put $x = a \cos^3 \theta$, $y = a \sin^3 \theta$.]

11. Find the equation of the locus of the point of intersection of two perpendicular tangents to the curve $4y^3 = 27ax^2$. [Put $x = 2at^3$, $y = 3at^2$.]

12. Express the co-ordinates of any point on the curve $y^2 = x^2(1 + x)$ in terms of the parameter m, where $y = mx$.

If P, Q are two points on the curve such that the angle POQ is a right angle, prove that the equation of the locus of the point of intersection of the tangents at P and Q is $2y^2 = x^3$.

§ 214. The Cycloid.

—The cycloid is the curve described by a point on the circumference of a circle rolling on a straight line.

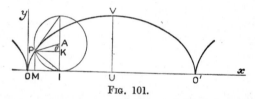

FIG. 101.

Let a circle of radius a, centre A, roll along the axis of x, starting with the point P of the circumference at the origin; and let (x, y) be the co-ordinates of P when the circle has rolled through an angle θ radians (Fig. 101). Then

$$x = OM = OI - MI, \quad y = MP = IK = IA - KA.$$

Now PA makes an angle θ with the vertical, because PA was vertical at the start and has turned through an angle θ; therefore, since the arc PI has rolled off OI,

$$OI = \text{arc } PI = a\theta.$$

Also $\quad MI = PK = a \sin \theta, \quad IA = a, \quad KA = a \cos \theta.$

$$\therefore x = a\theta - a \sin \theta, \quad y = a - a \cos \theta. \tag{1}$$

These are the parametric equations of the cycloid.

The rolling circle is called the *generating circle*. The points O, O′ are called *cusps*, the line OO′ the *base*, the point V a *vertex*, and the line UV an *axis* of the cycloid.

The portion of the curve from O to O' is continually repeated as the circle rolls along. Each such portion is sometimes called an *arch* of the cycloid.

§ 215. The Trochoid.—The trochoid is the curve described by a point rigidly attached to, but not on the circumference of, a circle rolling on a straight line.

Let a be the radius of the rolling circle, c the distance of the tracing point from the centre of the circle, θ the angle turned through by the circle. Then, if the tracing point be on the axis of y when $\theta = 0$, and below the centre of the circle, the parametric equations of the trochoid are found to be

$$x = a\theta - c \sin\theta, \quad y = a - c \cos\theta. \tag{2}$$

The Epicycloid, Pericycloid, and Hypocycloid.—An epicycloid is the curve traced by a point on the circumference of a circle rolling on and outside a fixed circle.

A pericycloid is an epicycloid in the tracing of which the rolling circle surrounds the fixed circle.

A hypocycloid is the curve traced by a point on the circumference of a circle rolling on and inside a fixed circle.

§ 216. Areas. Lengths of Arcs. Surfaces of Revolution.— When an integration has to be performed, and x and y are expressed in terms of a parameter t, the parameter is usually the most convenient variable of integration.

Thus, the area A, bounded by the (x, y) graph, the x-axis, and the ordinates at the points where $t = a$, $t = b$, is given by

$$A = \int y \, dx = \int_a^b y\dot{x} \, dt. \tag{1}$$

The volume V, generated when the area A revolves about the x-axis, is given by

$$V = \int \pi y^2 \, dx = \int_a^b \pi y^2 \dot{x} \, dt. \tag{2}$$

Again, if dx, dy, ds are differentials with respect to t,

$$ds^2 = dx^2 + dy^2,$$
$$\therefore \dot{s}^2 = \dot{x}^2 + \dot{y}^2,$$
$$\therefore \dot{s} = \sqrt{(\dot{x}^2 + \dot{y}^2)}.$$

Hence, the length s of the arc of the (x, y) graph, from the point where $t = a$ to the point where $t = b$, is given by

$$s = \int_a^b \sqrt{(\dot{x}^2 + \dot{y}^2)} \, dt. \tag{3}$$

The area S, of the surface of revolution generated when the arc s revolves about the x-axis, is given by

$$S = \int 2\pi y \, ds = \int_a^b 2\pi y \sqrt{(\dot{x}^2 + \dot{y}^2)} dt. \qquad (4)$$

Ex. 1. Find the length of an arch of the cycloid

$$x = a\theta - a\sin\theta, \quad y = a - a\cos\theta.$$

Using dots to indicate differentiation with respect to θ,

$$\dot{x} = a - a\cos\theta = a(1 - \cos\theta), \quad \dot{y} = a\sin\theta,$$
$$\therefore \dot{x}^2 + \dot{y}^2 = a^2\{(1 - \cos\theta)^2 + \sin^2\theta\}$$
$$= 2a^2(1 - \cos\theta) = 4a^2\sin^2\tfrac{1}{2}\theta,$$
$$\therefore \dot{s} = \sqrt{(\dot{x}^2 + \dot{y}^2)} = 2a\sin\tfrac{1}{2}\theta.$$

Now θ increases from 0 to 2π, while the tracing point describes one arch of the cycloid. Hence, the length of one arch

$$= \int_0^{2\pi} \dot{s} \, d\theta = \int_0^{2\pi} 2a\sin\tfrac{1}{2}\theta \, d\theta = 8a.$$

Ex. 2. Find (i) the area bounded by one arch of the cyloid in Ex. 1 and its base, (ii) the volume generated when this area revolves about the base. Let A = the area, V = the volume, required. Then

$$dx = a \, d\theta - a\cos\theta \, d\theta = a(1 - \cos\theta)d\theta,$$
$$\therefore A = \int y \, dx = \int_0^{2\pi} a^2(1 - \cos\theta)^2 \, d\theta$$
$$= a^2 \int_0^{2\pi} (1 - 2\cos\theta + \cos^2\theta) \, d\theta$$
$$= a^2(2\pi - 0 + \tfrac{1}{2} \cdot 2\pi),$$
$$\therefore A = 3\pi a^2.$$

Also,
$$V = \int \pi y^2 \, dx = \pi a^3 \int_0^{2\pi} (1 - \cos\theta)^3 \, d\theta$$
$$= \pi a^3 \int_0^{2\pi} (1 - 3\cos\theta + 3\cos^2\theta - \cos^3\theta) \, d\theta$$
$$= \pi a^3(2\pi - 0 + 3 \cdot \tfrac{1}{2} \cdot 2\pi - 0),$$
$$\therefore V = 5\pi^2 a^3.$$

Note.—In working out such integrals as these, it is well to keep in mind the reduction formula (21), § 188, and the average values of $\cos\theta$, $\cos^2\theta$.

Examples CII.

1. Find the area bounded by the (x, y) graph, the x-axis, and the ordinates at the given points :—

   (i) $x = at^2$, $y = 2at$; $t = 0$, $t = 3$.

   (ii) $x = ct$, $y = ct^{-1}$; $t = 1$, $t = 10$.

   (iii) $x = a \cos \phi$, $y = b \sin \phi$; $\phi = 0$, $\phi = \pi$.

   (iv) $x = 2a \log u$, $y = a(u + u^{-1})$; $u = 1$, $u = 2$.

   (v) $x = a \sin \theta$, $y = a \cos^3 \theta$; $\theta = -\frac{1}{2}\pi$, $\theta = \frac{1}{2}\pi$.

   (vi) $x = 2a \cos^2 \theta$, $y = a \sin 2\theta$; $\theta = 0$, $\theta = \frac{1}{2}\pi$.

   (vii) $x = a \sec \theta$, $y = b \tan \theta$; $\theta = 0$, $\theta = \frac{1}{3}\pi$.

2. Find the volumes generated when the areas in Ex. 1 revolve about the x-axis.

3. Find the length of the arc of the (x, y) graph between the given points :—

   (i) $x = 3t^2$, $y = 3t - t^3$; $t = 0$, $t = 1$.

   (ii) $x = 4u$, $y = u^2 - 2 \log u$; $u = 1$, $u = 3$.

   (iii) $x = 8 \sin \theta$, $y = 2\theta - \sin 2\theta$; $\theta = 0$, $\theta = \frac{1}{2}\pi$.

   (iv) $x = 3t^2$, $y = 2t^3$; $t = 0$, $t = 1$.

4. Find the areas of the surfaces of revolution generated when the arcs given in Ex. 3 revolve about the x-axis.

5. In the cycloid $x = a(\theta - \sin \theta)$, $y = a(1 - \cos \theta)$:

   (i) Find the distance of the centre of gravity of the arc of one arch from the base.

   (ii) Find the distance of the centre of gravity of the area bounded by one arch and its base from the base.

6. In the astroid $x = a \cos^3 \theta$, $y = a \sin^3 \theta$:

   (i) Find the whole length of the curve.

   (ii) Find the area enclosed by the curve.

   (iii) Find the volume of the surface of revolution generated when the curve revolves about the x-axis.

   (iv) Find the area of this surface of revolution.

7. The equations of the epicycloid traced by a point on the circumference of a circle of radius b, rolling on a circle of radius a, can be written

$$x = (a + b) \cos \theta - b \cos \frac{(a + b)\theta}{b},$$

$$y = (a + b) \sin \theta - b \sin \frac{(a + b)\theta}{b}.$$

When $b/a = 1/n$, where n is a positive integer, prove that the whole length of the curve is $8(n + 1)a/n$.

Examine the limit of this expression when $n \to \infty$.

§ 217. **Area of a Sector.**—Let (x, y) be the co-ordinates of a point P on a curve, and Q a neighbouring point (Fig. 102). Let

$OP = r$, $OQ = r + \delta r$, $\angle xOP = \theta$, $\angle POQ = \delta\theta$. Let PS, QR be circular arcs with O as centre.

Let δA be the area of the sector OPQ. Then δA lies between the areas of the two circular sectors OPS, OQR, ; that is, δA

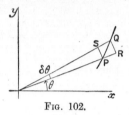

Fig. 102.

lies between $\tfrac{1}{2}r^2\delta\theta$ and $\tfrac{1}{2}(r + \delta r)^2\delta\theta$.

Hence, in the notation of differentials, by theorem (1), § 79,

$$dA = \tfrac{1}{2}r^2 d\theta. \tag{1}$$

Now

$$x = r\cos\theta, \quad y = r\sin\theta,$$
$$\therefore dx = dr\cos\theta - r\sin\theta\, d\theta, \quad dy = dr\sin\theta + r\cos\theta\, d\theta,$$
$$\therefore x\, dy - y\, dx = r^2\, d\theta, \tag{2}$$
$$\therefore dA = \tfrac{1}{2}(x\, dy - y\, dx). \tag{3}$$

Hence, if x and y are functions of a parameter t,

$$\frac{dA}{dt} = \tfrac{1}{2}\left(x\frac{dy}{dt} - y\frac{dx}{dt}\right); \tag{4}$$

and, if A is the area of the sector bounded by the curve and the lines joining the origin to the points where $t = a$, $t = b$,

$$A = \tfrac{1}{2}\int_a^b \left(x\frac{dy}{dt} - y\frac{dx}{dt}\right)dt = \tfrac{1}{2}\int_a^b (x\dot{y} - \dot{x}y)dt. \tag{5}$$

In particular, putting $t = x$, we deduce that the area of the sector bounded by a curve and the lines joining the origin to the points where $x = a$, $x = b$, is given by

$$A = \tfrac{1}{2}\int_a^b \left(x\frac{dy}{dx} - y\right)dx. \tag{6}$$

§ 218. Sign of the Area of a Sector.—It follows from (2) that (5) can be written

$$A = \int_a^b \tfrac{1}{2}r^2\frac{d\theta}{dt}\, dt. \tag{7}$$

Now r^2 is necessarily positive. Consequently, if t *increases* from a to b, the sign of the area A, given by (5) or (7), is *positive or negative according as the angle θ increases or decreases as t increases.*

Examples CIII.

In Exs. 1-4 find the areas of the sectors bounded by the given curves and the lines joining the origin to the points where the parameter has the given values :—

1. The ellipse $x = a \cos \phi$, $y = b \sin \phi$; $\phi = \alpha$, $\phi = \beta$.

2. The hyperbola $x = a \sec \theta$, $y = b \tan \theta$; $\theta = 0$, $\theta = \alpha$.

3. The parabola $x = at^2$, $y = 2at$; $t = t_1$, $t = t_2$.

4. $x = a(\cos \theta + \theta \sin \theta)$, $y = a(\sin \theta - \theta \cos \theta)$; $\theta = \alpha$, $\theta = \beta$.

5. Find the area enclosed by the curve

$$x = a + \alpha \cos \theta + \beta \sin \theta, \quad y = b + \gamma \cos \theta + \delta \sin \theta.$$

6. Find the area enclosed by the epicycloid whose equations are given in Exs. CII., No. 7, when $b/a = 1/n$, where n is a positive integer.

CHAPTER XVI.

POLAR CO-ORDINATES.

§ **219. Polar Co-ordinates.**—Let O be a fixed point, OX a fixed straight line.

Let P be any point on a line R′OR drawn through O in a direction making an angle θ with OX (Fig. 103).

Let $r = $ OP, and let r be positive or negative according as P is on the same side of O as R or R′.

Then (r, θ) are called the *polar co-ordinates* of the point P, O is called the *pole*, OX the *initial line*, OP the *radius vector*, and θ the *vectorial angle* of the point P.

When the point P describes a curve, its polar co-ordinates (r, θ) are connected by an equation, which is called the *polar equation* of the curve.

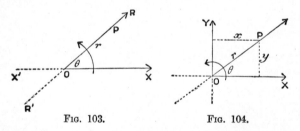

FIG. 103.　　　　FIG. 104.

§ **220. Relation between Polar and Cartesian Co-ordinates.**— In Fig. 104 let (x, y) be the Cartesian co-ordinates of the point P referred to OX, OY as co-ordinate axes, and let (r, θ) be its polar co-ordinates referred to O as pole and OX as initial line. Then x and y are given in terms of r and θ by the equations

$$x = r \cos \theta, \qquad y = r \sin \theta; \tag{1}$$

while r and ρ are given in terms of x and y by

$$r^2 = x^2 + y^2, \qquad \tan \theta = \frac{y}{x}. \tag{2}$$

By means of (1) and (2) we can transform a Cartesian equation into a polar equation, or vice versa.

A few important polar equations and the curves they represent are given below:—

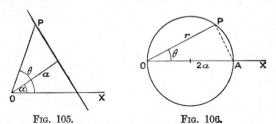

FIG. 105. FIG. 106.

§ 221. Straight Line. $r = a \sec (\theta - \alpha)$.

This is the polar equation of a straight line; a is the perpendicular from the pole on the line; α is the angle between this perpendicular and the initial line (Fig. 105).

§ 222. Circles.   (1) $r = 2a \cos \theta$.

The polar equation of a circle of radius a, with the pole on the circumference, and the diameter through the pole as initial line (Fig. 106).

$$(2)   r = 2a \cos (\theta - \alpha).$$

A circle of radius a, with the pole on the circumference, and the diameter through the pole making an angle α with the initial line.

$$(3)   r^2 + c^2 - 2cr \cos \theta = a^2.$$

A circle of radius a, with the pole at a distance c from the centre, and the diameter through the pole as initial line.

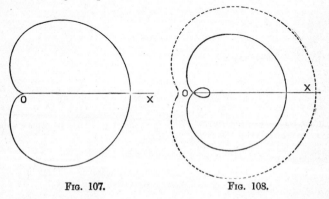

FIG. 107. FIG. 108.

§ 223. **Cardioid.** $r = a(1 + \cos \theta)$.

The polar equation of a heart-shaped curve called the *cardioid*. The initial line is the axis of the curve (Fig. 107).

Limaçon. $r = a \cos \theta + c$.

The polar equation of a curve called the *limaçon*. The initial line is the axis of the curve.

In Fig. 108, the full-line curve is a limaçon in which $c < a$. The dotted curve is a limaçon in which $c > a$. When $c = a$ the limaçon becomes a cardioid.

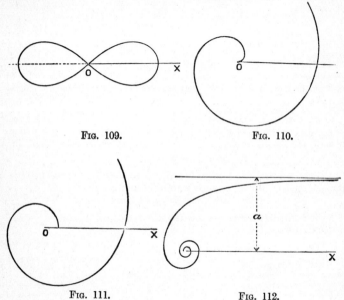

FIG. 109.   FIG. 110.

FIG. 111.   FIG. 112.

§ 224. **Lemniscate.**   (1) $r^2 = a^2 \cos 2\theta$,

(2) $r^2 = a^2 \sin 2\theta$.

Each of these is the polar equation of a *lemniscate*.

In (1) the axis of the curve is the initial line (Fig. 109). In (2) the axis of the curve makes 45° with the initial line.

§ 225. **Spirals.**   (1) $r = a\theta$.   Archimedean spiral (Fig. 110).

(2) $r = ae^{b\theta}$.   Equiangular spiral (Fig. 111).

(3) $r\theta = a$.   Reciprocal spiral (Fig. 112).

§ 226. Conics. $\dfrac{l}{r} = 1 + e \cos \theta.$

This is the general polar equation of a conic, in which l = the semi-latus rectum, e = the eccentricity. The pole is at a focus, and the initial line is an axis of the conic. The conic is an ellipse if $e < 1$, a parabola if $e = 1$, a hyperbola if $e > 1$.

Examples CIV.

In Exs. 1-14 sketch the curves whose polar equations are given. (It may be helpful to transform the given equations into Cartesian equations) :—

1. $r = 3$.   2. $r = a$.   3. $\theta = 0$.   4. $\theta = \frac{1}{2}\pi$.
5. $r = 6 \cos \theta$.   6. $r = 2 \sin \theta$.   7. $r \sin \theta = 2$.
8. $r = 4 \cos \theta + 2 \sin \theta$.   9 $r^2 - 2r \cos \theta = 3$.
10. $r^2 = 4 \sin 2\theta$.   11. $r^2 \sin 2\theta = 4$.
12. $r = a \cos 2\theta$ (four-leaved rose). Also $r = a \sin 2\theta$.
13. $r = a \cos 3\theta$ (three-leaved rose). Also $r = a \sin 3\theta$.
14. $r = a \sec^2 \frac{1}{2}\theta$ (parabola).
15. Draw the circle $r = 2 \cos \theta$. Use it to draw the curves

  (i) $r = 2 \cos \theta + 3$,   (ii) $r = 2 \cos \theta + 2$,   (iii) $r = 2 \cos \theta + 1$.

16. In the curve $r\theta = a$ (the Reciprocal Spiral), express x and y in terms of θ, and deduce that $y \to a$ when $\theta \to 0$.

17. In the curve $r^2\theta = a^2$ (the Lituus), express x and y in terms of θ, and deduce that $y \to 0$ when $\theta \to 0$. Sketch the curve.

18. Prove that the epicycloid traced by a point on the circumference of a circle rolling on an equal circle is a cardioid.

§ 227. The Angles ϕ and ψ.—In polar co-ordinates, the angle between the tangent and the radius vector is denoted by ϕ, the angle between the tangent and the initial line by ψ. Thus, in Fig. 113, $\phi = \angle OPT$, $\psi = \angle XTP$.

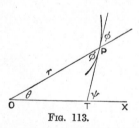
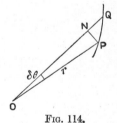

FIG. 113.   FIG. 114.

From the triangle OTP follows

$$\psi = \theta + \phi. \tag{1}$$

§ 228. Let P, Q be two neighbouring points on a curve (Fig. 114). Let (r, θ) be the polar co-ordinates of P, and

$(r + \delta r, \theta + \delta \theta)$ those of Q. Let PN be the perpendicular from P on OQ, and let NQ $= \Delta r$. We shall first prove that

$$\lim_{\delta\theta \to 0} \left(\frac{\Delta r}{\delta r} \right) = 1. \qquad (2)$$

Proof. Since

$$NQ = OQ - ON = OQ - OP \cos \angle POQ,$$
$$\therefore \Delta r = (r + \delta r) - r \cos \delta\theta = \delta r + (1 - \cos \delta\theta)r,$$
$$\therefore \frac{\Delta r}{\delta r} = 1 + \frac{1 - \cos \delta\theta}{(\delta\theta)^2} \cdot \frac{r\delta\theta}{\delta r} \cdot \delta\theta ;$$

hence, by (2), § 44,

$$\lim_{\delta\theta \to 0} \left(\frac{\Delta r}{\delta r} \right) = 1 + \frac{1}{2} \cdot \frac{r\,d\theta}{dr} \cdot 0 = 1.$$

§ 229. Next, let $\delta s =$ arc PQ. We shall prove that

$$\tan \phi = \frac{r\,d\theta}{dr}, \qquad \sin \phi = \frac{r\,d\theta}{ds}, \qquad \cos \phi = \frac{dr}{ds}. \qquad (3)$$

Proof. Suppose P, Q joined and put $\Delta s = chord$ PQ. Then

$$\tan PQN = \frac{PN}{NQ} = \frac{r \sin \delta\theta}{\Delta r} = \frac{r\delta\theta}{\delta r} \cdot \frac{\sin \delta\theta}{\delta\theta} \cdot \frac{\delta r}{\Delta r} ;$$

$$\sin PQN = \frac{PN}{PQ} = \frac{r \sin \delta\theta}{\Delta s} = \frac{r\delta\theta}{\delta s} \cdot \frac{\sin \delta\theta}{\delta\theta} \cdot \frac{\delta s}{\Delta s} ;$$

$$\cos PQN = \frac{NQ}{PQ} = \frac{\Delta r}{\Delta s} = \frac{\delta r}{\delta s} \cdot \frac{\Delta r}{\delta r} \cdot \frac{\delta s}{\Delta s}$$

Now, when $\delta\theta \to 0$, $\angle$ PQN $\to \phi$, $\sin \delta\theta/\delta\theta \to 1$, $\delta s/\Delta s \to 1$ and $\delta r/\Delta r \to 1$ (just proved). Hence, in the limit,

$$\tan \phi = \frac{r\,d\theta}{dr}, \qquad \sin \phi = \frac{r\,d\theta}{ds}, \qquad \cos \phi = \frac{dr}{ds}.$$

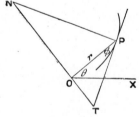

Fig. 115.

§ 230. Polar Subtangent and Polar Subnormal.—In Fig. 115 let PT be the tangent, and PN the normal, at P, and let TN be the line drawn through the pole O perpendicular to the radius vector OP.

Then OT is called the *polar subtangent*, and ON the *polar subnormal*. Further, PT is called the *polar tangent*, and PN the *polar normal*.

From formulæ (3) follow

$$\text{polar subtangent} = \text{OT} = r \tan \phi = \frac{r^2 \, d\theta}{dr}; \qquad (4)$$

$$\text{polar subnormal} = \text{ON} = r \cot \phi = \frac{dr}{d\theta}; \qquad (5)$$

$$\text{polar tangent} = \text{PT} = \frac{r}{\cos \phi} = \frac{r \, ds}{dr}; \qquad (6)$$

$$\text{polar normal} = \text{PN} = \frac{r}{\sin \phi} = \frac{ds}{d\theta}. \qquad (7)$$

Ex. In the parabola $r = a \sec^2 (\tfrac{1}{2}\theta)$, find (i) the angle ϕ, (ii) the angle ψ, (iii) the polar subtangent, (iv) the polar subnormal, all in terms of θ.

(i) By logarithmic differentiation, or otherwise, we find

$$\frac{1}{r}\frac{dr}{d\theta} = \tan \tfrac{1}{2}\theta,$$

$$\therefore \cot \phi = \tan \tfrac{1}{2}\theta,$$

$$\therefore \phi = \tfrac{1}{2}\pi - \tfrac{1}{2}\theta.$$

(ii) $\psi = \theta + \phi = \tfrac{1}{2}\pi + \tfrac{1}{2}\theta.$

(iii) The polar subtangent $= r \tan \phi = r \cot \tfrac{1}{2}\theta = 2a \operatorname{cosec} \theta.$

(iv) The polar subnormal $= r \cot \phi = a \sec^2 \tfrac{1}{2}\theta \tan \tfrac{1}{2}\theta.$

The reader should draw a figure to illustrate these results.

Examples CV.

In Exs. 1-6 find ϕ and ψ in terms of θ :—

1. $r = ae^\theta.$ **2.** $r = ae^{\theta \cot \alpha}.$ **3.** $r^2 \sin 2\theta = a^2.$

4. $r = 2a \cos \theta.$ **5.** $r = a(1 - \cos \theta).$ **6.** $r^n \cos n\theta = a^n.$

7. If $r = a \tan \left(\dfrac{\pi}{4} + \dfrac{\theta}{2} \right)$, prove that $\tan \phi = \dfrac{2ar}{a^2 + r^2}.$

8. If $r = a\theta$, prove that $\dfrac{dr}{ds} = \dfrac{a}{\sqrt{(a^2 + r^2)}}, \dfrac{d\theta}{ds} = \dfrac{1}{\sqrt{(a^2 + r^2)}}.$

9. If $r^n = a^n \cos n\theta$, prove that $\dfrac{d^2r}{ds^2} = - \dfrac{nr^{2n-1}}{a^{2n}}.$

10. In the Equiangular Spiral $r = ae^{b\theta}$, prove that $\phi = $ constant (hence the name).

11. In the curve $r = 6e^{\frac{4}{3}\theta}$, find the lengths of the polar tangent, normal, subtangent, and subnormal, when $\theta = 0$.

12. In the curve $r = ae^{\theta \cot \alpha}$, find the lengths of the polar tangent, normal, subtangent, and subnormal, at any point.

13. In the Archimedean Spiral $r = a\theta$, prove that the polar subnormal is constant.

14. In the Reciprocal Spiral $r\theta = a$, prove that the polar subtangent is constant, and that the polar tangent $= \sqrt{(r^2 + a^2)}$.

15. In the Lemniscate $r^2 = a^2 \cos 2\theta$, prove that the polar normal $= a^2/r$.

16. The normal to the curve $r^2 = a^2 \cos 2\theta$ at the point $P(r, \theta)$ cuts the initial line in G. Prove that $PG = a^2r/(a^2 + 2r^2)$.

17. Prove that the radius vectors of the points of contact of three parallel tangents to the cardioid $r = a(1 - \cos \theta)$ are equally inclined to one another.

18. A point P moves along the curve $r^n = a^n \sin n\theta$ so that the radius vector OP rotates with constant angular velocity ω. Prove that the tangent at P rotates with angular velocity $(n + 1)\omega$.

In Exs. 19-22 find the angles of intersection of the given pairs of curves :—

19. $r = a, r = 2a \cos \theta$.   **20.** $r^2 \sin 2\theta = 4a^2, r = a \sec \theta$.

21. $r = a \cos \theta, r = a(1 - \cos \theta)$.   **22.** $r^2 \sin 2\theta = 9, r^2 = 25 \sin 2\theta$.

In Exs. 23-26 prove that the given pairs of curves intersect at right angles :

23. $r = a\theta, r\theta = a$.   **24.** $r = a(1 + \cos \theta), r = b(1 - \cos \theta)$.

25. $r = ae^\theta, r = be^{-\theta}$.   **26.** $r^2 \cos 2\theta = a^2, r^2 \sin 2\theta = b^2$.

§ 231. Area of a Sector in Polar Co-ordinates.

—From (1), § 217, it follows that the area A of a sector bounded by a curve and the radius vectors $\theta = a$, $\theta = \beta$, is given by

$$A = \int_a^\beta \tfrac{1}{2} r^2 d\theta. \tag{1}$$

Ex. Find the area enclosed by the cardioid $r = a(1 + \cos \theta)$.

Let A = area enclosed = twice the area from $\theta = 0$ to $\theta = \pi$,

$$\therefore A = 2\int_0^\pi \tfrac{1}{2} a^2 (1 + \cos \theta)^2 d\theta = \tfrac{3}{2}\pi a^2.$$

§ 232. Volumes of Revolution about the Initial Line.

—Let V be the volume generated when the sector bounded by a curve and the radius vectors $\theta = a$, $\theta = \beta$, revolves about the initial line.

Now, in the limit when $\delta\theta \to 0$, the centre of gravity of the elementary sector OPQ, of area δA, in Fig. 114, is at a distance $\tfrac{2}{3}r$ from O, and therefore at a distance $\tfrac{2}{3}r \sin \theta$ from OX. Hence, by (19), § 142, when this sector revolves about OX it generates a volume dV given by

$$dV = dA \cdot 2\pi \cdot \tfrac{2}{3}r \sin \theta = \tfrac{1}{2}r^2 d\theta \cdot 2\pi \cdot \tfrac{2}{3}r \sin \theta = \tfrac{2}{3}\pi r^3 \sin \theta \, d\theta,$$

$$\therefore V = \frac{2\pi}{3}\int_a^\beta r^3 \sin \theta \, d\theta. \tag{2}$$

§ 233. **Length of an Arc in Polar Co-ordinates.**—From the right-angled triangle PNQ in Fig. 114, we have

$$PQ = \surd(PN^2 + NQ^2),$$

and therefore, using differentials in the limit when $\delta\theta \to 0$,

$$ds = \surd\{(r\,d\theta)^2 + (dr)^2\}.$$

Hence, the length s of the arc of the curve is given by

$$s = \int \left\{ r^2 + \left(\frac{dr}{d\theta} \right)^2 \right\}^{\frac{1}{2}} d\theta, \tag{3}$$

or by

$$s = \int \left\{ \left(\frac{r\,d\theta}{dr} \right)^2 + 1 \right\}^{\frac{1}{2}} dr. \tag{4}$$

Ex. Find the whole length of the cardioid $r = a(1 + \cos\theta)$.
Let s = whole length = twice the length from $\theta = 0$ to $\theta = \pi$.

Since $\qquad r^2 + \left(\dfrac{dr}{d\theta} \right)^2 = a^2(1 + \cos\theta)^2 + a^2\sin^2\theta$

$$= 2a^2(1 + \cos\theta) = 4a^2\cos^2\tfrac{1}{2}\theta,$$

$$\therefore\ ds = 2a\cos\tfrac{1}{2}\theta\,d\theta,$$

$$\therefore\ s = 2\int_0^\pi 2a\cos\tfrac{1}{2}\theta\,d\theta = 8a.$$

§ 234. **Surfaces of Revolution about the Initial Line.**—When an arc of a curve, whose polar equation is given, revolves about the initial line, the area S of the surface of revolution generated is given by the formula

$$S = \int 2\pi y\,ds = 2\pi \int r\sin\theta \left\{ r^2 + \left(\frac{dr}{d\theta} \right)^2 \right\}^{\frac{1}{2}} d\theta, \tag{5}$$

or by the alternative formula obtained by taking r, instead of θ, as the variable of integration.

Examples CVI.

In Exs. 1-5 find the areas bounded by the given curves and radius vectors :—

1. $r = 2a\cos\theta$; $\theta = 0, \theta = \alpha$.   2. $r = a\sec^2\tfrac{1}{2}\theta$; $\theta = 0, \theta = \alpha$.
3. $r^2\sin 2\theta = a^2$; $\theta = \tfrac{1}{4}\pi, \theta = \alpha$.
4. $\dfrac{1}{r^2} = \dfrac{\cos^2\theta}{a^2} - \dfrac{\sin^2\theta}{b^2}$; $\theta = 0, \theta = \alpha$.
5. $\dfrac{l}{r} = 1 + \tfrac{5}{3}\cos\theta$; $\theta = 0, \theta = \tfrac{1}{2}\pi$.

In Exs. 6-9 find the areas enclosed by the given curves :—
6. $r = 2a\sin^2\tfrac{1}{2}\theta$.   7. $r = a\cos\theta + c,\ (c > a)$.
8. $\dfrac{1}{r^2} = \dfrac{\cos^2\theta}{a^2} + \dfrac{\sin^2\theta}{b^2}$.   9. $\dfrac{l}{r} = 1 + e\cos\theta,\ (e < 1)$.

10. Find the area of a loop of the curve $r^2 = a^2 \cos 2\theta$.

11. Find the area of a loop of the curve $r = a(\sin 2\theta + 2 \sin \theta)$.

12. Prove that the area of the portion of the circle $r = 2a \cos \theta$ outside the circle $r = a\sqrt{2}$ is a^2.

13. Find the ratio of the areas of the two portions into which the circle $r = a$ divides a loop of the curve $r = 2a \sin 2\theta$.

14. Prove that the sum of the areas of the two loops of the curve

$$r = a(2 \cos \theta + 1) \text{ is } 3\pi a^2.$$

15. Find the area of each of the loops of the limaçon

$$r = a \cos \theta + c, \ (c < a).$$

In Exs. 16-19 find the volumes generated when the areas bounded by the given curves and radius vectors revolve about the initial line :—

16. $r = a$; $\theta = 0, \theta = \alpha$.   **17.** $r = 2a \sin^2 \frac{1}{2}\theta$; $\theta = 0, \theta = \pi$.

18. $r = a\theta$; $\theta = 0, \theta = \frac{1}{2}\pi$.   **19.** $r = a \sec^2 \frac{1}{2}\theta$; $\theta = 0, \theta = \alpha$.

In Exs. 20-23 find the (x, y) co-ordinates of the centres of gravity of the areas bounded by the given curves and radius vectors :—

20. $r = a$; $\theta = -\alpha, \theta = +\alpha$.   **21.** $r = 2a \cos \theta$; $\theta = 0, \theta = \alpha$.

22. $r = a\theta$; $\theta = 0, \theta = 2\pi$.   **23.** $r = a(1 + \cos \theta)$; $\theta = 0, \theta = 2\pi$.

In Exs. 24-31 find the lengths of the arcs of the given curves between the points where θ, or r, has the given values :—

24. $r = ae^{\theta \cot \alpha}$; $\theta = \theta_1, \theta = \theta_2$.   **25.** $r = ae^{-\beta\theta}$; $\theta = 0, \theta = \infty$.

26. $r = a \sin^3 \dfrac{\theta}{3}$; $\theta = 0, \theta = 3\pi$.   **27.** $r = a \sin^n \dfrac{\theta}{n}$; $\theta = 0, \theta = n\pi$.

28. $r = a \sec^2 \frac{1}{2}\theta$; $\theta = 0, \theta = \alpha$.   **29.** $r = 4\theta$; $r = 0, r = 3$.

30. $r = a(\sec \theta - \cos \theta)$; $\theta = 0, \theta = \frac{1}{4}\pi$.   **31.** $r\theta = 12$; $r = 16, r = 9$.

In Exs. 32-38, find the areas of the surfaces generated when the given curves, between the points whose vectorial angles are given, revolve about the initial line :—

32. $r = a$; $\theta = \alpha, \theta = \beta$.   **33.** $r = 2a \sin \theta$; $\theta = 0, \theta = \pi$.

34. $r = a \cos \theta$; $\theta = 0, \theta = \frac{1}{2}\pi$.   **35.** $r = a(1 + \cos \theta)$; $\theta = 0, \theta = \pi$.

36. $r = ae^{-\beta\theta}$; $\theta = 0, \theta = \pi$.   **37.** $r = a \sec^2 \frac{1}{2}\theta$; $\theta = 0, \theta = \alpha$.

38. $r = 2a \cos (\theta + \alpha)$; $\theta = 0, \theta = \frac{1}{2}\pi - \alpha, (\alpha < \frac{1}{2}\pi)$.

39. Find the distance from the pole to the centre of gravity of the *arc* of the cardioid $r = a(1 + \cos \theta)$.

40. Find the distance from the pole to the centre of gravity of the *surface* generated when the cardioid $r = a(1 + \cos \theta)$ revolves about the initial line.

§ 235. The Perpendicular from the Pole on the Tangent.

Let p be the length of the perpendicular from the pole on the tangent at any point P. Then (Fig. 116),

$$p = r \sin \phi. \tag{1}$$

To express p in terms of r and θ, we have

$$\frac{1}{p^2} = \frac{1}{r^2 \sin^2 \phi} = \frac{1}{r^2} (\text{cosec}^2 \phi) = \frac{1}{r^2}(1 + \cot^2 \phi),$$

and hence, since $\cot\phi = dr/r\,d\theta$,

$$\frac{1}{p^2} = \frac{1}{r^2} + \frac{1}{r^4}\left(\frac{dr}{d\theta}\right)^2. \tag{2}$$

It is sometimes more convenient to work with $1/r$ than r. When we do so, we put $u = 1/r$. Then

$$u = \frac{1}{r}, \qquad \frac{du}{d\theta} = -\frac{1}{r^2}\frac{dr}{d\theta},$$

$$\therefore \frac{1}{p^2} = u^2 + \left(\frac{du}{d\theta}\right)^2. \tag{3}$$

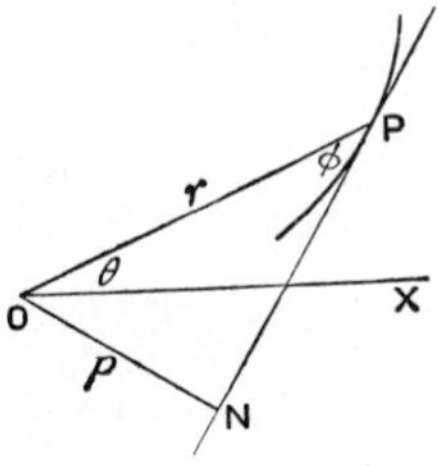

FIG. 116. 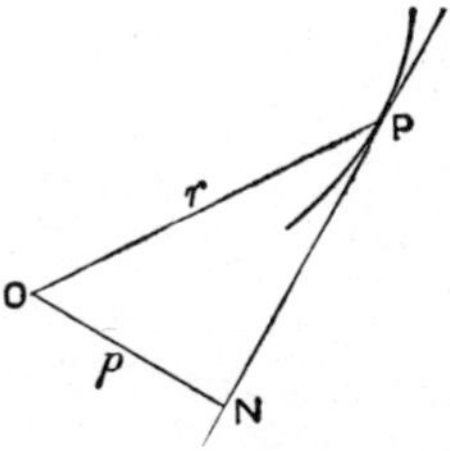   FIG. 117.

§ 236. **The (p, r) Equation of a Curve.**—Let P be any point on a curve, and let O be any fixed point. Let $r = \mathrm{OP}$, and $p =$ the perpendicular from O on the tangent at P (Fig. 117).

The relation between p and r that holds good for every point on the curve is called the (p, r) *equation* of the curve, with reference to O as pole.

When the polar equation, $f(r, \theta) = 0$, is given with reference to a pole O and an initial line OX, the (p, r) equation with reference to O as pole can be found by eliminating θ from the given polar equation and equation (3). In practice, however. it is easier to eliminate θ and ϕ from the three equations

$$f(r, \theta) = 0, \quad \tan\phi = r\,d\theta/dr, \quad p = r\sin\phi.$$

§ 237. **Radius of Curvature.**—We shall prove the formulæ

$$\rho = r\frac{dr}{dp}, \tag{4}$$

$$\frac{1}{\rho} = \frac{r^2 + 2\dot{r}^2 - r\ddot{r}}{(r^2 + \dot{r}^2)^{\frac{3}{2}}}, \tag{5}$$

where, in the second formula, dots denote differentiation with respect to θ.

Proof of (4). Since

$$p = r \sin \phi,$$

$$\therefore \frac{dp}{dr} = \sin \phi + r \cos \phi \frac{d\phi}{dr}$$

$$= r \frac{d\theta}{ds} + r \frac{dr}{ds} \frac{d\phi}{dr},$$

$$\therefore \frac{1}{r} \frac{dp}{dr} = \frac{d\theta}{ds} + \frac{d\phi}{ds} = \frac{d\psi}{ds} = \frac{1}{\rho} \text{ (since } \theta + \phi = \psi),$$

$$\therefore \rho = r \frac{dr}{dp}.$$

Proof of (5).—Using dots to indicate differentiation with respect to θ, we have, since $\psi = \theta + \phi$,

$$\frac{1}{\rho} = \frac{d\psi}{ds} = \frac{\dot\psi}{\dot s} = \frac{1 + \dot\phi}{(r^2 + \dot r^2)^{\frac{1}{2}}}. \tag{i}$$

But
$$\phi = \tan^{-1}\left(\frac{r\,d\theta}{dr}\right) = \tan^{-1}\left(\frac{r}{\dot r}\right),$$

from which we find

$$\dot\phi = \frac{\dot r^2 - r\ddot r}{r^2 + \dot r^2},$$

and hence, from (i),

$$\frac{1}{\rho} = \frac{r^2 + 2\dot r^2 - r\ddot r}{(r^2 + \dot r^2)^{\frac{3}{2}}}.$$

In practice, to find ρ from a polar equation, it is usually easier first to derive the (p, r) equation, and then apply the simple formula (4), than to make a direct application of (5).

§ 238. **Points of Inflexion.**—Since $\rho = \infty$ at a point of inflexion, a necessary condition for a point of inflexion is, from (i),

$$\frac{d\phi}{d\theta} = -1, \tag{6}$$

or, from (4),
$$\frac{dp}{dr} = 0, \tag{7}$$

or, from (5),
$$r^2 + 2\dot r^2 - r\ddot r = 0. \tag{8}$$

Ex. Find the (p, r) equation of the Archimedean Spiral $r = a\theta$, and the radius of curvature in terms of r.

Since
$$\tan \phi = \frac{r\,d\theta}{dr} = \frac{r}{a},$$

$$\therefore \sin \phi = \frac{r}{\sqrt{(a^2 + r^2)}}.$$

Hence, since $p = r \sin \phi$, the (p, r) equation is

$$p = \frac{r^2}{\sqrt{(a^2 + r^2)}}.$$

From this equation we find

$$\frac{dp}{dr} = \frac{r(2a^2 + r^2)}{(a^2 + r^2)^{\frac{3}{2}}},$$

and hence

$$\rho = r\frac{dr}{dp} = \frac{(a^2 + r^2)^{\frac{3}{2}}}{2a^2 + r^2}.$$

Examples CVII.

In Exs. 1-12 derive the (p, r) equation from the given polar equation, and find the radius of curvature in terms of r :—

1. $r = 2a \cos \theta$.   **2.** $r = a(1 + \cos \theta)$.   **3.** $r\theta = a$.

4. $r = ae^{\theta \cot \alpha}$.   **5.** $r = a \sec^2 \frac{1}{2}\theta$.   **6.** $r^2\theta = a^2$.

7. $r^2 \sin 2\theta = a^2$.   **8.** $r^n = a^n \cos n\theta$.

9. $\frac{a}{r} = 1 + \cos \theta$.   **10.** $\frac{1}{r^2} = \frac{\cos^2 \theta}{a^2} + \frac{\sin^2 \theta}{b^2}$.

11. $\frac{l}{r} = 1 + e \cos \theta$.   **12.** $\frac{1}{r^2} = \frac{\cos^2\theta}{a^2} - \frac{\sin^2 \theta}{b^2}$.

13. In the Equiangular Spiral $r = ae^{b\theta}$, prove that the radius of curvature at any point is equal to the polar normal.

14. (i) In the conic $l = r(1 + e \cos \theta)$, prove that $\rho = l \operatorname{cosec}^3 \phi$.

(ii) In the spiral $r\theta = a$, prove that $\rho = r \operatorname{cosec}^3 \phi$.

15. In the Lituus $2r^2\theta = 3$, find the value of the radius of curvature at the point where $r = 2$.

16. Prove that the polar co-ordinates of the point of inflexion of the Lituus $r^2\theta = a^2$ are $(a\sqrt{2}, \frac{1}{2})$.

17. Prove that the Limaçon $r = a \cos \theta + c$ has real points of inflexion if c lies between a and $2a$.

18. If $r = f(\theta)$, and $u = 1/r$, prove that the radius of curvature is given by

$$\frac{1}{\rho} = \frac{u^3(u + \ddot{u})}{(u^2 + \dot{u}^2)^{\frac{3}{2}}}.$$

where dots indicate differentiation with respect to θ. Deduce that a necessary condition for a point of inflexion is $\ddot{u} + u = 0$.

Prove that the curve $l/r = 1 + e \cos n\theta$ has points of inflexion where $r = l(n^2 - 1)/n^2$.

CHAPTER XVII.

HYPERBOLIC FUNCTIONS.

§ 239. Hyperbolic Functions.—Two functions of x closely related to $\cos x$ and $\sin x$ are defined by

$$\cosh x = \tfrac{1}{2}(e^x + e^{-x}), \quad \sinh x = \tfrac{1}{2}(e^x - e^{-x}). \tag{1}$$

They are called the *hyperbolic* cosine and sine of x (pronounced "cosh" and "shine").

From $\cosh x$ and $\sinh x$ other hyperbolic functions are defined by analogy with the trigonometric functions; thus

$$\tanh x = \frac{\sinh x}{\cosh x} = \frac{e^x - e^{-x}}{e^x + e^{-x}} \tag{2}$$

$$\coth x = \frac{1}{\tanh x}, \quad \operatorname{sech} x = \frac{1}{\cosh x}, \quad \operatorname{cosech} x = \frac{1}{\sinh x}. \tag{3}$$

Note that :—

(i) $\cosh 0 = 1$, $\sinh 0 = 0$, $\tanh 0 = 0$.

(ii) $\cosh x > 1$, for all values of x (except $x = 0$).

(iii) $\tanh (+ \infty) = + 1$, $\tanh (- \infty) = - 1$; $\tanh x$ lies between $+ 1$ and $- 1$, since $\sinh x$ is numerically less than $\cosh x$.

(iv) $\cosh x$ is an *even* function ; for

$$\cosh (- x) = \tfrac{1}{2}(e^{-x} + e^x) = \cosh x ;$$

$\sinh x$ and $\tanh x$ are *odd* functions.

§ 240. *Graph of $\cosh x$.*—Let the graphs of e^x and e^{-x} be drawn (dotted in Fig. 118). Let any ordinate cut them in the points A, B, the x-axis in M, and the graph of $\cosh x$ in C. Now, by definition, $\cosh x$ is the mean of e^x and e^{-x}. Therefore, MC is the mean of MA and MB, and C bisects AB.

Hence, we can obtain points on the graph of $\cosh x$ by drawing a set of ordinates and bisecting the segments of these ordinates between the graphs of e^x and e^{-x}.

§ 241. *Graph of $\sinh x$.*—Since $\sinh x$ can be written

$$\sinh x = \tfrac{1}{2}\{e^x + (- e^{-x})\}$$

it follows that the graph of $\sinh x$ can be drawn from those of e^x and $-e^{-x}$ in the same way as the graph of $\cosh x$ can be drawn from those of e^x and e^{-x} (Fig. 119).

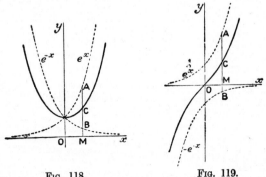

Fig. 118.   Fig. 119.

§ 242. *Graph of* $\tanh x$.—The graph of $\tanh x$ lies between the lines $y = 1$, $y = -1$, approaching the former asymptotically when $x \to +\infty$, the latter when $x \to -\infty$ (Fig. 120).

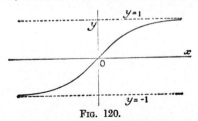

Fig. 120.

Examples CVIII.

1. Using the exponential series (§ 164), obtain the expansions :—

$$\sinh x = \frac{x}{1!} + \frac{x^3}{3!} + \frac{x^5}{5!} + \dots, \qquad \cosh x = 1 + \frac{x^2}{2!} + \frac{x^4}{4!} + \dots$$

2. From the series in Ex. 1, calculate the values of $\cosh x$ and $\sinh x$, when $x = 1$, to four decimal places.

3. Sketch the graphs of (i) $\operatorname{sech} x$, (ii) $\operatorname{cosech} x$, (iii) $\coth x$.

4. Sketch the graphs of (i) $\cosh x \cos x$, (ii) $\sinh x \sin x$ (see § 48).

5. Factorise $(x^2 - 2xy \cosh \alpha + y^2)$, and solve the quadratic equation

$$x^2 - 2x \cosh \alpha + 1 = 0.$$

8

6. In any triangle ABC, if $\alpha = \log_e (b/c)$, prove that
$$a^2 = 2bc \, (\cosh \alpha - \cos A).$$

7. If $e^y = \coth x$, prove that $e^{2x} = \coth \frac{y}{2}$.

8. If $v = e^x$ and $t = \tanh \frac{1}{2}x$, prove that (i) $t = \dfrac{v-1}{v+1}$, (ii) $v = \dfrac{1+t}{1-t}$.

9. Prove that $\tan^{-1}(e^x) - \tan^{-1}(\tanh \frac{1}{2}x) = \frac{1}{4}\pi$.

§ 243. Hyperbolic Identities.—To every identity satisfied by the circular functions, there is an analogous one satisfied by the hyperbolic functions. We shall prove the first of the following four identities; the others can be proved similarly:—

$$\sinh (x + y) = \sinh x \cosh y + \cosh x \sinh y, \qquad (1)$$
$$\sinh (x - y) = \sinh x \cosh y - \cosh x \sinh y, \qquad (2)$$
$$\cosh (x + y) = \cosh x \cosh y + \sinh x \sinh y, \qquad (3)$$
$$\cosh (x - y) = \cosh x \cosh y - \sinh x \sinh y. \qquad (4)$$

Proof of (1).
$$\sinh x \cosh y = \tfrac{1}{2}(e^x - e^{-x}) \cdot \tfrac{1}{2}(e^y + e^{-y})$$
$$= \tfrac{1}{4}(e^{x+y} + e^{x-y} - e^{-x+y} - e^{-x-y}),$$
$$\cosh x \sinh y = \tfrac{1}{2}(e^x + e^{-x}) \cdot \tfrac{1}{2}(e^y - e^{-y})$$
$$= \tfrac{1}{4}(e^{x+y} - e^{x-y} + e^{-x+y} - e^{-x-y}).$$

By addition,
$$\sinh x \cosh y + \cosh x \sinh y = \tfrac{1}{2}(e^{x+y} - e^{-x-y}) = \sinh (x + y).$$

Next, put $y = x$ in (1), (3), and (4). We get
$$\sinh 2x = 2 \sinh x \cosh x, \qquad (5)$$
$$\cosh 2x = \cosh^2 x + \sinh^2 x, \qquad (6)$$
$$1 = \cosh^2 x - \sinh^2 x. \qquad (7)$$

From (7),
$$\cosh^2 x = \sinh^2 x + 1, \qquad (8)$$
$$\sinh^2 x = \cosh^2 x - 1. \qquad (9)$$

Also, dividing (7) in turn by $\cosh^2 x$ and $\sinh^2 x$, we get
$$\operatorname{sech}^2 x = 1 - \tanh^2 x, \qquad (10)$$
$$\operatorname{cosech}^2 x = \coth^2 x - 1. \qquad (11)$$

From (6) and (7), by addition and subtraction, we get
$$\cosh 2x + 1 = 2 \cosh^2 x, \qquad (12)$$
$$\cosh 2x - 1 = 2 \sinh^2 x. \qquad (13)$$

From (12) and (13),
$$\cosh^2 x = \tfrac{1}{2}(\cosh 2x + 1), \qquad (14)$$
$$\sinh^2 x = \tfrac{1}{2}(\cosh 2x - 1). \qquad (15)$$

Note.—Each of these identities can be obtained from the corresponding trigonometric one by writing *cosh* in place of *cos*, and *i sinh* in place of *sin*, where $i = \sqrt{(-1)}$. [See § 267.]

Examples CIX.

In Exs. 1-9 prove the given identities directly from the definitions of $\sinh x$ and $\cosh x$:—

1. $e^x = \cosh x + \sinh x, \quad e^{-x} = \cosh x - \sinh x.$
2. $(\cosh x + \sinh x)^n = \cosh nx + \sinh nx.$
3. $\cosh^2 x - \sinh^2 x = 1.$
4. $2 \sinh^2 x = \cosh 2x - 1.$
5. $2 \cosh^2 x = \cosh 2x + 1.$
6. $4 \sinh^3 x = \sinh 3x - 3 \sinh x.$
7. $4 \cosh^3 x = \cosh 3x + 3 \cosh x.$
8. $8 \sinh^4 x = \cosh 4x - 4 \cosh 2x + 3.$
9. $8 \cosh^4 x = \cosh 4x + 4 \cosh 2x + 3.$

In Exs. 10-18 prove the given identities :—

10. $\tanh (x + y) = \dfrac{\tanh x + \tanh y}{1 + \tanh x \tanh y}.$
11. $2 \sinh x \cosh y = \sinh (x + y) + \sinh (x - y).$
12. $2 \cosh x \cosh y = \cosh (x + y) + \cosh (x - y).$
13. $2 \sinh x \sinh y = \cosh (x + y) - \cosh (x - y).$
14. $\sinh u + \sinh v = 2 \sinh \dfrac{u + v}{2} \cosh \dfrac{u - v}{2}.$
15. $\cosh u + \cosh v = 2 \cosh \dfrac{u + v}{2} \cosh \dfrac{u - v}{2}.$
16. $\cosh u - \cosh v = 2 \sinh \dfrac{u + v}{2} \sinh \dfrac{u - v}{2}.$
17. $\sin^2 x \cosh^2 y + \cos^2 x \sinh^2 y = \tfrac{1}{2}(\cosh 2y - \cos 2x).$
18. $\cos^2 x \cosh^2 y - \sin^2 x \sinh^2 y = \tfrac{1}{2}(1 + \cos 2x \cosh 2y).$
19. Express c and h in terms of a and b when, for all values of x,
    (i) $a \cosh x + b \sinh x = c \cosh (x + h), \quad (a^2 > b^2)$;
    (ii) $a \cosh x + b \sinh x = c \sinh (x + h), \quad (a^2 < b^2).$
20. If $u = \log (\sec \theta + \tan \theta)$, prove that $\tanh \tfrac{1}{2}u = \tan \tfrac{1}{2}\theta$, and that
    $\cosh u = \sec \theta, \quad \sinh u = \tan \theta, \quad \tanh u = \sin \theta.$

§ 244. **Differentiation of Hyperbolic Functions.**—The two standard differential coefficients are :—

$$\frac{d}{dx}(\sinh x) = \cosh x, \qquad \frac{d}{dx}(\cosh x) = \sinh x.$$

Proof.

$$\frac{d}{dx}(\sinh x) = \frac{d}{dx}\{\tfrac{1}{2}(e^x - e^{-x})\} = \tfrac{1}{2}(e^x + e^{-x}) = \cosh x.$$

This proves the first. The second is proved similarly.

By means of the standard rules of differentiation, the other hyperbolic functions can now be differentiated.

§ 245. **Reason for the Term "Hyperbolic".**—If $x = a \cos \theta$, $y = a \sin \theta$, then $x^2 + y^2 = a^2$.

Hence, any point P whose co-ordinates are $(a \cos \theta,\ a \sin \theta)$ lies on the circle $x^2 + y^2 = a^2$ (Fig. 121). Further, if this circle cuts Ox in the point A, the area of the sector AOP $= \frac{1}{2}a^2\theta$. Thus, θ is proportional to the area of the sector AOP.

On account of their relation to the circle, the trigonometric functions are also called *circular* functions.

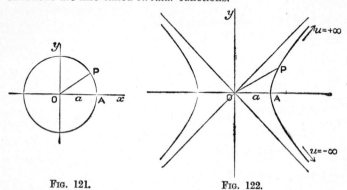

FIG. 121.   FIG. 122.

The *hyperbolic* functions are so called on account of an analogous relation, which will now be explained :—

If $x = a \cosh u$, $y = a \sinh u$, then $x^2 - y^2 = a^2$, by (7).

Hence, any point P whose co-ordinates are $(a \cosh u,\ a \sinh u)$ lies on the rectangular hyperbola $x^2 - y^2 = a^2$. [Since $\cosh u$ is always positive, this point lies on the right-hand half of the hyperbola (Fig. 122), and describes the whole of that half when u varies from $- \infty$ to $+ \infty$, coinciding when $u = 0$ with the point A where the curve crosses the x-axis.]

Moreover, the parameter u is proportional to the area of the hyperbolic sector AOP, as we shall prove :—

Proof.—If dots denote differentiation with respect to u,

$$x = a \cosh u, \qquad y = a \sinh u,$$
$$\dot{x} = a \sinh u, \qquad \dot{y} = a \cosh u,$$
$$\therefore x\dot{y} - \dot{x}y = a^2 (\cosh^2 u - \sinh^2 u) = a^2, \text{ by (7)}.$$

Hence, by (5), § 217,

$$\text{area of sector AOP} = \frac{1}{2}\int_0^u a^2\, du = \frac{1}{2}a^2 u,$$

which is proportional to u.

Examples CX.

Differentiate the given functions with respect to x :—

1. $\tanh x$.
2. $\text{sech } x$.
3. $x + \sinh x \cosh x$.
4. $\sinh^2 x$.
5. $\tanh^2 x$.
6. $\log (\cosh x)$.
7. $\sinh nx$.
8. $\cosh n(a - x)$.
9. $\log (\tanh x)$.
10. $\cosh^n x$.
11. $\cos x \cosh x$.
12. $\tan^{-1} (\tanh \frac{1}{2}x)$.

13. Prove that $e^{-x} \sinh x$ is an increasing function of x for all values of x. Sketch the graph of this function.

14. Sketch the graph of $y = e^{-2x} \sinh x$, for positive values of x. Find the maximum value of y. [Put $v = e^{-x}$.]

15. If $y = e^{-ax} \sinh bx$, find the value of x for which y is a maximum, given that $a > b > 0$.

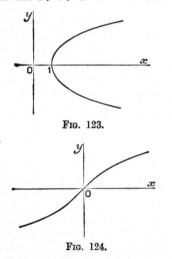

Fig. 123.

Fig. 124.

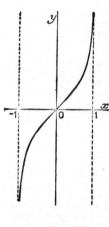

Fig. 125.

§ 246. **Inverse Hyperbolic Functions.**—*The inverse cosh.* If we interchange x and y in the equation $y = \cosh x$, we get

$$x = \cosh y, \quad \text{or } \cosh y = x, \quad \text{or } y = \cosh^{-1} x,$$

which defines y as the *inverse cosh* of x (see § 49).

The graph of $y = \cosh^{-1} x$ is shown in Fig. 123. It is the reflection of the graph of $y = \cosh x$ in the line $y = x$ (§ 50).

If $x > 1$, we see from the graph that $\cosh^{-1} x$ has two values, equal in magnitude but opposite in sign. The positive value is called the *principal value* of $\cosh^{-1} x$.

The inverse sinh. The equation $\sinh y = x$, or $y = \sinh^{-1} x$, defines y as the *inverse sinh* of x. The graph is shown in Fig. 124.

For every value of x the function $\sinh^{-1} x$ has one and only one real value, as we see from the graph.

The inverse tanh. The equation $\tanh y = x$, or $y = \tanh^{-1} x$, defines y as the *inverse tanh* of x. The graph is shown in Fig. 125.

For every value of x *between* 1 *and* -1, the function $\tanh^{-1} x$ has one and only one real value (see graph).

§ 247. Inverse Hyperbolic Functions expressed as Logarithms.
—We shall prove that

$$\sinh^{-1} x = \log \{x + \sqrt{(x^2 + 1)}\}, \tag{1}$$

$$\cosh^{-1} x = \log \{x + \sqrt{(x^2 - 1)}\}, \tag{2}$$

$$\tanh^{-1} x = \tfrac{1}{2} \log \frac{1 + x}{1 - x}, \tag{3}$$

where $\cosh^{-1} x$ has its principal value.

Proof.—By the definitions of $\cosh y$ and $\sinh y$,

$$e^y = \cosh y + \sinh y, \tag{i}$$

$$e^{-y} = \cosh y - \sinh y. \tag{ii}$$

From (i),

$$y = \log (\cosh y + \sinh y). \tag{iii}$$

In (iii), put $y = \sinh^{-1} x$. Then

$$\sinh y = x, \qquad \cosh y = + \sqrt{(x^2 + 1)},$$
$$\therefore \sinh^{-1} x = \log \{x + \sqrt{(x^2 + 1)}\}.$$

Again, in (iii) put $y = \cosh^{-1} x$, where $\cosh^{-1} x$ means the principal value of this function. Then y is positive, and

$$\cosh y = x, \qquad \sinh y = + \sqrt{(x^2 - 1)},$$
$$\therefore \cosh^{-1} x = \log \{x + \sqrt{(x^2 - 1)}\}.$$

Further, dividing (i) by (ii), we have

$$e^{2y} = \frac{\cosh y + \sinh y}{\cosh y - \sinh y} = \frac{1 + \tanh y}{1 - \tanh y},$$

$$\therefore y = \tfrac{1}{2} \log \frac{1 + \tanh y}{1 - \tanh y}. \tag{iv}$$

In (iv), put $y = \tanh^{-1} x$. Then $\tanh y = x$,

$$\therefore \tanh^{-1} x = \tfrac{1}{2} \log \frac{1 + x}{1 - x}.$$

§ 248. Differentiation of Inverse Hyperbolic Functions.

We shall prove the first of the following standard differential coefficients of the inverse hyperbolic functions. The others can be proved in a similar way:—

$$\frac{d}{dx}\sinh^{-1}x = \frac{1}{\sqrt{(x^2+1)}}, \qquad \frac{d}{dx}\sinh^{-1}\frac{x}{a} = \frac{1}{\sqrt{(x^2+a^2)}}; \quad (1)$$

$$\frac{d}{dx}\cosh^{-1}x = \frac{1}{\sqrt{(x^2-1)}}, \qquad \frac{d}{dx}\cosh^{-1}\frac{x}{a} = \frac{1}{\sqrt{(x^2-a^2)}}; \quad (2)$$

$$\frac{d}{dx}\tanh^{-1}x = \frac{1}{1-x^2}, \qquad \frac{d}{dx}\tanh^{-1}\frac{x}{a} = \frac{a}{a^2-x^2}; \quad (3)$$

where the inverse cosh functions have their principal values.

Proof.—Put $y = \sinh^{-1}x$. Then

$$x = \sinh y, \qquad \therefore \frac{dx}{dy} = \cosh y,$$

$$\therefore \frac{dy}{dx} = \frac{1}{\cosh y} = \frac{1}{\sqrt{(\sinh^2 y + 1)}} = \frac{1}{\sqrt{(x^2+1)}}.$$

Examples CXI.

1. If $7\cosh x = 5 + 5\sinh x$, find x.

2. If $x = \sinh y$, prove that $(e^y)^2 - 2x(e^y) - 1 = 0$. Find y from this quadratic equation, and deduce (1), § 247. In the same kind of way, prove (2) and (3), § 247.

3. Calculate the values of

       (i) $\sinh^{-1}\frac{3}{4}$,   (ii) $\cosh^{-1}\frac{5}{3}$,   (iii) $\tanh^{-1}\frac{1}{2}$.

In Exs. 4-9 differentiate the given functions :—

4. $\sinh^{-1}\frac{x}{2}$.   **5.** $\sinh^{-1}\frac{x-1}{2}$.   **6.** $\cosh^{-1}\frac{2x-3}{x+1}$.

7. $\tanh^{-1}\frac{x}{3}$.   **8.** $\sinh^{-1}\frac{x-1}{x}$.   **9.** $\tanh^{-1}\frac{a+x}{1+ax}$.

§ 249. Hyperbolic Integrands.

We shall prove the results :—

$$\int \sinh x\,dx = \cosh x. \tag{1}$$
$$\int \cosh x\,dx = \sinh x. \tag{2}$$
$$\int \tanh x\,dx = \log(\cosh x). \tag{3}$$
$$\int \coth x\,dx = \log(\sinh x). \tag{4}$$
$$\int \operatorname{sech} x\,dx = 2\tan^{-1}(e^x). \tag{5}$$
$$\int \operatorname{cosech} x\,dx = \log(\tanh \tfrac{1}{2}x). \tag{6}$$

Proof of (1) and (2).—These follow at once from § 244.

Proof of (3). $\int \tanh x\,dx = \int \frac{\sinh x\,dx}{\cosh x} = \int \frac{d(\cosh x)}{\cosh x} = \log(\cosh x)$

The proof of (4) is similar.

Proof of (5). $\int \text{sech } x \, dx = \int \dfrac{2dx}{e^x + e^{-x}} = \int \dfrac{2e^x dx}{e^{2x} + 1} = 2 \int \dfrac{dv}{v^2 + 1},$

where $v = e^x$.   Hence

$$\int \text{sech } x \, dx = 2 \tan^{-1} v = 2 \tan^{-1} (e^x).$$

Proof of (6). $\int \text{cosech } x \, dx = \int \dfrac{2\,dx}{e^x - e^{-x}} = \int \dfrac{2e^x dx}{e^{2x} - 1} = \int \dfrac{2dv}{v^2 - 1},$

where $v = e^x$.   Hence

$$\int \text{cosech } x \, dx = \log \frac{v - 1}{v + 1} = \log \frac{e^x - 1}{e^x + 1} = \log \left(\tanh \frac{x}{2} \right).$$

§ 250. All integrals with hyperbolic integrands can be evaluated by methods analogous to those that would be used for the corresponding trigonometric integrands.

Ex. Evaluate $\int \cosh^2 u \, du$.

$$\int \cosh^2 u \, du = \tfrac{1}{2}\int(\cosh 2u + 1)du = \tfrac{1}{2}(\tfrac{1}{2} \sinh 2u + u),$$
$$\therefore \int \cosh^2 u \, du = \tfrac{1}{2}(\sinh u \cosh u + u).$$

§ 251. The method used in the proofs of (5) and (6), § 249, suggests the following rule :—

Rule.—To evaluate an integral in which the integrand is a rational function of e^x, where x is the variable of integration, make the substitution

$$v = e^x, \quad x = \log v, \quad dx = \frac{dv}{v}.$$

The integral is thereby transformed into one in which the integrand is a *rational* function of v, and hence can be evaluated (§ 180).

Examples CXII.

Evaluate the given integrals :—

1. $\int \sinh^2 x \, dx$.
2. $\int \text{sech}^2 x \, dx$.
3. $\int \tanh^2 x \, dx$.
4. $\int \sinh^3 x \, dx$.
5. $\int \tanh^3 x \, dx$.
6. $\int \text{sech}^3 x \, dx$.
7. $\int x \sinh x \, dx$.
8. $\int \cosh ax \cos bx \, dx$.
9. $\int \sinh^{-1} x \, dx$.
10. $\int \tanh^{-1} x \, dx$.
11. $\int x \tanh^{-1} x \, dx$.
12. $\int \dfrac{dx}{a + e^x}$.
13. $\int \dfrac{e^x + 1}{e^x + 2} \, dx$.
14. $\int \dfrac{dx}{(e^x - 1)^2}$.
15. $\int_0^1 \cosh x \, dx$.
16. $\int_0^1 \cosh^2 x \, dx$.
17. $\int_0^1 x \cosh x \, dx$.
18. $\int_0^\infty \text{sech}^2 x \, dx$.
19. $\int_0^\infty \text{sech } x \, dx$.
20. $\int_0^\infty e^{-2x} \sinh x \, dx$.

21. $\int_0^\infty \frac{dx}{\sqrt{(3e^x + 1)}}.$ **22.** $\int_0^\infty x \operatorname{sech} x \tanh x \, dx.$

23. $\int_0^b \cosh n(b - x) dx.$ **24.** $\int_0^\pi \sinh a(\pi - x) \sin x \, dx.$

In Exs. 25-27 prove the given reduction formulæ :—

25. $n\int\cosh^n x \, dx = \sinh x \cosh^{n-1} x + (n - 1) \int\cosh^{n-2} x \, dx.$
26. $(n - 1) \int\tanh^n x \, dx = - \tanh^{n-1} x + (n - 1) \int\tanh^{n-2} x \, dx.$
27. $(n-1) \int\operatorname{sech}^n x \, dx = \tanh x \operatorname{sech}^{n-2} x + (n - 2) \int\operatorname{sech}^{n-2} x \, dx.$

§ 252. Integrals involving Inverse Hyperbolic Functions.

From (1) and (2), § 248, follow, inversely,

$$\int \frac{dx}{\sqrt{(x^2 + a^2)}} = \sinh^{-1}\frac{x}{a} = \log\{x + \sqrt{(x^2 + a^2)}\} + C, \qquad (1)$$

$$\int \frac{dx}{\sqrt{(x^2 - a^2)}} = \cosh^{-1}\frac{x}{a} = \log\{x + \sqrt{(x^2 - a^2)}\} + C, \qquad (2)$$

where $C = - \log a$. Both these integrals, in their logarithmic forms, are particular cases of (2), § 193. Other integrals can often be expressed conveniently in terms of inverse hyperbolic functions, which usually arise as the result of a hyperbolic substitution, made with the object of rationalising the square root of a quadratic function in the integrand :—

§ 253. **Hyperbolic Substitutions.**—The following *hyperbolic* substitutions are sometimes preferable to the corresponding trigonometric ones (the second and third at the top of p. 186) :—

$\sqrt{(x^2 + a^2)}$; $x = a \sinh u,$ $dx = a \cosh u \, du,$ $\sqrt{(x^2 + a^2)} = a \cosh u.$
$\sqrt{(x^2 - a^2)}$; $x = a \cosh u,$ $dx = a \sinh u \, du,$ $\sqrt{(x^2 - a^2)} = a \sinh u.$

Ex. Prove that

$$\int\sqrt{(x^2 + a^2)}dx = \tfrac{1}{2}x\sqrt{(x^2 + a^2)} + \tfrac{1}{2}a^2 \sinh^{-1}\frac{x}{a}, \qquad (3)$$

$$\int\sqrt{(x^2 - a^2)}dx = \tfrac{1}{2}x\sqrt{(x^2 - a^2)} - \tfrac{1}{2}a^2 \cosh^{-1}\frac{x}{a}. \qquad (4)$$

Both these integrals are particular cases of (6), § 196. Here we prove them by means of hyperbolic substitutions.

Proof of (3).—Put
$\quad x = a \sinh u,$ $dx = a \cosh u \, du,$ $\sqrt{(x^2 + a^2)} = a \cosh u,$
$\quad \therefore \int\sqrt{(x^2 + a^2)}dx = a^2 \int \cosh^2 u \, du$
$\qquad\qquad\qquad\qquad = \tfrac{1}{2}a^2(\sinh u \cosh u + u),$ as in § 250.

But $\qquad\qquad \sinh u = \frac{x}{a},$ $\therefore \cosh u = \frac{\sqrt{(x^2 + a^2)}}{a},$

$\qquad \therefore \int\sqrt{(x^2 + a^2)}dx = \tfrac{1}{2}x\sqrt{(x^2 + a^2)} + \tfrac{1}{2}a^2 \sinh^{-1}\frac{x}{a}.$

Proof of (4).—Put $x = a \cosh u,$ and proceed similarly.

Examples CXIII.

Evaluate the given integrals, using hyperbolic substitutions :—

1. $\int \dfrac{dx}{\sqrt{(x^2+1)}}$.

2. $\int \dfrac{dx}{\sqrt{(x^2-1)}}$.

3. $\int \dfrac{x^2 dx}{\sqrt{(x^2+1)}}$.

4. $\int \dfrac{dx}{\sqrt{(x^2+3)}}$.

5. $\int \dfrac{x+1}{\sqrt{(4x^2-1)}} dx$.

6. $\int \dfrac{dx}{\sqrt{(x^2-x)}}$.

7. $\int \sqrt{(x^2+4)} dx$.

8. $\int \sqrt{(x^2-4)} dx$.

9. $\int \sqrt{(x^2-6x+5)} dx$.

10. $\int \dfrac{\sqrt{(x^2-1)}}{x^2} dx$.

11. $\int \dfrac{dx}{x^2 \sqrt{(x^2+1)}}$.

12. $\int \dfrac{dx}{x^4 \sqrt{(x^2-1)}}$.

13. $\int \dfrac{dx}{(x^2+1)\sqrt{(x^2+5)}}$.

14. $\int \dfrac{dx}{(3x^2+1)\sqrt{(x^2-1)}}$.

§ 254. The Catenary.—The catenary is the curve in which a uniform chain hangs under its own weight.

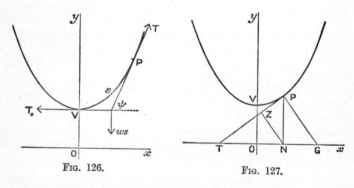

Fig. 126.   Fig. 127.

The lowest point V is called the *vertex* (Fig. 126). Let P be any other point of the chain. Let T be the tension at P, T_0 the tension at V, s the length of the arc VP, w the weight per unit length of the chain, ψ the angle which the tangent at P makes with the horizontal.

The weight of the portion VP is ws, and this portion is in equilibrium under the three forces T, T_0, and ws. Resolving vertically and horizontally, we find

$$T \sin \psi = ws, \quad T \cos \psi = T_0,$$

$$\therefore \tan \psi = \frac{ws}{T_0} = \frac{s}{c},$$ (i)

where $c = T_0/w$.   Hence the relation between s and ψ is

$$s = c \tan \psi. \tag{1}$$

This is the *intrinsic equation* of the catenary.[1]

The horizontal line drawn at a depth c below the vertex is called the *directrix* of the catenary.

The simplest (x, y) equation of the catenary is obtained by taking the directrix for the x-axis, and the y-axis through the vertex.   Then

$$x = 0 \text{ and } y = c, \quad \text{when } s = 0. \tag{ii}$$

By (i), we have

$$\frac{dx}{ds} = \cos \psi = \frac{c}{\sqrt{(s^2 + c^2)}}, \quad \frac{dy}{ds} = \sin \psi = \frac{s}{\sqrt{(s^2 + c^2)}}, \tag{iii}$$

and hence, by integration,

$$x = c \sinh^{-1} \frac{s}{c}, \quad y = \sqrt{(s^2 + c^2)}, \tag{2}$$

the constants of integration being zero, in virtue of (ii).

Equations (2) are parametric equations of the catenary, s being the parameter.

Eliminating s from them, we find the (x, y) equation :

$$y = c \cosh \frac{x}{c}. \tag{3}$$

Examples CXIV.

1. Prove that, with the angle ψ as parameter, the equations of the catenary are

$$x = c \log (\sec \psi + \tan \psi), \quad y = c \sec \psi.$$

2. The catenary $y = c \cosh (x/c)$ is shown in Fig. 127. Let PN be the ordinate, PT the tangent, PG the normal, at any point P, and let NZ be the perpendicular from N on PT. Prove the following results :—

   (i) NZ = c.
   (ii) Arc VP = s = PZ.
   (iii) Area ONPV = cs = $2\triangle$NPZ.
   (iv) Radius of curvature at P = y^2/c = PG.
   (v) The centre of gravity of the *area* ONPV is vertically beneath the centre of gravity of the *arc* VP.

[1] The relation between s and ψ for any curve is called its *intrinsic* equation.

CHAPTER XVIII.

COMPLEX NUMBERS.

§ 255. All the positive and negative numbers are said to be *real*. There is no real number whose square is -1. The square root of -1 is therefore called an *imaginary* number. It is denoted by the letter i.

Because it is neither a positive nor a negative number, we must not conclude that the number i cannot be useful; it is, in fact, of great use, not only in Pure Mathematics but in practical problems.

Expressions involving the number i are called *complex numbers*. The simplest form of a complex number is $a + ib$, where a and b are real numbers. Of this complex number, a is called the *real part* and ib the *imaginary part*. A number of the form ib, where b is real, is called a *pure imaginary*. Two numbers of the form $a + ib$, $a - ib$, that differ only in the signs before their imaginary parts, are called a *conjugate pair*.

Ex. 1. The successive powers of the number i are
$$i, \ i^2 = -1, \ i^3 = -i, \ i^4 = 1, \ i^5 = i, \ i^6 = -1, \ \ldots$$

Ex. 2. The roots of the quadratic equation

(i) $x^2 + 1 = 0$, or $x^2 = -1$, are $\pm i$;

(ii) $x^2 + 3 = 0$, or $x^2 = -3$, are $x = \pm i\sqrt{3}$;

(iii) $x^2 - 2x + 5 = 0$, or $(x - 1)^2 = -4$, are $x = 1 \pm 2i$.

§ 256. Factors of the Sum of Two Squares.—Since
$$(a + ib)(a - ib) = a^2 - i^2b^2 = a^2 + b^2,$$
$$\therefore \ a^2 + b^2 = (a + ib)(a - ib).$$

Thus the *sum* of two squares can be factorised, the factors being a conjugate pair of complex numbers.

§ 257. Equating of Real and Imaginary Parts.—Let $x + iy$ and $a + ib$ be two equal complex numbers, where $x, y, a \ b$ are all real. Then
$$x + iy = a + ib,$$
$$\therefore \ x - a = -i(y - b),$$
$$\therefore \ (x - a)^2 = -(y - b)^2,$$

i.e. a positive real number equal to a negative one, which is impossible unless both are zero.   Hence

$$x - a = 0, \qquad y - b = 0,$$
$$\therefore x = a, \quad y = b.$$

It follows that, when two complex numbers are equal, we can *equate their real parts and their imaginary parts.*

Examples CXV.

In Exs. 1-7 simplify the given expressions, i.e. reduce them to the form $a + ib$, where a and b are real :—

1. $(1 + 5i) + (3 - 2i).$ **2.** $(1 + 5i) - (3 - 2i).$
3. $(3 + 2i)^2.$ **4.** $(i - 1)^3.$ **5.** $(1 + i)^{15}.$
6. $(2 + 3i)(2 + i).$ **7.** $(3 + i)^4 + (3 - i)^4.$

8. If $f(x) = 2 + x + 3x^2 - x^3$, express $f(3 + 2i)$ in the form $a + ib$, where a and b are real.

9. Find real values of x and y that satisfy the equations

(i) $(2 - 5i)x + (1 + 3i)y - 3 + 13i = 0,$
(ii) $(x + iy)^2 = 5 - 12i.$

10. Let $x + iy = \sqrt{(3 - 4i)}$.   Square both sides, equate real and imaginary parts, and hence find the two square roots of $(3 - 4i)$ in the form $\pm(a + ib)$, where a and b are real.

11. Find the square roots of

(i) $4 + 3i$,   (ii) $16 - 30i$,   (iii) i.

12. Solve the quadratic equations

(i) $x^2 + x + 1 = 0$;   (ii) $x^2 - 2ax + a^2 + b^2 = 0$;
(iii) $x^2 - x + 1 + i = 0$;   (iv) $x^2 - 4ix - 7 - 4i = 0.$

§ 258. Powers with Complex Indices.

Every new expression in mathematics has to be *defined* before we can use it.

The simplest power with a real base and an imaginary index is $e^{i\theta}$, where e is the base of natural logarithms and θ is a real number.   To define $e^{i\theta}$ we make use of the expansion

$$e^x = 1 + \frac{x}{1!} + \frac{x^2}{2!} + \frac{x^3}{3!} + \frac{x^4}{4!} + \cdots$$

which holds good when x is real (§ 164).   We let this expansion *define* $e^{i\theta}$ when we replace x by $i\theta$.   Thus $e^{i\theta}$ is *defined* by

$$e^{i\theta} = 1 + \frac{i\theta}{1!} + \frac{(i\theta)^2}{2!} + \frac{(i\theta)^3}{3!} + \frac{(i\theta)^4}{4!} + \cdots$$

After simplifying the powers of i on the right, we get

$$e^{i\theta} = \left(1 - \frac{\theta^2}{2!} + \frac{\theta^4}{4!} - \cdots\right) + i\left(\frac{\theta}{1!} - \frac{\theta^3}{3!} + \frac{\theta^5}{5!} - \cdots\right),$$

$$\therefore \ e^{i\theta} = \cos\theta + i\sin\theta.$$

(See Exs. LXXIV., Nos. 1 and 2.)

§ 259. *Definition of e^{x+iy}.*—We can now define e^{x+iy} thus:

$$e^{x+iy} = e^x \times e^{iy} = e^x(\cos y + i\sin y).$$

§ 260. We shall verify that the Law of Indices $e^m \times e^n = e^{m+n}$ remains true when m and n are pure imaginaries.

Let $m = i\theta$, $n = i\phi$. Then

$$e^m \times e^n = e^{i\theta} \times e^{i\phi}$$

$$= (\cos\theta + i\sin\theta)(\cos\phi + i\sin\phi)$$
$$= (\cos\theta\cos\phi - \sin\theta\sin\phi) + i(\sin\theta\cos\phi + \cos\theta\sin\phi)$$
$$= \cos(\theta + \phi) + i\sin(\theta + \phi)$$
$$= e^{i(\theta+\phi)} = e^{i\theta+i\phi} = e^{m+n},$$

which verifies the law stated. Similarly it may be verified that this law holds good when m and n are any complex numbers.

§ 261. It follows that

$$(e^{i\theta})^2 = e^{i\theta} \times e^{i\theta} = e^{2i\theta},$$
$$(e^{i\theta})^3 = e^{i\theta} \times e^{i\theta} \times e^{i\theta} = e^{2i\theta} \times e^{i\theta} = e^{3i\theta},$$

and so on. Hence the Law of Indices $(e^m)^n = e^{mn}$ holds good when m is a pure imaginary and n a positive integer.

Ex. Verify that $\cos 2\theta = \cos^2\theta - \sin^2\theta$, $\sin 2\theta = 2\sin\theta\cos\theta$.

We have $\qquad\qquad e^{2i\theta} = (e^{i\theta})^2,$

that is, $\qquad \cos 2\theta + i\sin 2\theta = (\cos\theta + i\sin\theta)^2,$

$$\therefore \ \cos 2\theta + i\sin 2\theta = \cos^2\theta - \sin^2\theta + 2i\sin\theta\cos\theta.$$

Equating real and imaginary parts, we get

$$\cos 2\theta = \cos^2\theta - \sin^2\theta, \quad \sin 2\theta = 2\sin\theta\cos\theta.$$

§ 262. **Every Complex Number can be Written in the Form** $re^{i\theta}$, **where r and θ are real, and r is positive.**—Let $x + iy$ be any complex number, and let (r, θ) be the polar co-ordinates of the point whose Cartesian co-ordinates are (x, y), where r is taken positive. Then

$$x = r\cos\theta, \quad y = r\sin\theta,$$
$$\therefore \ x + iy = r(\cos\theta + i\sin\theta) = re^{i\theta},$$

where $r = +\sqrt{(x^2 + y^2)}$, $\tan\theta = y/x$.

The quadrant in which θ lies is the same as that in which the point (x, y) lies.

Ex. Express $(1 + i)$ in the form $re^{i\theta}$.

The polar co-ordinates of the point whose Cartesian co-ordinates are $(1, 1)$ are $(\sqrt{2}, \tfrac{1}{4}\pi)$. Hence

$$1 + i = \sqrt{2}e^{\frac{\pi i}{4}}.$$

§ 263. The nth Roots of any Real or Complex Number.—Let $x + iy$ denote any number, and put

$$x + iy = re^{i\theta}, \text{ where } r = +\sqrt{(x^2 + y^2)}, \tan\theta = y/x.$$

Now, if k is any integer,

$$e^{2k\pi i} = \cos 2k\pi + i\sin 2k\pi = 1;$$

hence we may also put

$$x + iy = re^{i\theta} \cdot e^{2k\pi i} = re^{(\theta + 2k\pi)i}.$$

It follows that an nth root of $(x + iy)$ is given by

$$(x + iy)^{\frac{1}{n}} = r^{\frac{1}{n}}e^{\frac{(\theta + 2k\pi)i}{n}}.$$

By giving k the n values $0, 1, 2, \ldots (n - 1)$, we find that $(x + iy)$ has n different nth roots, viz.

$$r^{\frac{1}{n}}e^{\frac{\theta i}{n}}, \quad r^{\frac{1}{n}}e^{\frac{(\theta + 2\pi)i}{n}}, \quad r^{\frac{1}{n}}e^{\frac{(\theta + 4\pi)i}{n}}, \quad \ldots$$

Ex. Putting $r = 1$, $\theta = 0$, $n = 3$, we obtain the three cube roots of unity, viz.,

$$1, \quad e^{\frac{2\pi i}{3}}, \quad e^{\frac{4\pi i}{3}},$$

that is,

$$1, \quad \cos\frac{2\pi}{3} + i\sin\frac{2\pi}{3}, \quad \cos\frac{4\pi}{3} + i\sin\frac{2\pi}{3},$$

or,

$$1, \quad \tfrac{1}{2}(-1 + i\sqrt{3}), \quad \tfrac{1}{2}(-1 - i\sqrt{3}).$$

§ 264. The Logarithm of any Real or Complex Number.—Let $x + iy$ denote any number. Then, as in § 263, we can put

$$x + iy = re^{(\theta + 2k\pi)i},$$

where $r = +\sqrt{(x^2 + y^2)}$, $\tan\theta = y/x$, and k is any integer.

It follows that a logarithm of $(x + iy)$ is given by

$$\log(x + iy) = \log r + (\theta + 2k\pi)i.$$

Since k is any integer, the logarithm of any number has an infinite number of values. The *principal value* is the one in which $(\theta + 2k\pi)$ lies between π and $-\pi$.

Ex. Since 3 can be written in the form $3e^{2k\pi i}$, where k is any integer, the general value of the logarithm of 3 to base e is given by

$$\log\left(3e^{2k\pi i}\right) = \log 3 + 2k\pi i.$$

The principal value is obtained by putting $k = 0$, which gives the ordinary real logarithm $\log 3$.

Examples CXVI.

1. Express in the form $re^{i\theta}$:—
(i) $\sqrt{3} + i$, (ii) $1 - i$, (iii) i, (iv) -5, (v) $-3i$, (vi) $3 + 4i$,
(vii) $(\cos \alpha + i \sin \alpha)(\cos \beta + i \sin \beta)$, (viii) $\left(\dfrac{\cos \alpha + i \sin \alpha}{\cos \beta + i \sin \beta}\right)^2$.

2. Show that $\cos 3\theta + i \sin 3\theta = (\cos \theta + i \sin \theta)^3$. Deduce that
$$\cos 3\theta = \cos^3 \theta - 3 \cos \theta \sin^2 \theta = 4 \cos^3 \theta - 3 \cos \theta,$$
$$\sin 3\theta = 3 \cos^2 \theta \sin \theta - \sin^3 \theta = 3 \sin \theta - 4 \sin^3 \theta.$$

3. Prove that $(1 + i)^n = 2^{\frac{n}{2}}\left(\cos \dfrac{n\pi}{4} + i \sin \dfrac{n\pi}{4}\right)$.

4. Find the three cube roots of
(i) $8i$, (ii) $-27i$, (iii) $2(1 + i)$, (iv) $4 + 3i$.

5. Find the four fourth roots of (i) 1, (ii) -4.

6. Find the principal values of the logarithms of
(i) i, (ii) -1, (iii) $1 + i$, (iv) $3 + i$.

7. Put $a = e^{\log a}$, and deduce that $a^{x + iy}$ must be defined by
$$a^{x+iy} = a^x\{\cos (y \log a) + i \sin (y \log a)\}.$$

8. Express in the form $a + ib$, where a and b are real,
(i) 2^{3+i}, (ii) $3^i + 3^{-i}$.

§ 265. The Real and Imaginary Parts of a Product.—Let $x + iy$, $a + ib$ be two complex numbers. To separate the real and imaginary parts of their product :—

First Method.—
$$(x + iy)(a + ib) = ax - by + i(ay + bx).$$

Second Method.—Put
$$x + iy = re^{i\theta}, \text{ where } r = + \sqrt{(x^2 + y^2)}, \text{ tan } \theta = y/x;$$
$$a + ib = se^{i\phi}, \text{ where } s = + \sqrt{(a^2 + b^2)}, \text{ tan } \phi = b/a.$$
Then
$$(x + iy)(a + ib) = re^{i\theta} \cdot se^{i\phi} = rse^{i(\theta + \phi)},$$
$$\therefore (x + iy)(a + ib) = rs\{\cos (\theta + \phi) + i \sin (\theta + \phi)\}.$$

§ 266. The Real and Imaginary Parts of a Quotient.—

First Method.—Multiply numerator and denominator by the conjugate of the denominator ; thus

$$\frac{x + iy}{a + ib} = \frac{(x + iy)(a - ib)}{(a + ib)(a - ib)} = \frac{ax + by + i(ay - bx)}{a^2 + b^2}.$$

Second Method.—In the notation of § 265,

$$\frac{x + iy}{a + ib} = \frac{re^{i\theta}}{se^{i\phi}} = \frac{r}{s}e^{i(\theta - \phi)},$$

$$\therefore \frac{x + iy}{a + ib} = \frac{r}{s}\{\cos(\theta - \phi) + i\sin(\theta - \phi)\}.$$

Ex. 1. Evaluate $\int e^{ax} \cos bx\, dx$. [Compare § 175 (ii).]

Put $\qquad u = \int e^{ax} \cos bx\, dx, \quad v = \int e^{ax} \sin bx\, dx.$

Then $\qquad u + iv = \int e^{ax}(\cos bx + i\sin bx)dx$

$$= \int e^{ax}e^{ibx}\,dx = \int e^{(a+ib)x}\,dx = \frac{e^{(a+ib)x}}{a + ib}.$$

Multiplying numerator and denominator by $(a - ib)$,

$$u + iv = \frac{e^{ax}(\cos bx + i\sin bx)(a - ib)}{a^2 + b^2}.$$

Hence, equating *real* parts,

$$u = \frac{e^{ax}(a\cos bx + b\sin bx)}{a^2 + b^2}.$$

Alternative method.

$$u + iv = \frac{e^{(a+ib)x}}{a + ib} = \frac{e^{ax}e^{ibx}}{\sqrt{(a^2 + b^2)}e^{i\phi}} = \frac{e^{ax}e^{i(bx-\phi)}}{\sqrt{(a^2 + b^2)}},$$

where $\phi = \tan^{-1}(b/a)$. Hence, equating real parts,

$$u = \frac{e^{ax}}{\sqrt{(a^2 + b^2)}} \cos(bx - \phi).$$

Ex. 2. Find the nth differential coefficient of $e^{ax} \sin bx$.

Put $\qquad u = D^n(e^{ax} \cos bx), \quad v = D^n(e^{ax} \sin bx),$

$$\therefore u + iv = D^n\{e^{(a+ib)x}\} = (a + ib)^n e^{(a+ib)x},$$

$$\therefore u + iv = (a^2 + b^2)^{\frac{n}{2}} e^{ax} e^{i(bx+n\phi)},$$

where $\phi = \tan^{-1}(b/a)$. Hence, equating *imaginary* parts,

$$v = (a^2 + b^2)^{\frac{n}{2}} e^{ax} \sin(bx + n\phi).$$

§ 267. Euler's Formulæ.

—Changing the sign of θ in

$$e^{i\theta} = \cos\theta + i\sin\theta,$$

we get

$$e^{-i\theta} = \cos\theta - i\sin\theta.$$

Hence, after adding and subtracting, we get

$$\cos\theta = \frac{e^{i\theta} + e^{-i\theta}}{2}, \quad \sin\theta = \frac{e^{i\theta} - e^{-i\theta}}{2i}.$$

These are known as *Euler's formulæ*. They may be compared with (1), § 239.

We can use Euler's formulæ to *define* $\cos \theta$ and $\sin \theta$ when θ is not real. After thus defining them, we deduce, on replacing θ by $i\theta$, that

$$\cos i\theta = \cosh \theta, \quad \sin i\theta = i \sinh \theta,$$

which explains the Note at the end of § 243.

Further, we could verify, by the method of § 243, that all the ordinary identities of Trigonometry hold good whether the angles are real or complex.

Ex. Separate the real and imaginary parts of

$$\text{(i) } \sin (x + iy), \quad \text{(ii) } \tan (x + iy).$$

(i) $\sin (x + iy) = \sin x \cos iy + \cos x \sin iy$

$$= \sin x \cosh y + i \cos x \sinh y.$$

(ii) $\tan (x + iy) = \dfrac{\sin (x + iy)}{\cos (x + iy)} = \dfrac{2 \sin (x + iy) \cos (x - iy)}{2 \cos (x + iy) \cos (x - iy)},$

$$\therefore \tan (x + iy) = \frac{\sin 2x + i \sinh 2y}{\cos 2x + \cosh 2y}.$$

Examples CXVII.

1. Separate the real and imaginary parts of

$$\text{(i) } \frac{1}{3 + i}; \quad \text{(ii) } \frac{1}{(1 + 2i)^2}; \quad \text{(iii) } \frac{e^{1+2i}}{3 + 4i} \quad \text{(iv) } \frac{1}{1 - re^{i\theta}}$$

2. Find (i) $\dfrac{d^4}{dx^4} (e^x \cos x)$; (ii) $\dfrac{d^n}{dx^n} (e^x \cos x)$.

3. Evaluate the integrals :—

$$\text{(i) } \int_0^{2\pi} e^x \cos x \, dx; \quad \text{(ii) } \int_0^{2\pi} x e^x \cos x \, dx; \quad \text{(iii) } \int_0^\infty x e^{-x} \sin x \, dx;$$

$$\text{(iv) } \int_0^\infty e^{-ax} \cos bx \, dx; \quad \text{(v) } \int_0^\infty e^{-ax} \sin bx \, dx; \quad (a > 0).$$

4. Separate the real and imaginary parts of

$$\text{(i) } \cos (x + iy); \quad \text{(ii) } \sec (x + iy); \quad \text{(iii) } \cot (x + iy).$$

5. Separate the real and imaginary parts of

$$\text{(i) } \sinh (x + iy); \quad \text{(ii) } \cosh (x + iy); \quad \text{(iii) } \tanh (x + iy).$$

6 Let $\sin (x + iy) = 2$. Expand the left side, equate real and imaginary parts, and deduce that

$$\sin^{-1} 2 = \tfrac{1}{2}\pi \pm i \log (2 + \sqrt{3}).$$

7. If $x + iy = \sin^{-1}(a + ib)$, where x, y, a, b are real, show that

$$\sin x \cosh y = a, \quad \cos x \sinh y = b.$$

Deduce that, if x lies between $\frac{1}{2}\pi$ and $-\frac{1}{2}\pi$, the point (x, y) lies in the same quadrant as the point (a, b).

Also show that

$$\frac{a^2}{\sin^2 x} - \frac{b^2}{\cos^2 x} = 1, \quad \frac{a^2}{\cosh^2 y} + \frac{b^2}{\sinh^2 y} = 1.$$

8. Express in the form $x + iy$, where x and y are real,

(i) $\sin^{-1}(1 + i)$; (ii) $\sin^{-1}(-2 + 3i)$;

given that, in each case, x lies between $\frac{1}{2}\pi$ and $-\frac{1}{2}\pi$. [Use Ex. **7.**]

9. If $x + iy = \tan^{-1}(a + ib)$, where x, y, a, b are real, show that

$$\frac{\sin 2x}{\cos 2x + \cosh 2y} = a, \quad \frac{\sinh 2y}{\cos 2x + \cosh 2y} = b.$$

Deduce that, if x lies between $\frac{1}{2}\pi$ and $-\frac{1}{2}\pi$, the point (x, y) lies in the same quadrant as the point (a, b).

Also show that

$$\tan 2x = \frac{2a}{1 - a^2 - b^2}, \quad \tanh 2y = \frac{2b}{1 + a^2 + b^2}.$$

10. Express in the form $x + iy$, where x and y are real,

(i) $\tan^{-1}(1 + i)$; (ii) $\tan^{-1}(-2 + 3i)$;

given that, in each case, x lies between $\frac{1}{2}\pi$ and $-\frac{1}{2}\pi$. [Use Ex. **9.**]

11. Using Euler's formulæ, prove the identities:

$$4 \sin^3 \theta = 3 \sin \theta - \sin 3\theta,$$
$$4 \cos^3 \theta = 3 \cos \theta + \cos 3\theta,$$
$$8 \sin^4 \theta = 3 - 4 \cos 2\theta + \cos 4\theta,$$
$$8 \cos^4 \theta = 3 + 4 \cos 2\theta + \cos 4\theta.$$

12. Using Euler's formulæ, prove the identities:

$$32 \sin^2 \theta \cos^4 \theta = 2 + \cos 2\theta - 2 \cos 4\theta - \cos 6\theta,$$
$$32 \sin^4 \theta \cos^2 \theta = 2 - \cos 2\theta - 2 \cos 4\theta + \cos 6\theta,$$
$$64 \sin^4 \theta \cos^3 \theta = 3 \cos \theta - 3 \cos 3\theta - \cos 5\theta + \cos 7\theta,$$
$$64 \sin^3 \theta \cos^4 \theta = 3 \sin \theta + 3 \sin 3\theta - \sin 5\theta - \sin 7\theta.$$

Hence indicate a method of evaluating $\int \sin^m \theta \cos^n \theta \, d\theta$,

CHAPTER XIX.

DIFFERENTIAL EQUATIONS.

§ 268. **Differential Equations.**—A differential equation is an equation that contains differential coefficients. The equation is said to be *ordinary* or *partial* according as it contains ordinary or partial differential coefficients. Here we consider ordinary differential equations only.

The *order* of a differential equation is the order of the highest differential coefficient it contains, the *degree* of the equation is its degree considered as an algebraic equation in the highest differential coefficient. For example,

$$\left(\frac{dy}{dx}\right)^2 = x^2 + y^2$$

is a differential equation of the first order and second degree; while

$$x^2\frac{d^2y}{dx^2} + x\frac{dy}{dx} + (x^2 - n^2)y = 0$$

is of the second order and first degree.

§ 269. **Solution of an Ordinary Differential Equation.**—If x and y are the variables in an ordinary differential equation, the most general relation between x and y that satisfies the equation is called the *general solution* or the *complete integral* or the *primitive* of the equation.

Any particular relation between x and y that satisfies the equation is called a *particular solution*.

When we find the general solution we are said to *solve* or *integrate* the equation.

Ex. 1.
$$\frac{dy}{dx} = 2x.$$

$$\therefore y = \int 2x\,dx + \text{A},$$
$$\therefore y = x^2 + \text{A}.$$

This is the general solution, where A denotes an arbitrary constant.

Ex. 2. $$\frac{dy}{dx} = 2y.$$

$$\therefore \frac{dy}{y} = 2dx,$$

$\therefore \log y = 2x + A$, by integration,

$$\therefore y = e^{2x+A} = e^{2x} \cdot e^A = e^A \cdot e^{2x} = Ce^{2x},$$

$$\therefore y = Ce^{2x}.$$

This is the general solution, where C is an arbitrary constant. Here it is easy to express y explicitly in terms of x. We put C in place of e^A, which is merely an arbitrary constant, since A is arbitrary.

§ 270. **The Arbitrary Constant. Particular Solutions.**—In the examples above an arbitrary constant appears in the general solution. By giving a particular value to the constant, a particular solution is obtained. Thus, if we put $A = 0$ in the general solution of Ex. 1, we obtain the particular solution $y = x^2$. If we put $C = 3$ in the general solution of Ex. 2 we obtain the particular solution $y = 3e^{2x}$.

Ex. Given that y satisfies the equation

$$\frac{dy}{dx} = 3 - y,$$

and that $y = 0$ when $x = 0$, express y in terms of x.

The equation may be written

$$\frac{dy}{3 - y} = dx.$$

$\therefore -\log(3 - y) = x + A$, by integration,

$$\therefore 3 - y = e^{-x-A} = e^{-A} \cdot e^{-x} = Ce^{-x},$$

$$\therefore y = 3 - Ce^{-x}.$$

But $y = 0$ when $x = 0$,

$$\therefore 0 = 3 - C, \quad \therefore C = 3,$$

$$\therefore y = 3(1 - e^{-x}).$$

Here, a *particular solution* is required. The method is to find the general solution containing the arbitrary constant C, and then to obtain the particular solution required by using the additional information that $y = 0$ when $x = 0$.

§ 271. **Geometrical Meaning.** — Geometrically, a differential equation expresses a property common to every member of an infinite number of curves. Thus, consider the following differential equation and its general solution :

$$dy/dx = 2x, \quad y = x^2 + c.$$

For any particular value of the constant c, the curve $y = x^2 + c$ is a parabola with its vertex at the point $(0, c)$ and its axis along the y-axis. If we imagine c to take all values, we obtain an infinite *system* or *family* of such parabolas that covers the whole of the xy plane, and at every point on every curve of the system the differential equation $dy/dx = 2x$ is satisfied, i.e. every curve has the property that at every point on it the gradient is equal to twice the abscissa.

The infinite system of curves represents the general solution; any particular curve of the system represents a particular solution.

Examples CXVIII.

In Exs. 1-16, solve the given equations :—

1. $dy/dx = x^3$.
2. $dy/dx = y^3$.
3. $dy/dx = ax$.
4. $dy/dx = ay$.
5. $dy/dx = x^2 - 1$.
6. $dy/dx = y^2 - 1$.
7. $dy/dx = (x - 2)(x + 1)$.
8. $dy/dx = (y - 2)(y + 1)$.
9. $dy/dx = \sin nx$.
10. $dy/dx = \sin ny$.
11. $dy/dx = \sec^2 x$.
12. $dy/dx = \sec^2 y$.
13. $dy/dx = \sec x \tan x$.
14. $dy/dx = \sec y \tan y$.
15. $x\, dy/dx = \sqrt{(x^2 - 1)}$.
16. $y\, dy/dx = \sqrt{(y^2 - 1)}$.

In Exs. 17-26, solve the given equations and sketch roughly the systems of curves that represent the general solutions :—

17. $dy/dx = 1$.
18. $dy/dx = x^2$.
19. $y\, dy/dx = 1$.
20. $x\, dy = 2y\, dx$.
21. $(dy/dx)^2 = 4y$.
22. $(dy/dx)^2 = x$.
23. $x\, dx + y\, dy = 0$.
24. $(x - a)dx + (y - b)dy = 0$.
25. $x\, dy + y\, dx = 0$.
26. $x\, dy = (y - 2)dx$.

In Exs. 27-30, express y in terms of x, and draw the graph of y :—

27. $dy/dx = y^2$; $y = \frac{1}{2}$ when $x = 0$.
28. $dy/dx + y = 0$; $y = 2$ when $x = 0$.
29. $dy/dx + y = 3$; $y = 0$ when $x = 0$.
30. $dy/dx = \sin x$; $y = 0$ when $x = 0$.

§ 272. **Equations of the First Order and First Degree.**—A differential equation of the first order and first degree can always be reduced to the form

$$dy/dx = f(x, y).$$

The problem of finding y when $f(x, y)$ denotes any function of x and y has no general solution in finite terms, as we might expect, since this is not even true of the simpler problem of finding y when $dy/dx = f(x)$, i.e. the problem of integration.

Just as we find it necessary to keep in mind certain standard integrals, so it is worth while to be able to recognise certain standard types of differential equations which can be readily solved. A few of these are given below.

§ 273. **Variables Separable.**—When the equation can be put in the form

$$f(x)dx + F(y)dy = 0,$$

where $f(x)$ is a function of x only, and $F(y)$ a function of y only, the variables are said to be *separable*. The solution can be found at once by integration.

Ex. 1.
$$x\,dy + (y^2 - 1)dx = 0,$$
$$\therefore \frac{dy}{y^2 - 1} + \frac{dx}{x} = 0,$$
$$\therefore \tfrac{1}{2} \log \frac{y-1}{y+1} + \log x = \log A, \text{ by integration };$$
$$\therefore \log \frac{y-1}{y+1} = 2 \log A - 2 \log x = \log \frac{A^2}{x^2},$$

and hence
$$y = \frac{x^2 + A^2}{x^2 - A^2}.$$

Here, when we perform the integration, both terms on the left-hand side are logarithms, so it is a convenience to write the arbitrary constant as a logarithm for the sake of the subsequent simplification.

Ex. 2.
$$\frac{dy}{dx} = \frac{1 + y^2}{1 + x^2}.$$
$$\therefore \frac{dy}{1 + y^2} = \frac{dx}{1 + x^2}.$$
$$\therefore \tan^{-1} y = \tan^{-1} x + \tan^{-1} A, \text{ by integration }$$
$$\therefore y = \tan (\tan^{-1} x + \tan^{-1} A),$$
$$\therefore y = \frac{x + A}{1 - Ax}.$$

Here it is convenient to write the arbitrary constant as $\tan^{-1} A$, because the other terms are of this form.

§ 274. **Exact Equations. Integrating Factors.**—When an equation has the form $dz = 0$, where dz is the *exact* or *total* differential of a function z of x and y (§ 207), the equation is said to be *in the exact form*. Its solution can then be written down at once: it is $z = C$, where C is an arbitrary constant.

Other forms in which an exact equation can be written are

$$\frac{\partial z}{\partial x}dx + \frac{\partial z}{\partial y}dy = 0, \quad du + dv - dw \ldots = 0,$$

where du, dv, dw are total or exact differentials.

An equation can sometimes be made exact by multiplying by a factor, which is then called an *integrating factor*.

Ex. 1. $(x^2 + y^2)dy + 2xy\, dx = 0.$

This can be written

$$(x^2\, dy + 2xy\, dx) + y^2\, dy = 0,$$
$$\therefore\ d(x^2y) + d(\tfrac{1}{3}y^3) = 0,$$
$$\therefore\ x^2y + \tfrac{1}{3}y^3 = C.$$

Ex. 2. $x\, dy + y\, dx = 2xy^2\, dy.$

Here $1/xy$ is an integrating factor; for, on multiplying by $1/xy$, we have

$$\frac{d(xy)}{xy} = 2y\, dy,$$
$$\therefore\ \log(xy) = y^2 + C.$$

§ 275. **Linear Equations.**—When an equation can be reduced to the form

$$dy/dx + Py = Q, \tag{1}$$

where P and Q are functions of x only, i.e. when the equation is a linear relation between the dependent variable and its differential coefficient, it is called a *linear* equation.

Here, $e^{\int P\, dx}$ is an integrating factor. For, put $u = e^{\int P\, dx}$

$$\therefore\ \log u = \int P\, dx, \quad \therefore\ \frac{du}{u} = P\, dx, \quad \therefore\ uP = \frac{du}{dx}. \tag{2}$$

Now, multiplying (1) by u, and using (2), we get

$$u\frac{dy}{dx} + uPy = u\frac{dy}{dx} + y\frac{du}{dx} = uQ,$$

$$\therefore\ \frac{d}{dx}(uy) = uQ.$$

This is in the exact form, since uQ is a function of x only. Integrating, we get the general solution

$$uy = \int uQ\, dx + C.$$

Ex. 1. $\dfrac{dy}{dx} - 2y = 3e^{2x}.$

Here $\int P\, dx = \int -2dx = -2x, \quad \therefore\ e^{\int P\, dx} = e^{-2x}.$

Hence, multiplying by e^{-2x}, we obtain

$$\frac{dy}{dx}e^{-2x} - 2ye^{-2x} = 3,$$

$$\therefore \frac{d}{dx}(ye^{-2x}) = 3,$$

$$\therefore ye^{-2x} = 3x + \text{A, by integration,}$$

$$\therefore y = \text{A}e^{2x} + 3xe^{2x}.$$

Ex. 2. $\qquad\qquad \cos x \dfrac{dy}{dx} + y \sin x = 1.$

Dividing by $\cos x$, so as to put the equation in the above standard form, in which the coefficient of dy/dx is unity, we have

$$dy/dx + y \tan x = \sec x.$$

Here $\quad \int \text{P}\,dx = \int \tan x\,dx = \log \sec x, \quad \therefore e^{\int \text{P}\,dx} = \sec x.$

Hence, multiplying by $\sec x$, we obtain

$$\sec x \frac{dy}{dx} + y \sec x \tan x = \sec^2 x,$$

$$\therefore \frac{d}{dx}(y \sec x) = \sec^2 x,$$

$$\therefore y \sec x = \tan x + \text{A, by integration,}$$

$$\therefore y = \sin x + \text{A} \cos x.$$

§ 276. Homogeneous Equations.—An equation that can be reduced to the form

$$\frac{dy}{dx} = f\left(\frac{y}{x}\right)$$

is called a *homogeneous* equation. It can be solved by means of the substitution

$$\frac{y}{x} = v, \qquad \therefore y = xv, \qquad \therefore \frac{dy}{dx} = v + x\frac{dv}{dx}.$$

For, when y is eliminated the equation reads

$$v + x\frac{dv}{dx} = f(v).$$

The variables are now separable, and we obtain

$$\int \frac{dv}{f(v) - v} = \int \frac{dx}{x} = \log x + \text{C},$$

where C is an arbitrary constant. After the integral on the left has been evaluated, the required solution is obtained by replacing v by y/x.

Examples CXIX.

Solve the given equations (variables separable) :—

1. $x^2\,dy + y^2\,dx = 0.$ $\qquad\qquad$ **2.** $2(x + a)dy = 3(y + b)dx.$

3. $\dfrac{dy}{dx} = \dfrac{y}{\sqrt{(x^2 + c)}}.$ $\qquad\qquad$ **4.** $y - x\dfrac{dy}{dx} = 1 + x^2\dfrac{dy}{dx}.$

5. $\left(\dfrac{dy}{dx}\right)^2 = y^3.$ **6.** $y\dfrac{dy}{dx} + y\left\{1 + \left(\dfrac{dy}{dx}\right)^2\right\}^{\frac{1}{3}} = a.$

7. $x\,dy/dx = y \log y.$ **8.** $y \log y\,dy = \sec^2 x \tan x\,dx.$

9. $x^2\,dy = \sqrt{(1 - 2y)}dx.$ **10.** $\sin y\,dx + e^x\,dy = 0.$

11. $2e^x\,dx + (1 - e^x) \tan y\,dy = 0.$

12. $(3 + 2x)(1 + y^2)dy = (x - 1)y\,dx.$

13. $2dy = (1 + y^2) \operatorname{sech} x\,dx.$

14. $\{x + 2\sqrt{(x - 1)}\}dy + y^2\,dx = 0.$

Solve the given equations (exact) :—

15. $x\,dy + y\,dx = 0.$ **16.** $2xy^3\,dx + 3x^2y^2\,dy = 0.$

17. $(ax + hy + g)\,dx + (hx + by + f)\,dy = 0.$

18. $\dfrac{x\,dy - y\,dx}{x^2} = 3x^2\,dx.$ **19.** $\dfrac{y\,dx - x\,dy}{x^2 + y^2} = \dfrac{dx}{1 + x^2}.$

Solve the equations (find an integrating factor) :—

20. $x\,dy = y\,dx = 0.$ **21.** $2 \cos \theta\,dr - r \sin \theta\,d\theta = 0.$

22. $y\,dx + x\,dy = 2x^2y^3\,dy.$ **23.** $y\,dx - x\,dy = x^2y^3\,dy.$

24. $y\,dx - x\,dy + xy(x\,dy + y\,dx) = 0.$

25. $(x^3e^x - 2y^2)dx + 2xy\,dy = 0.$

26. $y(2y + x^2e^x)dx = x^2e^x\,dy.$

Solve the given equations (linear) :—

27. $\dfrac{dy}{dx} + 2y = 8.$ **28.** $\dfrac{dy}{dx} - 2y = 6e^{-x}.$

29. $\dfrac{dy}{dx} + \dfrac{3y}{x} = 4.$ **30.** $\dfrac{dy}{dx} + y = 5 \cos 2x.$

31. $\dfrac{dy}{dx} = \dfrac{xy + 2}{1 - x^2}.$ **32.** $\sin x \dfrac{dy}{dx} - y \cos x = 1.$

33. $\dfrac{dy}{dx} + \dfrac{ny}{x} = x^m.$ **34.** $x(x + 1)\dfrac{dy}{dx} + 2y = x(x + 2).$

35. $\sin 2x \dfrac{dy}{dx} + 2y = \cos 2x.$ **36.** $\dfrac{dy}{dx} + ny \tan x = \sin x.$

Solve the equations 37-43 (homogeneous) :—

37. $\dfrac{dy}{dx} = \dfrac{x^2 + y^2}{xy}.$ **38.** $\dfrac{dy}{2xy} = \dfrac{dx}{x^2 - y^2}.$ **39.** $\dfrac{dy}{dx} = \dfrac{y + x}{y - x}.$

40. $2xy \dfrac{dy}{dx} = x^2 + y^2.$ **41.** $x\left(\dfrac{dy}{dx} - \tan \dfrac{y}{x}\right) = y.$

42. $x\,dx + y\,dx = 2y\,dx.$ **43.** $y\,dx + \sqrt{x}(\sqrt{y} - \sqrt{x})dy = 0.$

44. If $dy/dx = y + b$, and $y = 0$ when $x = 0$, prove that $y = b(e^x - 1).$

45. If $\dfrac{dy}{dx} = \dfrac{a}{y} + b$, and $y = 0$ when $x = 0$, prove that

$$x = y/b - (a/b^2) \log \{(a + by)/a\}.$$

46. If $(3x + 1)(2x - 1)dy + 5y\,dx = 0$, and $y \to 3$ when $x \to \infty$, express y in terms of x, and sketch the graph.

47. If $(x^2 - 1)dy + 2x(y + 1)\,dx = 0$, and $y = 0$ when $x = 2$, express y in terms of x, and sketch the graph.

48. If $x^2\,dy/dx - 2y = x^{-1}$, and if $y = 1$ when $x = \infty$, express y in terms of x.

49. Solve the equation $dy/dx + 2y \tan x = \sin x$. If $y = 0$ when $x = \pi/3$, show that the maximum value of y is $1/8$.

50. If $x\,dy/dx = y - \sqrt{(x^2 + y^2)}$, and $y = 0$ when $x = a$, prove that $2ay = a^2 - x^2$.

51. If $x\,dy/dx = y - n\sqrt{(x^2 + y^2)}$, and $y = 0$ when $x = 1$, prove that $2y = x^{1-n} - x^{1+n}$.

§ 277. Formation of Differential Equations by Eliminating Constants.

From algebra, we know that *one* unknown can be eliminated from *two* equations, *two* unknowns from *three* equations, and in general n unknowns from $n + 1$ equations.

Now suppose we have an equation containing x, y, A. By differentiation we obtain a second equation containing x, y, dy/dx, A. From these two equations we can eliminate A, obtaining an equation in x, y, dy/dx, i.e. a differential equation of the *first* order.

Again, suppose we have an equation containing x, y, A, B. By differentiating we obtain a second equation containing x, y, dy/dx, A, B; and by differentiating again, a third equation containing x, y, dy/dx, d^2y/dx^2, A, B. From these three equations we can eliminate A, B and obtain an equation in x, y, dy/dx, d^2y/dx^2, i.e. a differential equation of the *second* order.

In general, if we have an equation containing x, y, and n constants $A_1, A_2, \ldots A_n$, after differentiating n times we have $(n + 1)$ equations from which the n constants can be eliminated, and the result will be a differential equation of the nth order.

§ 278.

Conversely, we expect that the general solution of a differential equation will contain *a number of arbitrary constants equal to the order of the equation*. For, if it involved fewer constants, they could be eliminated as above, leading to a differential equation of order less than that of the given equation; while, if the number of arbitrary constants were greater than the order of the equation, their elimination would lead to an equation of higher order than that of the given equation.

Ex. 1.
$$y = Ax^2 + Bx.$$
$$y' = 2Ax + B.$$
$$y'' = 2A.$$

Eliminating A and B from these three equations, we find
$$x^2 y'' - 2xy' + 2y = 0.$$
2nd method.

$$\frac{y}{x} = Ax + B, \qquad \therefore \frac{d^2}{dx^2}\left(\frac{y}{x}\right) = 0,$$

which reduces to the same result.

Ex. 2.
$$y = A \cos nx + B \sin nx.$$
$$\frac{d^2 y}{dx^2} = -n^2 A \cos nx - n^2 B \sin nx,$$
$$\therefore \frac{d^2 y}{dx^2} = -n^2 y.$$

Ex. 3.
$$y = e^{-kx}(A \cos nx + B \sin nx).$$
$$\therefore ye^{kx} = A \cos nx + B \sin nx,$$

hence, by the last example,
$$\frac{d^2}{dx^2}(ye^{kx}) = -n^2(ye^{kx}),$$

which reduces to
$$\frac{d^2 y}{dx^2} + 2k\frac{dy}{dx} + (k^2 + n^2)y = 0.$$

Examples CXX.

In Exs. 1-4, derive a differential equation of the first order, not containing the constant A :—

1. $y = \sin(x + A)$.   **2.** $y = e^{Ax}$.

3. $x \cos A + y \sin A = p$.   **4.** $y = (x + A)/(1 - Ax)$.

In Exs. 5-19, derive a differential equation of the second order, not containing the constants A, B :—

5. $y = Ax + B$.   **6.** $y = x^2 + Ax + B$.

7. $y = Ax^2 + B$.   **8.** $y = Ax^3 + Bx^2$.

9. $y = 1/(Ax + B)$.   **10.** $y = A/x^3 + B/x^4$.

11. $y = Ax/(x + B)$.   **12.** $y^2 + Ay + B = x$.

13. $y = A \log x + B$.   **14.** $y = A(\log x)^2 + B \log x$.

15. $y = Ae^{nx} + Be^{-nx}$.   **16.** $y = A \cosh nx + B \sinh nx$.

17. $y = (Ae^{nx} + Be^{-nx})/x$.   **18.** $y = (Ax + B)e^{2x}$.

19. $y = (A \cos x + B \sin x)e^{-x}$.

20. If $y = Ax^2 + Bx + C$, prove that $d^3 y/dx^3 = 0$.

21. If $(x - A)^2 + (y - B)^2 = C^2$, prove that $y'''(1 + y'^2) = 3y'y''^2$.

22. If $x^2 + y^2 - 2Ax = c^2$ (coaxal circles), prove that
$$2xy\, dy/dx = y^2 - x^2 - c^2.$$

23. If $\dfrac{x^2}{A} + \dfrac{y^2}{A - c^2} = 1$ (confocal conics), prove that
$$xy(dy/dx)^2 + (x^2 - y^2 - c^2)dy/dx - xy = 0.$$

24. If $y = A \sin(n\theta + B)$, and $x = \sin\theta$, prove that
$$(1 - x^2)y'' - xy' + n^2 y = 0.$$

§ 279. **Equations of Higher Order than the First.**—If an equation can be written in the form

$$dz/dx = 0, \quad \text{or} \quad dz/dx = f(x)$$

where z may contain x, y, dy/dx, d^2y/dx^2, . . . one step towards the solution can be made at once by integration.

Ex. $$\frac{d}{dx}\left(x\frac{dy}{dx}\right) = \frac{1}{x}.$$

$$\therefore x\frac{dy}{dx} = \log x + \text{A, by integration,}$$

$$\therefore \frac{dy}{dx} = \frac{\log x}{x} + \frac{\text{A}}{x},$$

$$\therefore y = \tfrac{1}{2}(\log x)^2 + \text{A} \log x + \text{B}.$$

§ 280. **Equations of the Second Order with one Variable Absent.**—If either variable is absent explicitly in an equation of the second order, its solution can be made to depend upon two first-order equations.

(1) *Dependent Variable Absent.*—If the equation has the form

$$f(d^2y/dx^2, dy/dx, x) = 0,$$

so that y is not present explicitly, we put

$$p = dy/dx, \quad dp/dx = d^2y/dx^2,$$

and the equation becomes

$$f(dp/dx, p, x) = 0,$$

which is of the first order in p and x. Solving it, we obtain an equation in p, x, and A, an arbitrary constant. Since $p = dy/dx$, this is another first order equation, whose solution, containing x, y, A, and B, a second arbitrary constant, is the solution of the original equation.

(2) *Independent Variable Absent.*—If the equation has the form

$$f(d^2y/dx^2, dy/dx, y) = 0,$$

so that x is not present explicitly, we put

$$\frac{dy}{dx} = p, \quad \frac{d^2y}{dx^2} = \frac{dp}{dx} = \frac{dp}{dy}\frac{dy}{dx} = \frac{dp}{dy}\cdot p = p\frac{dp}{dy}$$

and the equation becomes

$$f(p\, dp/dy, p, y) = 0,$$

which is of the first order in p and y. The solution now proceeds as in the previous case.

Ex. 1.
$$\frac{d^2y}{dx^2} = -n^2y.$$

Putting $d^2y/dx^2 = p\, dp/dy$, where $p = dy/dx$, we obtain

$$p\, dp = -n^2 y\, dy,$$
$$\therefore \tfrac{1}{2}p^2 = -\tfrac{1}{2}n^2y^2 + A, \text{ by integration.}$$

The left-hand side is positive, so the right-hand side must be positive, and hence A must be positive. Putting $A = \tfrac{1}{2}n^2a^2$ for convenience, we get

$$p^2 = n^2(a^2 - y^2).$$
$$\therefore p = dy/dx = \pm n\sqrt{(a^2 - y^2)},$$
$$\therefore -dy/\sqrt{(a^2 - y^2)} = \pm n\, dx,$$
$$\therefore \cos^{-1}(y/a) = \pm (nx + \epsilon),$$
$$\therefore y = a \cos (nx + \epsilon).$$

This is the general solution, involving two arbitrary constants, a, ϵ. If we put

$$A = a \cos \epsilon, \qquad B = -a \sin \epsilon,$$

we obtain the general solution in the equivalent form

$$y = A \cos nx + B \sin nx,$$

where A, B are two arbitrary constants.

Both forms of the solution should be remembered, because of the important applications of this equation.

Ex. 2.
$$\frac{d^2y}{dx^2} = n^2y.$$

By the same method, the general solution can be obtained in the form

$$y = A \cosh nx + B \sinh nx,$$

which can also be written

$$y = \tfrac{1}{2}A(e^{nx} + e^{-nx}) + \tfrac{1}{2}B(e^{nx} - e^{-nx}),$$
or
$$y = Ce^{nx} + De^{-nx},$$
where
$$C = \tfrac{1}{2}(A + B), \qquad D = \tfrac{1}{2}(A - B).$$

Examples CXXI.

Solve the given equations :—

1. $\dfrac{d^3y}{dx^3} = 6x^2.$

2. $\dfrac{d}{dx}\left\{ x \dfrac{d}{dx}\left(x \dfrac{dy}{dx} \right) \right\} = 0.$

3. $x^2 \dfrac{d^3y}{dx^3} + 1 = 0.$

4. $\dfrac{d}{dx}\left\{ (1 - x^2) \dfrac{dy}{dx} \right\} = 0.$

5. $x \dfrac{d^2y}{dx^2} + \dfrac{dy}{dx} = 0.$

6. $(1 - x^2) \dfrac{d^2y}{dx^2} - x \dfrac{dy}{dx} = 2.$

7. $\dfrac{d^2y}{dx^2} = \dfrac{1}{y^3}.$

8. $(1 - y) \dfrac{d^2y}{dx^2} = \left(\dfrac{dy}{dx} \right)^2.$

9. $y \dfrac{d^2y}{dx^2} = 2\dfrac{dy}{dx} + \left(\dfrac{dy}{dx} \right)^2.$

10. $\sin \theta \dfrac{d^2\theta}{d\phi^2} = \cos \theta \left(\dfrac{d\theta}{d\phi} \right)^2.$

11. $\dfrac{d^2y}{dt^2} = g - n^2y.$ $\left[\text{Put } \cdot = y - \dfrac{g}{n^2}. \right]$

In the following examples, express y in terms of x :—

12. $d^2y/dx^2 = -y$; $y = 5$ and $dy/dx = 0$ when $x = 0$.

13. $d^2y/dx^2 = -4y$; $y = 3$ and $dy/dx = 4$ when $x = 0$.

14. $y \dfrac{d^2y}{dx^2} = 2\left(\dfrac{dy}{dx}\right)^2$; $y = 2$ when $x = 1$, $y = 4$ when $x = 0$.

15. $y \dfrac{d^2y}{dx^2} + \left(\dfrac{dy}{dx}\right)^3 = 0$; $y = 1$ and $dy/dx = \frac{1}{2}$ when $x = 0$.

16. $\dfrac{d}{dx}\left\{(1 + x^2)\dfrac{dy}{dx}\right\} = 2$; $y = 1$ and $dy/dx = 0$ when $x = 0$.

17. $x\, d^2y/dx^2 = n\{1 + (dy/dx)^2\}^{\frac{1}{2}}$; $y = 0$ and $dy/dx = 0$ when $x = 1$.

18. If $d^2\theta/dt^2 = -n^2 \sin\theta$, and if $\theta = 0$ and $d\theta/dt = 2n$ when $t = 0$, express θ in terms of t.

§ **281. Linear Equations.**—A linear differential equation is a linear relation between the dependent variable and its differential coefficients. The linear equation of the first order has already been considered (§ 275) ; we now consider the linear equation of the second order which, being linear in y, dy/dx and d^2y/dx^2, can be reduced to the form

$$\frac{d^2y}{dx^2} + \mathrm{P}\frac{dy}{dx} + \mathrm{Q}y = \mathrm{V}, \quad \text{or} \quad \mathrm{D}^2y + \mathrm{P\,D}y + \mathrm{Q}y = \mathrm{V}, \qquad (1)$$

where P, Q, V are functions of x.

§ **282. Properties of the Linear Equation of the Second Order when V = 0.**—When $\mathrm{V} = 0$ equation (1) reduces to

$$\mathrm{D}^2y + \mathrm{PD}y + \mathrm{Q}y = 0. \qquad (2)$$

This equation has the following properties, of which the first two can be easily proved by the reader :—

(1) If $y = u$ is a solution, then $y = \mathrm{A}u$ is also a solution, where A is an arbitrary constant.

(2) If $y = u_1$ and $y = u_2$ are solutions, then $y = u_1 + u_2$ is a solution.

(3) If $y = u_1$ and $y = u_2$ are two *independent* solutions (i.e. one is not a mere multiple of the other), then $y = \mathrm{A}u_1 + \mathrm{B}u_2$ is the *general solution*.

Proof.—Since $y = u_1$ and $y = u_2$ are solutions, it follows from (1) that $y = \mathrm{A}u_1$, $y = \mathrm{B}u_2$ are solutions, where A, B are arbitrary constants. Hence, by (2), $y = \mathrm{A}u_1 + \mathrm{B}u_2$ is a solution. But this solution contains two arbitrary constants, and must, therefore, be the general solution (§ 278).

(4) If the coefficients P, Q are *constants*, the equation has particular solutions of the form $y = e^{\lambda x}$. The values of the constant λ can be determined by substituting $y = e^{\lambda x}$ in the equation (see § 285).

§ 283. **Properties of the Linear Equation of the Second Order when V $\neq$ 0.**—The linear equation (1) has the following properties:—

(1) The *general* solution can be found by adding a *particular* solution to the general solution of (2). That is, if $y = v$ is a particular solution of (1), and $y = u$ is the general solution of (2), then $y = u + v$ is the general solution of (1).

Proof.—Since $y = u$ satisfies (2), $\therefore$ D²u + P Du + Qu = 0, and since $y = v$ satisfies (1), $\therefore$ D²v + P Dv + Qv = V ; hence, by addition,

$$\text{D}^2(u + v) + \text{P D}(u + v) + \text{Q}(u + v) = \text{V}.$$

Thus $y = u + v$ is a solution of (1). But this solution contains two arbitrary constants, since $y = u$ is the general solution of (2). Hence $y = u + v$ is the general solution of (1).

The particular solution v is called the *particular integral*, and u is called the *complementary function*. Thus the general solution (G.S.) of (1) can be written

$$y = \text{G.S.} = \text{C.F.} + \text{P.I.},$$

the particular integral (P.I.) being any solution of (1), and the complementary function (C.F.) being the general solution of (2).

(2) If the coefficients P, Q are constants, the particular integral v can be found in simple cases by the method of undetermined coefficients (see § 286).

(3) If $y = u$ is *any solution of equation* (2), equation (1) can be reduced to the type discussed in § 280, (1), by the substitution $y = uz$.

Proof.—If $y = uz$, Dy = u Dz + z Du,

$$\text{D}^2y = u \text{ D}^2z + 2 \text{ Du Dz} + z \text{ D}^2u,$$

and with this substitution the equation becomes

$$u \text{ D}^2z + (2\text{Du} + \text{Pu})\text{Dz} + (\text{D}^2u + \text{P Du} + \text{Qu})z = \textbf{V}.$$

But D²u + P Du + Qu = 0, since u satisfies (2),

$$\therefore u\text{D}^2z + (2\text{Du} + \text{Pu})\text{Dz} = \text{V},$$

which is of the type stated.

§ 284. **The Linear Equation of the Second Order with Constant Coefficients.**—When the coefficients P, Q are constants, equation (1), § 281, is of special importance on account of its applications. In this case we write the equation

$$\text{D}^2y + a\,\text{D}y + by = \textbf{V}. \tag{1}$$

where a, b denote constants. To obtain the general solution we have to find the complementary function and the particular integral and add them together (§ 283).

§ 285. **The Complementary Function.**—The C.F. is the general solution of the equation

$$D^2y + aDy + by = 0. \tag{2}$$

Put $y = e^{\lambda x}$, and we get

$$e^{\lambda x}(\lambda^2 + a\lambda + b) = 0,$$

from which it follows that $y = e^{\lambda x}$ is a solution of the differential equation (2), if λ is a root of the algebraic equation

$$\lambda^2 + a\lambda + b = 0. \tag{3}$$

This is called the *auxiliary equation*. Its roots are

$$\lambda_1, \lambda_2 = -\tfrac{1}{2}a \pm \sqrt{(\tfrac{1}{4}a^2 - b)}. \tag{4}$$

There are now three cases to be noticed :—

(1) $a^2 > 4b$. The roots λ_1, λ_2 of the auxiliary equation are real and different; $y = e^{\lambda_1 x}$, $y = e^{\lambda_2 x}$ are two independent solutions and the general solution, by (3), § 282, is

$$y = Ae^{\lambda_1 x} + Be^{\lambda_2 x}.$$

(2) $a^2 < 4b$. The roots of the auxiliary equation are again different and $y = Ae^{\lambda_1 x} + Be^{\lambda_2 x}$ is again the general solution. But this is not its most useful form, because λ_1, λ_2 are a conjugate pair of complex numbers. A more useful form is obtained as follows: We have from (4)

$$\lambda_1, \lambda_2 = -\tfrac{1}{2}a \pm i\beta, \quad \text{where } \beta = \sqrt{(b - \tfrac{1}{4}a^2)},$$

and therefore the general solution can be written

$$y = Ae^{(-\frac{1}{2}a + i\beta)x} + Be^{(-\frac{1}{2}a - i\beta)x}$$

$$= e^{-\frac{1}{2}ax}\{A(\cos \beta x + i \sin \beta x) + B(\cos \beta x - i \sin \beta x)\}$$

$$\therefore y = e^{-\frac{1}{2}ax}(C \cos \beta x + D \sin \beta x), \tag{5}$$

where $C = A + B$, $D = i(A - B)$. An equivalent form is

$$y = Ee^{-\frac{1}{2}ax} \cos(\beta x - \epsilon), \tag{6}$$

where E, ϵ are now the arbitrary constants.

9

(3) $a^2 = 4b$.   In this case equation (2) can be written

$$D^2y + a\,Dy + \tfrac{1}{4}a^2y = 0, \tag{7}$$

with the auxiliary equation

$$\lambda^2 + a\lambda + \tfrac{1}{4}a^2 = 0, \quad \text{or } (\lambda + \tfrac{1}{2}a)^2 = 0. \tag{8}$$

The auxiliary equation has now equal roots, $\lambda = -\tfrac{1}{2}a$, and leads to only one solution $y = e^{-\frac{1}{2}ax}$.   But knowing one solution we can make use of § 283, (3).

To do so, we make the substitution $y = e^{-\frac{1}{2}ax}z$, and find that the differential equation reduces to

$$e^{-\frac{1}{2}ax}\,D^2z = 0, \quad \therefore \; D^2z = 0, \quad \therefore \; z = Ax + B, \tag{9}$$

so that in this case the general solution is

$$y = (Ax + B)e^{-\frac{1}{2}ax}. \tag{10}$$

Ex. 1. $\qquad\qquad D^2y + Dy - 6y = 0.$
$$\lambda^2 + \lambda - 6 = 0; \quad (\lambda - 2)(\lambda + 3) = 0; \quad \lambda = 2, -3;$$
$$y = Ae^{2x} + Be^{-3x}.$$

Ex. 2. $\qquad\qquad D^2y + 2Dy + 5y = 0.$
$$\lambda^2 + 2\lambda + 5 = 0; \quad (\lambda + 1)^2 + 2^2 = 0; \quad \lambda = -1 \pm 2i;$$
$$y = e^{-x}(A \cos 2x + B \sin 2x).$$

Ex. 3. $\qquad\qquad D^2y + 4Dy + 4y = 0.$
$$\lambda^2 + 4\lambda + 4 = 0; \quad (\lambda + 2)^2 = 0; \quad \lambda = -2, -2;$$
$$y = (Ax + B)e^{-2x}.$$

§ 286. **The Particular Integral.**—We have to find a particular solution of equation (1).   The simplest cases are those in which V contains exponential terms, sines and cosines of multiples of x, or powers of x.

Rule.—Assume that a solution exists of the same form as V, but with undetermined coefficients.   Find the values of these coefficients by substituting the assumed solution in the equation. [There are exceptions to this rule when V is of the same form as part of the C.F.   (See Exs. 2, 3 below)].

(1) $V = he^{ax}$.

Ex. 1. $\qquad\qquad D^2y + Dy - 6y = 2e^x.$

The C.F. is $Ae^{2x} + Be^{-3x}$, from Ex. 1, § 285.

For the P.I. try $y = He^x$. This satisfies the equation if
$$H(1^2 + 1 - 6)e^x = 2e^x, \quad \therefore \ -4He^x = 2e^x, \quad \therefore \ H = -\tfrac{1}{2}.$$

G.S. $\qquad\qquad\qquad y = Ae^{2x} + Be^{-3x} - \tfrac{1}{2}e^x.$

Ex. 2. $\qquad\qquad\qquad D^2y + Dy - 6y = 10e^{2x}.$

The C.F. is $Ae^{2x} + Be^{-3x}$, as before.

We cannot find the P.I. by assuming $y = He^{2x}$, because e^{2x} is part of the C.F. The appropriate assumption in this case is $y = Hxe^{2x}$ (compare § 275, Ex. 1). Making this substitution, we find
$$H(4xe^{2x} + 4e^{2x}) + H(2xe^{2x} + e^{2x}) - 6Hxe^{2x} = 10e^{2x}, \quad \therefore \ 5He^{2x} = 10e^{2x},$$
$$\therefore \ H = 2.$$

G.S. $\qquad\qquad\qquad y = Ae^{2x} + Be^{-3x} + 2xe^{2x}.$

Ex. 3. $\qquad\qquad\qquad D^2y + 4Dy + 4y = 6e^{-2x}.$

The C.F. is $Axe^{-2x} + Be^{-2x}$, from Ex. 3, § 285. In this case e^{-2x} and also xe^{-2x} are parts of the C.F. The appropriate assumption for the P.I is $y = Hx^2e^{-2x}$. Making this substitution, we find $H = 3$.

G.S. $\qquad\qquad\qquad y = (Ax + B)e^{-2x} + 3x^2e^{-2x}.$

(2) $V = h \cos \alpha x + k \sin \alpha x.$

Ex. $\qquad\qquad\qquad D^2y + 2Dy - 5y = 10 \cos x.$

The C.F. is $e^{-x}(A \cos 2x + B \sin 2x)$, from Ex. 2, § 285.
For the P.I. try $y = H \cos x + K \sin x$; then we get
$$(4H + 2K) \cos x - (2H - 4K) \sin x = 10 \cos x.$$

Equating coefficients of $\cos x$ and $\sin x$, and dividing by 2,
$$2H + K = 5, \quad H - 2K = 0; \quad \therefore \ H = 2, K = 1.$$

G.S. $\quad y = e^{-x}(A \cos 2x + B \sin 2x) + 2 \cos x + \sin x,$
or $\qquad\qquad y = Ce^{-x} \cos (2x - \epsilon) + \sqrt{5} \cos (x - \phi),$
where $\phi = \tan^{-1} \tfrac{1}{2}.$

(3) $V = a$ power of x or a polynomial.

Ex. $\qquad\qquad\qquad D^2y + 4Dy + 4y = 8x^2.$

The C.F. is $(Ax + B)e^{-2x}$, from Ex. 3, § 285.
For the P.I. try $y = Hx^2 + Kx + L$; then we get
$$4Hx^2 + (8H + 4K)x + 2H + 4K + 4L = 8x^2.$$

Equating coefficients of like powers of x,
$$4H = 8, \quad 8H + 4K = 0, \quad 2H + 4K + 4L = 0,$$
$$\therefore \ H = 2, \quad K = -4, \quad L = 3.$$

G.S. $\qquad\qquad\qquad y = (Ax + B)e^{-2x} + 2x^2 - 4x + 3.$

§ 287. Linear Equation of any Order, with Constant Coefficients.—For the linear equation of order n (including $n = 1$)-

the auxiliary equation will be of the nth degree and will have n roots, and the C. F. will contain n arbitrary constants (§ 278); otherwise the above methods will apply.

Ex.
$$D^4y - 2D^3y + 5D^2y - 8Dy + 4y = 0.$$
$$\lambda^4 - 2\lambda^3 + 5\lambda^2 - 8\lambda + 4 = 0;$$
$$(\lambda - 1)^2(\lambda^2 + 4) = 0; \quad \lambda = 1, 1, 2i, -2i.$$

G.S. $\quad\quad y = (Ax + B)e^x + Ce^{2ix} + De^{-2ix},$

or $\quad\quad y = (Ax + B)e^x + E \cos 2x + F \sin 2x,$

or $\quad\quad y = (Ax + B)e^x + G \cos (2x - \epsilon).$

Examples CXXII.

Solve the given equations, where $D \equiv d/dx$:—

1. $D^2y + 5Dy + 6y = 0.$
2. $2D^2y - 9Dy + 9y = 0$
3. $D^2y + 6Dy + 13y = 0.$
4. $D^2y + Dy + y = 0.$
5. $D^2y - 6Dy + 9y = 0.$
6. $D^2y + 2nDy + n^2y = 0.$
7. $Dy + ay = b.$
8. $Dy - 4y = 10 \cos 3x.$
9. $D^2y + 2Dy - 3y = 10e^{2x}.$
10. $D^2y + 2Dy - 3y = 2e^x.$
11. $D^2y - 4Dy + 5y = 16 \sin x.$
12. $D^2y - y = 2 + 5x.$
13. $D^2y - 2Dy + y = 10 \cos 2x.$
14. $D^2y - y = 6 \cosh 2x.$
15. $D^2y + 3Dy + 2y = 4(x + 1).$
16. $D^2y - y = 6 \cosh x.$
17. $D^3y + 2D^2y + 2Dy = 6x^2.$
18. $D^2y + n^2y = \cos px.$
19. $D^2y = n^2y.$
20. $D^2y = -n^2y.$
21. $D^2y = n\,Dy.$
22. $D^4y = k^4y.$
23. $D^4y = -4y.$
24. $D^4y = k^2\,D^2y.$
25. $D^3y = k^3y.$
26. $D^3y + Dy = 0.$
27. $D^3y = a\,D^2y.$
28. $D^3y - 6D^2y + 11Dy - 6y = 0.$
29. $D^3y + D^2y - Dy - y = 0.$
30. $D^4y - 5D^2y + 4y = 0.$
31. $D^4y + 5D^2y + 4y = 0.$
32. $D^3y - 2Dy - 4y = 0.$
33. $D^3y - 3Dy + 2y = 0.$
34. $D^3y - 2D^2y - 3Dy = 0.$
35. $D^4y - 2D^2y + y = 0.$
36. $D^4y + D^2y + y = 0.$

In Exs. 37–41, express y in terms of x and sketch its graph :–

37. $dy/dx + y = 0$; $y = 1$ when $x = 0.$
38. $dy/dx + y = 1$; $y = 0$ when $x = 0.$
39. $dy/dx + y = 2 \cos x$; $y = 0$ when $x = 0.$
40. $d^2y/dx^2 = -y$; $y = 5$ and $dy/dx = 0$ when $x = 0.$
41. $d^2y/dx^2 = -4y$; $y = 3$ and $dy/dx = 8$ when $x = 0.$
42. If $dx/dt + y = 1$ and $x = dy/dt$, and if $x = 0$ and $y = 0$ when $t = 0,$ express x and y in terms of t and sketch their graphs.
43. If $d^2y/dt^2 + 2dy/dt + 2y = 0$ and $x = -dy/dt$, and if $x = 0$ and $y = 1$ when $t = 0$, express x and y in terms of t and sketch their graphs.
44. If $d^2y/dt^2 + 3dy/dt + 2y = 0$ and $x = -dy/dt$, and if $x = 0$ and $y = 1$ when $t = 0$, express x and y in terms of t and sketch their graphs.

45. If $d^2\theta/dt^2 + 2d\theta/dt + \theta = 1$, and if $\theta = 0$ and $d\theta/dt = 0$ when $t = 0$, express θ in terms of t and sketch its graph.

46. *Homogeneous Linear Equation.*—The equation

$$x^2\frac{d^2y}{dx^2} + ax\frac{dy}{dx} + by = f(x),$$

where a, b are constants, is called a *homogeneous linear* equation of the second order.

If $x = e^t$, and $D \equiv d/dt$, show that

$$x\frac{dy}{dx} = Dy, \qquad x^2\frac{d^2y}{dx^2} = D^2y - Dy,$$

and hence that the substitution $x = e^t$ reduces the homogeneous linear equation to a linear equation with *constant* coefficients.

Solve the equations

(i) $x^2\dfrac{d^2y}{dx^2} - 2y = 4x$; (ii) $x^2\dfrac{d^2y}{dx^2} + x\dfrac{dy}{dx} - n^2y = 0$;

(iii) $x^2\dfrac{d^2y}{dx^2} + y = 0$; (iv) $x^2\dfrac{d^2y}{dx^2} - 3x\dfrac{dy}{dx} + 4y = 5\cos(\log x)$;

(v) $(x-1)^2\dfrac{d^2y}{dx^2} + (x-1)\dfrac{dy}{dx} - 4y = 6x^2$.

47. By putting $x = \cos t$, solve the equation
$$(1 - x^2)d^2y/dx^2 - x\,dy/dx + n^2y = 0.$$

48. By putting $x = \sin t$, solve the equation
$$(1 - x^2)d^2y/dx^2 - x\,dy/dx + y = x^2.$$

49. By changing the dependent variable from y to z by means of the substitution $z = xy$, solve the equation

$$x\,d^2y/dx^2 + 2\,dy/dx + n^2xy = 0.$$

50. Use the last substitution to solve the equation
$$(x^2 + x)d^2y/dx^2 + 2\,dy/dx - 2y = (x + 1)^3.$$

§ 288. Geometrical Applications.

Ex. Find the equations of the curves along which the subnormal is constant and equal to $2a$.

By § 27, the subnormal $= y\,dy/dx$,

$$\therefore\ y\frac{dy}{dx} = 2a,$$

$$\therefore\ \tfrac{1}{2}y^2 = 2ax + A, \text{ by integration,}$$
$$\therefore\ y^2 = 4a(x - h),$$

where h is an arbitrary constant. For any value of h this is the equation of a parabola with its vertex at $(h, 0)$, its axis along the x-axis, and its latus rectum of length $4a$.

§ 289. Dynamical Applications. Rectilinear Motion..—The fundamental equation of dynamics is   mass × acceleration = force.

By (10) § 66, in the case of rectilinear motion, the acceleration can be put
in any of the forms

$$dv/dt, \qquad\qquad d^2x/dt^2, \qquad\qquad v\,dv/dx.$$

When any of these forms is substituted in the fundamental equation, we
get a differential equation, which may belong to one or other of the types
already discussed, according as the force is a function of one or more of the
variables t, v, x.   A few of the common types are indicated below, m being
the mass :—

(1) *Force = a function of* **t**.

$$m\,\frac{d^2x}{dt^2} = f(t).$$ [See § 279.]

(2) *Force = a function of* **v**.

$$m\,\frac{dv}{dt} = f(v), \quad \text{or } mv\,\frac{dv}{dx} = f(v).$$ [See § 273.]

(3) *Force = a function of* **x**.

$$mv\,\frac{dv}{dx} = f(x).$$ [See § 273.]

Examples CXXIII.

1. Find the curves in which the subtangent is proportional to the
abscissa.

2. Find the curves in which the subnormal is proportional to the abscissa.

3. Find the curves such that the portion of the tangent included between
the co-ordinate axes is bisected at the point of contact.

4. Find the curves in which the sum of the normal and subnormal is
constant and equal to a.

5. Find the curves in which the sum of the tangent and subtangent is
constant and equal to a.

6. Find the curves such that the tangent at any point (x, y) passes
through the point $(2y, 2x)$.

7. Find the curves in which the angle between the tangent and radius
vector is constant and equal to α.

8. Find the curves in which the angle between the tangent and radius
vector is half the vectorial angle θ.

9. Find the equation of the orthogonal trajectories of the rectangular
hyperbolas $xy = C$ (*i.e.* the curves every one of which cuts every one of the
system $xy = C$ at right angles).

10. Find the equation of the system of circles each of which touches the
x-axis at the origin.   Also find the equation of their orthogonal trajectories.

11. Find the equation of the system of coaxial circles, each of which passes
through the points $(c, 0)$, $(-c, 0)$.   Also find the equation of their orthogonal
trajectories.

12. A body is moving with constant acceleration f. If $v = u$ and $x = 0$ at time $t = 0$, prove that $v = u + ft$, $x = ut + \frac{1}{2}ft^2$, $v^2 = u^2 + 2fx$.

13. A body is moving with velocity u at time $t = 0$. It is then retarded with a retardation equal to kt. How far does it go before it stops ?

14. A particle starts from rest with acceleration f, and the acceleration diminishes uniformly with the time. Show that the distance moved before the particle acquires its maximum velocity u is $4u^2/3f$.

15. The acceleration of a certain body t seconds after it starts from rest is proportional to e^{-at} ($a > 0$). Show that the velocity approaches a limit V as $t \to \infty$, and find in how many seconds the velocity will reach 99 per cent. of this limiting velocity. Find also how far the body will travel in the first t seconds.

16. The brakes of a car are applied when the velocity is u, causing a constant resistance R per unit mass. If the air resistance is kv^2 per unit mass, show that the time T that elapses and the distance X travelled before the car stops are given by

$$T = \frac{1}{n} \tan^{-1} \frac{u}{V}, \quad X = \frac{V}{2n} \log\left(1 + \frac{u^2}{V^2}\right),$$

where
$$n = \sqrt{(Rk)}, \quad V = \sqrt{(R/k)}.$$

17. A body falls from rest under gravity. Assuming the air resistance to be kv^2 per unit mass, prove the following results, in which $v =$ velocity and $x =$ distance fallen after time t, and $V = \sqrt{(g/k)}$:—

$$v = V \tanh \frac{gt}{V}, \quad x = \frac{V^2}{g} \log \cosh \frac{gt}{V}, \quad v^2 = V^2(1 - e^{-2gx/V^2}).$$

18. Assuming the same law of resistance as in the last example, show that, if a body is projected upwards with the limiting velocity V, it will return to the starting point with velocity $V/\sqrt{2}$. Also find the ratio of the times on the upward and downward parts of the journey.

19. An engine pulling a train works at constant power H (absolute units). If M is the mass of the whole train and R the (constant) resistance, prove that the time of generating a velocity v from rest is given by

$$t = \frac{M}{R}\left(\frac{H}{R} \log \frac{H}{H - Rv} - v\right).$$

20. A weight of 100 lb. hangs from the end of a rope. The weight is hauled up from rest by a windlass. The pull in the rope starts at 150 pounds and then diminishes at the rate of 1 pound for every foot of rope wound in. Find the velocity of the weight after 50 ft. of rope have been wound. The weight of the rope may be neglected.

21. A particle is attracted towards a fixed point O with a force μx per unit mass, where x is the displacement from O, so that x satisfies the equation $d^2x/dt^2 = -\mu x$, where μ is a constant (simple harmonic motion). Express x in terms of t, given that

(i) $x = a$ and $dx/dt = 0$ when $t = 0$;
(ii) $x = 0$ and $dx/dt = u$ when $t = 0$.

22. If the same particle is acted upon by a resistance $k\, dx/dt$ per unit mass (damped oscillations), show that

$$\frac{d^2x}{dt^2} + k\frac{dx}{dt} + \mu x = 0.$$

If $k^2 < 4\mu$, and if $x = 0$ and $dx/dt = u$ when $t = 0$, express x in terms of t.

23. If the same particle is also acted upon by a force $f \cos pt$ per unit mass (forced oscillations), show that

$$\frac{d^2x}{dt^2} + k\frac{dx}{dt} + \mu x = f \cos pt.$$

Express x in terms of t and show that as t increases x approaches the limiting form

$$x = \frac{f \cos(pt - \epsilon)}{\sqrt{\{(\mu - p^2)^2 + k^2p^2\}}}, \qquad \left(\epsilon = \tan^{-1}\frac{kp}{\mu - p^2}\right).$$

24. A particle of unit mass starts from rest at a distance a from a centre of force which repels it with a force n^2x. Prove that $x = a \cosh nt$ after time t.

25. A particle of unit mass starts from rest at a distance a from a centre of force which attracts it with a force equal to k/x^3. Prove that it reaches the centre of force in time $a^2/\sqrt{k}$.

26. A particle of unit mass starts from rest at a distance a from a centre of force which attracts it with a force equal to μ/x^2. Find its velocity when $x = \frac{1}{2}a$, and show that it reaches the centre of force in time $\pi\sqrt{(a^3/8\mu)}$.

27. A particle is projected vertically upwards with initial velocity u. The resistance of the atmosphere may be taken as $nv^2/(x + a)$ per unit mass, where v is the velocity and x the height above the point of projection, n and a being constants. Show that the particle will reach a height h given by

$$\frac{h}{a} = \left\{1 + \frac{(2n + 1)u^2}{2ga}\right\}^{\frac{1}{2n+1}} - 1.$$

28. The equation $EI\, d^4y/dx^4 = w$ is satisfied by the deflection y of a horizontal beam subject only to its own weight and the reactions of its supports. Supposing E, I, w to be constants, express the deflection y in terms of x in the following cases :—

(i) $y = 0$ and $d^2y/dx^2 = 0$ at $x = 0$ and at $x = l$ (uniform beam of length l supported at its ends) ;

(ii) $y = 0$ and $dy/dx = 0$ at $x = 0$ and at $x = l$ (uniform beam clamped at the ends) ;

(iii) $y = 0$ and $dy/dx = 0$ at $x = 0$, $d^2y/dx^2 = 0$ and $d^3y/dx^3 = 0$ at $x =$ (uniform beam clamped at the end $x = 0$ and free at the end $x = l$).

29. When a thin strut is slightly bent by two equal thrusts P applied at its ends, the deflection y satisfies the equation $EI\, d^2y/dx^2 = -Py$. Supposing P/EI to be constant, express y in terms of x, and determine the value of P. [The end conditions are $y = 0$ at $x = 0$ and at $x = l$.]

30. When a rotating shaft is " whirling " the deflection y satisfies the equation $d^4y/dx^4 = w\omega^2 y/g\mathrm{EI}$. Supposing $w\omega^2/g\mathrm{EI}$ to be constant, express y in terms of x, given that $y = 0$ and $d^2y/dx^2 = 0$ at $x = 0$ and at $x = l$, and determine the critical angular velocity ω.

31. A rope laps a rough circular cylinder over an angle θ. The tensions at the ends of the rope are T and T_0 ($\mathrm{T} > \mathrm{T}_0$), and the coefficient of friction between rope and cylinder is μ. By considering the equilibrium of a small element of the rope, show that $\mathrm{T} = \mathrm{T}_0 e^{\mu\theta}$ when the rope is on the point of slipping.

A rope is given three complete turns round a capstan, and a man holds on to one end with a pull of 30 lb. What pull on the other end can he support if $\mu = 0\cdot3$?

32. A tank with vertical sides contains water which flows out through a hole in the bottom with a speed proportional to the square root of the depth. If the tank is full to begin with, and if the upper half empties in T seconds, how long will the lower half take to empty ?

33. The area of the horizontal cross-section of a cistern is a, a constant. When the depth of water in it is x, a volume ax/n escapes per second by a waste pipe. If the volume entering by the supply pipe per second is $\mathrm{V} + \mathrm{U}\sin pt$ ($\mathrm{V} > \mathrm{U}$), prove that ultimately

$$x = \frac{n}{a}\Big\{\mathrm{V} + \frac{\mathrm{U}}{1 + p^2n^2}(\sin pt - pn\cos pt)\Big\}.$$

34. A beaker of water is heated by supplying a units of heat per unit time. If b is the water-equivalent of the beaker and contents, and if heat is lost by radiation at the rate $h(\theta - \theta_0)$ per unit time, where θ is the temperature of the water, θ_0 that of the surrounding air, and h a constant, show that θ satisfies the equation

$$b\,d\theta/dt + h(\theta - \theta_0) = a.$$

Express θ in terms of t, given that $\theta = \theta_0$ at $t = 0$.

35. If p is the pressure of the atmosphere and ρ the density at a height z above the earth's surface, show that $dp = -g\rho\,dz$. Hence, assuming that p is proportional to ρ (i.e. the temperature is constant throughout the atmosphere), prove that $p = p_0 e^{-z/\mathrm{H}}$, where $\mathrm{H} = $ height of the homogeneous atmosphere $= p_0/g\rho_0$, and p_0 and ρ_0 are the pressure and density at $z = 0$.

36. When water flows through a capillary tube of length l and radius a, the pressure over the outflow end being p and that over the inflow end $\mathrm{P} + p$, the velocity v of the water, at a distance r from the axis of the tube, satisfies the equation

$$\mathrm{P}r = -\mu l\frac{d}{dr}\Big(r\frac{dv}{dr}\Big),$$

where μ is a constant. Express v in terms of r, given that $v = 0$ at $r = a$ and that v is finite at $r = 0$. Hence, prove that the volume that flows through the tube per unit time is $\pi\mathrm{P}a^4/8\mu l$.

37. When an electric current x is flowing in a circuit of self-induction L and resistance R, the equation

$$L\frac{dx}{dt} + Rx = E$$

is satisfied, where E is the external e.m.f.

(i) If $E = E_0$ = constant, express x in terms of t, given that $x = 0$ when $t = 0$.

(ii) If $E = E_0 \cos pt$, express x in terms of t, and show that it settles down to a steady oscillation of period $2\pi/p$.

38. If $L\frac{dx}{dt} + \frac{q}{C} = E$, and $x = \frac{dq}{dt}$, where L, C, E are constants, and if $x = 0$ and $q = 0$ when $t = 0$, express q in terms of t and show that q/C oscillates between 0 and 2E.

39. If $L\frac{d^2x}{dt^2} + R\frac{dx}{dt} + \frac{x}{C} = 0$, and $x = 0$ when $t = 0$, and

(i) if $R^2 < 4L/C$, show that $x = Ae^{-kt}\sin \omega t$, where
$$k = R/2L, \quad \omega = \sqrt{(4L/C - R^2)}/2L \ ;$$

(ii) if $R^2 > 4L/C$, show that $x = Ae^{-kt}\sinh nt$, where
$$k = R/2L, \quad n = \sqrt{(R^2 - 4L/C)}/2L \ ;$$

(iii) if $R^2 = 4L/C$, show that $x = Ate^{-kt}$.

40. If v and i satisfy the (transmission line) equations

$$-\frac{dv}{dx} = Ri, \qquad -\frac{di}{dx} = Gv,$$

where R, G are constants, express v and i in terms of x when

(i) $v = V$ at $x = 0$, $v = 0$ at $x = \infty$;

(ii) $v = V$ at $x = 0$, $v = 0$ at $x = l$;

(iii) $v = V$ at $x = 0$, $i = 0$ at $x = l$.

MISCELLANEOUS EXAMPLES.

Miscellaneous Examples I.

In Exs. 1-6 find dy/dx from first principles :—

1. $y = x^3 + x$.   **2.** $y = 1/(2 - x)$.   **3.** $y = \sqrt{(3x + 2)}$.
4. $y = \tan 3x$.   **5.** $y = \tan^{-1} x$.   **6.** $y = \log (ax + b)$.

In Exs. 7-30 differentiate the given functions :—

7. $\cos 4x$.   **8.** $x^3 \sin x$.   **9.** xe^{-x}.   **10.** $\sqrt[x]{x}$.   **11.** $a^{\sqrt{x}}$.
12. $\log (x^{\sin x})$.   **13.** $(\sin x)^{\tan x}$.   **14.** $\cos^{-1} (a \cos x)$.
15. $x \cos^{-1} x$.   **16.** $\sin^{-1} \sqrt{(\sin x)}$.   **17.** $(1 + \cos^2 x)^{-\frac{1}{2}}$.
18. $\tan (\sin^{-1} x)$.   **19.** $\sinh^{-1} (\tan x)$.   **20.** $\tan^{-1} (\tanh x)$.
21. $\dfrac{x^2}{(x + a)^2}$.   **22.** $\dfrac{\sqrt{(1 - x^2)}}{x}$.   **23.** $\dfrac{1 - \operatorname{cosec} x}{\cot x}$.
24. $\left(\dfrac{x^3}{x - a}\right)^{\frac{1}{3}}$.   **25.** $\sin^2 \left(\dfrac{a}{x}\right)$.   **26.** $\log \left(\dfrac{x^2 - 1}{x^2 + 1}\right)^{\frac{1}{3}}$.
27. $\dfrac{3x + 1}{\sqrt{(6x^2 + 4x + 1)}}$.   **28.** $\log \dfrac{\sqrt{(a^2 + x^2)} + x}{\sqrt{(a^2 + x^2)} - x}$.
29. $\tan^{-1} \left(\dfrac{\cos x}{1 + \sin x}\right)$ **30.** $\cos^{-1} \left(\dfrac{a + b \cos x}{b + a \cos x}\right)$.

In Exs. 31-36 find the second differential coefficients of the given functions :—

31. $x^2 \log x$.   **32.** $e^x \sin x$.   **33.** $\sinh^{-1} (\cos x)$.
34. $\sqrt{(1 + x + x^2)}$.   **35.** $\dfrac{3 - 2 \sin x}{1 - \sin x}$.   **36.** $\dfrac{x - 1}{(x - 3)(x - 5)}$.

In Exs. 37-39 find dy/dx in terms of x and y :—

37. $(x^3 + y^3)^2 = a^5(x - y)$.   **33.** $y \log (xy) = x$.   **39.** $y = x^y$.

In Exs. 40-54, dy/dx, d^2y/dx^2 are denoted by y', y'' :—

40. $y = (x^2 - 1)^n$; prove that $(x^2 - 1)y' = 2nxy$.
41. $y = \sqrt{(1 - x^2)} \cdot \sin^{-1} x$; prove that $(1 - x^2)y' + xy = 1 - x^2$.
42. $y\sqrt{(1 - x^2)} = \cos^{-1} x$; prove that $(1 - x^2)y' - xy + 1 = 0$.
43. $y = \left(\dfrac{1 - x^2}{1 + x^2}\right)^{\frac{1}{2}}$; prove that $y' = -\left(\dfrac{1 - y^4}{1 - x^4}\right)^{\frac{1}{3}}$.
44. $y = \log (1 + e^x)$; prove that $y'' = y'(1 - y')$.
45. $y = (\sin^{-1} x)^2$; prove that $(1 - x^2)y'' - xy' = 2$.

267

46. $y = \{x + \sqrt{(x^2 + 1)}\}^n$; prove that $(x^2 + 1)y'' + xy' - n^2y = 0$.

47. $y = \log \{x + \sqrt{(x^2 + 1)}\}$; prove that $(x^2 + 1)y'' + xy' = 0$.

48. $y = \sin (a \sin^{-1} x)$; prove that $(1 - x^2)y'' - xy' + a^2y = 0$.

49. $xy = A \cos nx + B \sin nx$; prove that $xy'' + 2y' + n^2 xy = 0$.

50. $y = ax \cos \left(\dfrac{n}{x} + b\right)$; prove that $x^4y'' + n^2y = 0$.

51. $y = \dfrac{ax + b}{cx - a}$; prove that $(y - x)y'' = 2y'(1 + y')$.

52. $y^3 + 3ax^2 + x^3 = 0$; prove that $y^5y'' = -2a^2x^2$.

53. $y^3 + 3x^2y + 1 = 0$; prove that $y'' = \dfrac{2(y^2 - x^2)}{(x^2 + y^2)^3}$.

54. $\dfrac{x^3}{a^3} + \dfrac{y^3}{b^3} = 1$; prove that $y'' = -\dfrac{2b^6x}{a^3y^5}$.

55. If $y = f(x)$, and $x = e^t$, prove that $x^2 \dfrac{d^2y}{dx^2} = \dfrac{d^2y}{dt^2} - \dfrac{dy}{dt}$.

In Exs. 56-61 find the stationary points and sketch the graphs :—

56. $a^2y = x^2(a - x)$. **57.** $y = x^5 - 5x^4 + 5x^3 + 2$.

58. $y = 2 \cos^4 x - \cos^2 x$. **59.** $y = \sin^3 x + \cos^3 x$.

60. $y = \dfrac{(x - 1)(x - 4)}{x - 5}$. **61.** $y = \dfrac{4}{2 - x} + \dfrac{9}{x - 3}$.

In Exs. 62-67 find the values of x at the turning-points and points of inflexion, and sketch the graphs of the given functions :—

62. $x - \sin x \cos x$. **63.** $x^2 \log x$. **64.** $x^2e^{-x^2}$.

65. $\dfrac{1}{x} + \log x$. **66.** $\dfrac{e^x}{x^2 + 1}$. **67.** $\dfrac{3 \sin x}{2 + \cos x}$.

68. If $x = r \cos \theta$, $y = r \sin \theta$, and x, y, r, θ are functions of t, prove that

(i) $\dot{x} \cos \theta + \dot{y} \sin \theta = \dot{r}$, $\dot{y} \cos \theta - \dot{x} \sin \theta = r\dot{\theta}$;

(ii) $\ddot{x} \cos \theta + \ddot{y} \sin \theta = \ddot{r} - r\dot{\theta}^2$, $\ddot{y} \cos \theta - \ddot{x} \sin \theta = \dfrac{1}{r} \dfrac{d}{dt}(r^2\dot{\theta})$.

69. If $r^2 = x^2 + y^2$, and $\tan \theta = y/x$, prove that

$$\left(\frac{\partial r}{\partial x}\right)^2 + \left(\frac{\partial r}{\partial y}\right)^2 = r^2\left\{\left(\frac{\partial \theta}{\partial x}\right)^2 + \left(\frac{\partial \theta}{\partial y}\right)^2\right\}.$$

70. If $u = (y - z)(z - x)(x - y)$, prove that

(i) $\dfrac{\partial u}{\partial x} + \dfrac{\partial u}{\partial y} + \dfrac{\partial u}{\partial z} = 0$; (ii) $x\dfrac{\partial u}{\partial x} + y\dfrac{\partial u}{\partial y} + z\dfrac{\partial u}{\partial z} = 3u$.

Miscellaneous Examples II.

1. Two tangents to the curve $y = x^3 - 4x^2 + 1$ are parallel to the line $y = 3x$. Find their equations, and the length of the x-axis and of the y-axis intercepted between them.

2. Find the maximum positive gradient of the curve whose equation is $y = x(1 + x - x^2)$.

3. The tangent to the curve $y = x(5 - x)^2$ at the point (3, 12) meets the curve again at P, the tangent at P meets the curve again at Q, and the tangent at Q meets the curve again at R. Find the equations of the tangents at P, Q, R.

4. Construct the cubic function of x which has the values 5, 3, 7, 3 when $x = 0$, 1, 2, $- 2$ respectively. Find the turning-points and sketch the graph of the function.

5. A function y is such that $y = 2x^2$ for values of x less than 1, and $y = ax^3 + bx - 4$ for values of x greater than 1. If the graph is a continuous smooth curve at $x = 1$, find a and b.

6. If the curve $y = A(x^2 - 1) + B \sin 2x + C \cos x$ cuts the y-axis at an angle of 45° at the point (0, 1), and if this point is a point of inflexion, find the constants A, B, and C.

7. If $z = x^3y^2$, and $2x + y = 4$, sketch the graph of z as a function of x, and find the maximum value of z.

8. Find the greatest breadth, measured parallel to the y-axis, of the loop of the curve $y^2 = x(x - 1)(2 - x)$.

9. Sketch the curve $xy^2 = (x + 1)^2$. Find the value of x where the gradient is zero ; and prove that, for greater values of x, the angle which the tangent makes with the x-axis does not exceed 11°.

10. The tangent at the point P to the curve $y(a^2 + x^2) = a^3$ meets the y-axis in T, and PN is the perpendicular from P on the y-axis. Find the maximum length of NT.

11. Sketch the graph of $y = x^3 + \dfrac{3}{x - 2}$, after proving that there is a maximum point where $x = 1 - \sqrt{2}$, a minimum point where $x = 1 + \sqrt{2}$, and a point of inflexion where $x = 1$.

12. Find the co-ordinates of the points of contact of the tangents drawn to the curve $3y = 3 + x^2$ from the origin.

13. The tangent at P to the curve $y = c \cosh (x/c)$ cuts the y-axis in the point U. Prove that $PU = xy/c$, where (x, y) are the co-ordinates of P.

14. Find the angle of intersection of the curves whose equations are $y = 20 - x^2$, $y = 3x^2 + 4$.

15. Sketch the graph, and the derived graph, of $y = e^{-x} \sin x$. Calculate the angle at which they intersect for the smallest positive value of x.

16. Find the differential coefficients of the two functions

$$x - \log (1 + x), \qquad \frac{2x}{2 + x} - \log (1 + x).$$

Hence prove that, when x is positive, the first is a positive increasing function, and the second a negative decreasing function.

17. Prove that $(9 - x)\{x + \sqrt{(x^2 + 9)}\}$ has a maximum or minimum value when $x = 4$, and determine which it is.

18. If $y = x^n + (a - x)^n$, where a is positive and n is any constant, prove that y has a stationary value when $x = \frac{1}{2}a$, and that this value is a maximum if $0 < n < 1$, but is a minimum for all other values of n (except 0 and 1).

19. AB is a diameter of a circle, and CD a chord parallel to AB. Prove that the maximum perimeter of the quadrilateral ABCD is five times the radius.

20. The sum of the lengths of the hypotenuse and one side of a right-angled triangle is given. Prove that the area is a maximum when the angle opposite the other side is 60°.

21. The area of the surface of a cylinder, including both ends, is constant and equal to C. If V is the maximum volume, prove that $54\pi V^2 = C^3$.

22. The volume of a right circular cone is 20 cub. ft. Find the base-radius when the area of the curved surface is a minimum.

23. A rectangle is inscribed in a quadrant of a circle of radius a, the sides of the rectangle making 45° with the bounding radii of the quadrant. Find the maximum area of the rectangle.

24. A cylindrical hole of length h is bored through a sphere of radius a, the axis of the hole passing through the centre of the sphere. Find the ratio of h to a when the total surface area (including that of the hole) of the part of the sphere that remains is a maximum.

25. The cost £C of a ship per hour is given by

$$C = 4 + \frac{v^3}{2500},$$

where v is the speed in knots through the water. What is the most economical speed through the water at which a voyage can be made against a current of 5 knots ?

26. The perimeter of a triangle is 36 ins., and one side is twice as long as another. Find the length of the shortest side when the area is a maximum.

27. If $s = Ae^{-t} \sin 2t$, prove that $\ddot{s} + 2\dot{s} + 5s = 0$.

28. If $s^2 = at^2 + 2bt + c$, prove that $\ddot{s} = (ac - b^2)/s^3$.

29. The co-ordinates of a moving point, t seconds after a certain instant, are given by $x = 3t^2(2 - t^2)$, $y = 8t^3$. Find its co-ordinates, resultant velocity, and resultant acceleration, when $t = 1$.

30. Water is pouring into a boiler, which has the shape of a circular cylinder of radius 2 ft., length 5 ft., with its axis horizontal. When the depth of water is 1 ft., the level is rising at the rate of one-tenth of an inch per second. How fast is the water pouring in, in cub. ft./min. ?

31. The length of a diagonal of each of two equal squares is c, and the distance between their centres is x. If they overlap so that the overlap is a square of area A, prove that $dA = - (c - x)dx$, and verify geometrically.

32. A point P moves on a straight line CP, passing through the centre C of a sphere of radius a. If S is the area of the part of the sphere visible from P, and if $x = CP$, prove that $dS = 2\pi a^3 dx/x^2$.

33. Write down the moment of inertia I of a solid sphere, of radius a and uniform density ρ, about a diameter. Find the differential of I with respect to a, and deduce the radius of gyration of a thin spherical shell, of radius a, about a diameter.

34. Prove that the radius of curvature at any point on the curve $(x/a)^{\frac{1}{2}} + (y/b)^{\frac{1}{2}} = 1$ is given by $\rho = 2 (ax + by)^{\frac{3}{2}}/ab$.

35. Prove that the radius of curvature at any point on the curve $x^{\frac{2}{3}} + y^{\frac{2}{3}} = a^{\frac{2}{3}}$ is given by $\rho = 3(axy)^{\frac{1}{3}}$.

36. Prove that the radius of curvature at the point t on the curve $x = 6t^2 - 3t^4$, $y = 8t^3$, is given by $\rho = 6t(1 + t^2)^2$.

37. In a certain curve. $x = a(\sec \psi + \tan \psi)$, where ψ is the angle of inclination of the tangent to the x-axis. Prove that the radius of curvature is given by $\rho = x \sec^2 \psi$.

38. Obtain the following expansions :—

(i) $\tan x = x + \dfrac{x^3}{3} + \dfrac{2x^5}{15} + \cdots$

(ii) $\sec x = 1 + \dfrac{x^2}{2} + \dfrac{5x^4}{24} + \cdots$

(iii) $\tan^{-1}(a + x) = \tan^{-1}a + \dfrac{x}{1 + a^2} - \dfrac{ax^2}{(1 + a^2)^2} \cdots$

(iv) $e^x \cos x = 1 + x - \dfrac{2x^3}{3!} - \dfrac{4x^4}{4!} - \cdots + 2^{\frac{n}{2}} \cos \dfrac{n\pi}{4} \dfrac{x^n}{n!} + \cdots$

39. Expand the differential coefficient of $\tan^{-1}x$ in ascending powers of x, and by integration obtain the expansion

(i) $\tan^{-1}x = x - \dfrac{x^3}{3} + \dfrac{x^5}{5} - \dfrac{x^7}{7} + \cdots$ [Gregory's Series.]

Similarly, obtain the expansions

(ii) $\sin^{-1}x = x + \dfrac{1}{2}\dfrac{x^3}{3} + \dfrac{1.3}{2.4}\dfrac{x^5}{5} + \dfrac{1.3.5}{2.4.6}\dfrac{x^7}{7} + \cdots$

(iii) $\log \{x + \sqrt{(x^2 + 1)}\} = x - \dfrac{1}{2}\dfrac{x^3}{3} + \dfrac{1.3}{2.4}\dfrac{x^5}{5} - \dfrac{1.3.5}{2.4.6}\dfrac{x^7}{7} + \cdots$

(iv) $\log (\sec x + \tan x) = x + \dfrac{x^3}{6} + \dfrac{x^5}{24} + \cdots$

40. If $f(a + h) = 0$, and if h is sufficiently small and $f'(a) \neq 0$, prove, by using Taylor's expansion, that, approximately,

$$h = -\dfrac{f(a)}{f'(a)} - \dfrac{f''(a)}{2f'(a)}\left(\dfrac{f(a)}{f'(a)}\right)^2.$$

Hence, given an approximation to a root of the equation $f(x) = 0$, show how to obtain a better approximation. [Newton's method.]

Find approximations, correct to four figures, to the real roots of the equations :

(i) $x^3 - x + 1 = 0$;   (ii) $x + e^x = 0$;   (iii) $x = \cos x$.

Find approximations, correct to four figures, to the smallest positive roots of the equations :

(iv) $x = \tan x$;   (v) $\tan x + \tanh x = 0$;   (vi) $\cos x \cosh x = 1$.

41. If $y = \tan (x + y)$, prove that $\dfrac{d^3y}{dx^3} = -\dfrac{2(y^2 + 1)(3y^2 + 5)}{y^5}$.

42. If $A + B + C = \pi$, and $\sin^2A + \sin^2 B + \sin^2 C = $ const., prove that

$$\dfrac{dB}{dA} = \dfrac{\tan A - \tan C}{\tan C - \tan B}.$$

43. In a triangle ABC, the side c and the angle C are constant, while the other sides and angles vary. Prove that

$$\frac{db}{da} = -\frac{\cos B}{\cos A}.$$

44. If the other sides and angles of a triangle are regarded as functions of A, b, c, prove that

$$\frac{\partial a}{\partial b} = -\frac{a}{b}\frac{\partial B}{\partial A} = \cos C.$$

45. The radius R of the circumcircle of a triangle ABC is calculated from measurements of a, b, C. Prove that the proportional error in R due to small errors δa, δb, δC in a, b, C, is given by

$$\frac{\delta R}{R} = \frac{\delta a \cos B + \delta b \cos A}{c} + \frac{\delta C \cos A \cos B}{\sin C}.$$

46. An angle of 45° was once drawn on a sheet of paper, with one leg of the angle parallel to the length of the paper. The paper has since shrunk α per cent. lengthways and β per cent. sideways. What does the angle measure now, in degrees, approximately ?

47. Find the minimum value of the radius of curvature on the curve $a^2y = x^3$.

48. By considering the graph of the function $x^3 - 3px$, show that the cubic equation $x^3 - 3px + 2q = 0$ has three real roots or only one according as $r^2 <$ or $> q^3$.

49. Prove that, for values of x between 0 and π, the function

$$3 \sin x + a \sin 3x$$

has two minima with an intermediate maximum if $a < -1$; one maximum if $-1 < a < \frac{1}{3}$; and two maxima with an intermediate minimum if $a > \frac{1}{3}$.

50. Prove that the abscissæ of the turning-points on the curve $y=(\sin x)/x$ are the roots of the equation $x = \tan x$: also, that the abscissæ of the points of contact of the tangents to the curve from the origin are the roots of the equation $x = 2 \tan x$.

51. The curve $y = ax^3 + bx^2 + cx + d$ touches the lines $y = 9x + 18$, $3x + y = 2$, at their points of intersection with the axes of x and y respectively. Find the values of a, b, c, d and show that the curve touches the x-axis.

52. The tangent at the point (1, 2) on the curve

$$2(x^2 + y^2) = xy(x + y) + 4$$

meets the curve again at P. Find the co-ordinates of P.

53. Prove that the length of the perpendicular from the origin on the tangent to the cycloid

$$x = a(\theta + \sin \theta), \quad y = a(1 - \cos \theta)$$

at the point θ is $a\theta \sin \frac{1}{2}\theta$.

54. The tangent at the point t on the curve

$$x = \frac{at}{t^3 + 1}, \quad y = \frac{at^2}{t^3 + 1},$$

meets the curve again at P, and the tangent at P meets the curve again at Q. Find the values of the parameter at P and Q.

55. In the epicycloid whose equations are given in Exs. CII., No. 7, prove that

$$\text{(i) } s = \frac{8b(a+b)}{a} \sin^2 \frac{a\theta}{4b}, \quad \text{(ii) } \rho = \frac{4b(a+b)}{a+2b} \sin \frac{a\theta}{2b},$$

where s is the length of the arc measured from the point $6 = 0$, and ρ is the radius of curvature.

56. Prove that the curves $r = 5 \cos \theta$, $r^2 \cos 2\theta = 12$, intersect at an angle equal to $3 \tan^{-1} \frac{1}{2}$.

57. If C is the centre of curvature at any point P on the curve $r^n = a^n \cos n\vartheta$, and if CN is the perpendicular from C on OP, prove that the ratio NP : OP is constant.

58. Prove that the abscissa x of a point of inflexion on the curve whose polar equation is $r = a \sec \theta + c$ (the Conchoid) satisfies the cubic equation

$$x^3 - 3a^2x + 2a(a^2 - c^2) = 0.$$

59. In the circle whose polar equation is $r^2 - 2cr \cos \theta + c^2 = a^2$, prove that $2ap = r^2 - c^2 + a^2$.

60. Prove that the locus of the point of intersection of two perpendicular tangents to the astroid $x = a \cos^3 \theta$, $y = a \sin^3 \theta$, is the rose-curve

$$r\sqrt{2} = a \cos 2\theta.$$

61. Four inextensible jointed bars form a quadrilateral ABCD. If x, y denote the lengths of the diagonals AC, BD, respectively, prove that in a small deformation of the quadrilateral

$$\frac{dA}{\triangle BCD} = -\frac{dB}{\triangle CDA} = \frac{dC}{\triangle DAB} = -\frac{dD}{\triangle ABC}$$

$$= -\frac{x\,dx}{2\triangle ABC . \triangle CDA} = \frac{y\,dy}{2\triangle DAB . \triangle BCD}.$$

Miscellaneous Examples III.

In Exs. 1-107 evaluate the given integrals :—

1. $\int_1^2 (x-2)^2\, dx.$

2. $\int_1^4 (x^{\frac{1}{2}} - x^{-\frac{1}{2}})dx.$

3. $\int_0^1 (1 - \sqrt[3]{x})dx.$

4. $\int \frac{x^2\, dx}{x^2 - x - 2}.$

5. $\int \frac{x^2\, dx}{(x+1)^2}.$

6. $\int \frac{x^3 + 1}{x^2 + 1}\, dx.$

7. $\int \frac{dx}{x(a^2 - x^2)}.$

8. $\int \frac{x^3\, dx}{x^4 + 1}.$

9. $\int \frac{dx}{x^4 + x^3 + x^2}.$

10. $\int_0^1 \frac{x\, dx}{x^2 - x + 1}.$

11. $\int_1^2 \frac{2 + 9x - 2x^2}{x(x+1)(2x-1)}\, dx.$

12. $\int_1^\infty \frac{dx}{x(x+1)^2}.$

13. $\int_0^\infty \frac{3x^2 + 2x + 1}{(x^2 + 1)(x+1)^2}\, dx.$

14. $\int \sin^2 x\, dx.$

15. $\int \sin^3 x\, dx.$

16. $\int \sin^4 x\, dx.$

17. $\int \tan x\, dx.$

18. $\int \tan^2 x\, dx.$

19. $\int \tan^3 x\, dx.$

20. $\int \sec x\, dx.$

21. $\int \sec^2 x\, dx.$

22. $\int \sec^3 x\, dx.$

23. $\int \cos \theta \cos 3\theta\, d\theta.$

24. $\int \tan \theta \sec^3 \theta\, d\theta.$

25. $\int \cot \theta \cos^2 \theta\, d\theta.$

26. $\int \frac{1 + \cos^3 \theta}{\cos^2 \theta}\, d\theta.$

27. $\int \frac{\tan \theta\, d\theta}{\sec \theta + \cos \theta}.$

28. $\int \frac{d\theta}{1 + \sec \theta}.$

29. $\int_0^{\frac{\pi}{2}} \frac{x \cos \theta \, d\theta}{1 - x^2 \cos^2 \theta}$.

30. $\int_0^{\pi} \frac{d\theta}{a^2 \sin^2 \theta + b^2 \cos^2 \theta + c^2}$.

31. $\int_0^{\frac{\pi}{4}} \cos^4 \theta \, d\theta$.

32. $\int_0^{\frac{\pi}{4}} \tan^4 \theta \, d\theta$.

33. $\int_0^{\frac{\pi}{4}} \sec^4 \theta \, d\theta$.

34. $\int_0^{\frac{\pi}{4}} \tan^5 \theta \, d\theta$.

35. $\int_0^{\frac{\pi}{2}} \sin^8 \theta \, d\theta$.

36. $\int_0^{\frac{\pi}{2}} \sin^3 \theta \cos^5 \theta \, d\theta$.

37. $\int_0^{\frac{\pi}{2}} \sin^{\frac{3}{2}} \theta \cos^3 \theta \, d\theta$.

38. $\int_0^{\frac{\pi}{2}} \cos^2 \theta \sin^2 2\theta \, d\theta$.

39. $\int_0^{\frac{\pi}{2}} \sin 3\theta \cos^2 \theta \, d\theta$.

40. $\int_0^{\pi} \cos 4\theta \cos^4 \theta \, d\theta$.

41. $\int_0^{\frac{\pi}{2}} \frac{d\theta}{5 + 4 \cos \theta}$.

42. $\int_0^{\frac{\pi}{2}} \frac{\sin \theta + \cos \theta}{1 + \sin^2 \theta} \, d\theta$.

43. $\int_0^{\frac{\pi}{2}} \frac{d\theta}{4 + 5 \cos \theta}$.

44. $\int_0^{\frac{\pi}{2}} \frac{\sin 2\theta \, d\theta}{\cos^2 \theta + 3 \cos \theta + 2}$.

45. $\int_0^{\frac{\pi}{2}} \frac{\sin^2 \theta \cos^2 \theta \, d\theta}{(\cos^3 \theta + \sin^3 \theta)^2}$.

46. $\int_0^{\frac{\pi}{3}} \frac{\log (\sec \theta + \tan \theta)}{\cos \theta} \, d\theta$.

47. $\int x \sin x \, dx$.

48. $\int x^2 \cos ax \, dx$.

49. $\int x^3 (\log x)^2 \, dx$.

50. $\int_0^{\pi} x^2 \sin x \, dx$.

51. $\int_0^1 \sin^{-1} x \, dx$.

52. $\int_0^1 x \log (1 + \frac{1}{2}x) dx$.

53. $\int_0^{\pi} x \sin^2 x \, dx$.

54 $\int_0^1 (\cos^{-1} x)^2 \, dx$.

55. $\int_0^{\frac{1}{4}} \tan^{-1}(2x) dx$.

56. $\int_0^1 x^n \log x \, dx$.

57. $\int_0^{\infty} \frac{dx}{1 + e^{2x}}$.

58. $\int_0^{\frac{1}{2}} \frac{\sin^{-1} x \, dx}{(1 - x^2)^{3/2}}$.

59. $\int_0^{2\pi} e^x (\sin x + \cos x) dx$.

60. $\int_0^{\infty} e^{-x} \sin ax \, dx$.

61. $\int_0^{\infty} e^{-x} \cos x \cos 2x \, dx$.

62. $\int_0^{\infty} x \operatorname{sech}^2 x \, dx$.

63. $\int \log \{x + \sqrt{(x^2 + c)}\} \, dx$.

64. $\int x^2 \sec^2 x \tan x \, dx$.

65. $\int \log \{a + \sqrt{(x^2 + a^2)}\} \, dx$.

66. $\int x^x e^{-x} \log x \, dx$.

67. $\int \frac{x \, dx}{\sqrt{(1 - x^2)}}$.

68. $\int \frac{dx}{x\sqrt{(1 - x^2)}}$.

69. $\int \frac{\sqrt{(1 - x^2)}}{x} dx$.

70. $\int \frac{x^2 \, dx}{\sqrt{(x^2 + c)}}$.

71. $\int \frac{dx}{x^2 \sqrt{(x^2 + c)}}$.

72. $\int \frac{\sqrt{(x^2 + c)}}{x^2} dx$.

73. $\int \frac{x^3 dx}{\sqrt{(ax^4 + c)}}$.

74. $\int \frac{\sqrt{x} \, dx}{\sqrt{(a^3 - x^3)}}$.

75. $\int \frac{(x - a) \, dx}{x\sqrt{(x^2 - a^2)}}$.

76. $\int (x + c)^{\frac{3}{2}} \, dx$.

77. $\int \sqrt{(e^x + 1)} dx$.

78. $\int x(x^2 + c)^{\frac{3}{2}} \, dx$.

79. $\int \sqrt{(2 + 4x - x^2)} dx$.

80. $\int x\sqrt{(x^2 + x + 1)} dx$.

81. $\int \frac{dx}{\sqrt{(2 + x + x^2)}}$.

82. $\int \frac{x \, dx}{\sqrt{(3x^2 + 2x + 1)}}$.

83. $\displaystyle\int \frac{(4x+3)dx}{\sqrt{(2x^2+3x-7)}}.$

84. $\displaystyle\int \frac{x^2 dx}{\sqrt{(x^2+4x+2)}}.$

85. $\displaystyle\int_0^1 \frac{1-\sqrt[3]{x}}{1+\sqrt[3]{x}}\,dx.$

86. $\displaystyle\int_0^1 \frac{dx}{x^{\frac{1}{2}}+x^{\frac{1}{3}}+x^{\frac{2}{3}}}.$

87. $\displaystyle\int_1^2 \frac{dx}{x-\sqrt{(x^2-1)}}.$

88. $\displaystyle\int_0^1 \left(1-\frac{1}{\sqrt{(1+x)}}\right)\frac{dx}{x}.$

89. $\displaystyle\int x^3 \left(\frac{a^2-x^2}{a^2+x^2}\right)^{\frac{1}{2}} dx.$

90. $\displaystyle\int \frac{3dx}{2\sqrt{(x-1)}+\sqrt{(x-4)}}.$

91. $\displaystyle\int_{\frac{1}{2}}^1 \sqrt{(1-x^2)}dx.$

92. $\displaystyle\int_{\frac{1}{2}}^1 \frac{\sqrt{(1-x^2)}}{x^2}dx.$

93. $\displaystyle\int_0^3 \frac{\sqrt{(9-x^2)}}{25-x^2}\,dx.$

94. $\displaystyle\int_4^5 \frac{x^3\,dx}{\sqrt{(x^2-16)}}.$

95. $\displaystyle\int_1^\infty \frac{dx}{x^2\sqrt{(x^2-1)}}.$

96. $\displaystyle\int_0^{\frac{\pi}{2}} \sqrt{(\tan\theta)}\,d\theta.$

97. $\displaystyle\int_0^3 \frac{x\,dx}{1+\sqrt{(1+x)}}.$

98. $\displaystyle\int_1^4 \frac{dx}{x\sqrt{(2x^2-2x+1)}}.$

99. $\displaystyle\int_0^1 \frac{dx}{x^{\frac{1}{2}}+1+x^{-\frac{1}{2}}}.$

100. $\displaystyle\int_2^\infty \frac{dx}{(x-1)\sqrt{(x^2+x-2)}}.$

101. $\displaystyle\int_0^1 \frac{x\,dx}{(3+x^2)\sqrt{(1-x^2)}}.$

102. $\displaystyle\int_0^a \frac{x\,dx}{\sqrt{(c^2+x^2)}\sqrt{(a^2-x^2)}}.$

103. $\displaystyle\int_0^{\frac{1}{2}} \frac{dx}{(1-2x^2)\sqrt{(1-x^2)}}.$

104. $\displaystyle\int_0^a \frac{x\,dx}{(c^2+x^2)\sqrt{(a^2-x^2)}}.$

105. $\displaystyle\int_0^4 x^3(4x-x^2)^{\frac{1}{2}}\,dx.$

106. $\displaystyle\int_0^2 (4x^2+1)\sqrt{(2x^2+1)}dx.$

107 $\displaystyle\int \frac{dx}{(x^2+1)\sqrt{(ax^2+c)}}.$ $\quad \left[\text{Put } x=\frac{1}{u}; \text{ then } a+cu^2=v^2.\right]$

108. By making the substitution $x=a-y$, prove the theorem

$$\int_0^a f(x)dx = \int_0^a f(a-x)dx.$$

Use this theorem to evaluate the integrals :—

(i) $\displaystyle\int_0^\pi x\sin^3 x\,dx$; (ii) $\displaystyle\int_0^\pi x\sin^4 x\cos^2 x\,dx$; (iii) $\displaystyle\int_0^\pi \frac{x\sin x\,dx}{1+\cos^2 x}.$

109. Use the theorem in the last example to prove that

(i) $\displaystyle\int_0^{\frac{\pi}{2}} \frac{\sin x\,dx}{\sin x+\cos x}=\frac{\pi}{4}$; (ii) $\displaystyle\int_0^{\frac{\pi}{2}} \log\tan x\,dx=0.$

In Exs. 110-118, find reduction formulæ for the given integrals :—

110. $\displaystyle\int (ax^2+c)^n\,dx.$ **111.** $\displaystyle\int \frac{dx}{(ax^2+c)^n}.$ **112.** $\displaystyle\int_0^\infty x^n e^{-x^2}\,dx.$

113. $\displaystyle\int_0^{\frac{\pi}{2}} e^x\cos^n x\,dx.$ **114.** $\displaystyle\int_0^\pi x^n\sin x\,dx.$ **115.** $\displaystyle\int_0^\infty \operatorname{sech}^n x\,dx.$

116. $\displaystyle\int \frac{x^n\,dx}{\sqrt{(ax+b)}}.$ **117.** $\displaystyle\int \frac{dx}{x^n\sqrt{(ax+b)}}.$ **118.** $\displaystyle\int \frac{x^n\,dx}{\sqrt{(ax^2+2bx+c)}}$

119. Evaluate the integral $\int_0^1 x^m(1-x^2)^n\,dx$, where m and n are positive integers.

120. Differentiate the identity

$$\int \frac{x^4\,dx}{\sqrt{(x^2+1)}} = (Ax^3 + Bx)\sqrt{(x^2+1)} + \int \frac{C\,dx}{\sqrt{(x^2+1)}},$$

and deduce the values of the constants A, B, C. Hence evaluate the integral on the left between the limits 0 and 1.

In Exs. 121-130 prove the given results by expanding the integrands in infinite series :—

121. $\dfrac{\pi}{4} = \displaystyle\int_0^1 \dfrac{dx}{1+x^2} = 1 - \dfrac{1}{3} + \dfrac{1}{5} - \dfrac{1}{7} + \dfrac{1}{9} - \dfrac{1}{11} + \cdots$

122. $\dfrac{\pi}{6} = \displaystyle\int_0^{\frac{1}{2}} \dfrac{dx}{\sqrt{(1-x^2)}} = \dfrac{1}{2} + \dfrac{1}{2}\dfrac{1}{3\cdot 2^3} + \dfrac{1\cdot 3}{2\cdot 4}\dfrac{1}{5\cdot 2^5} + \dfrac{1\cdot 3\cdot 5}{2\cdot 4\cdot 6}\dfrac{1}{7\cdot 2^7} + \cdots$

123. $\displaystyle\int_0^{\frac{\pi}{2}} \dfrac{d\phi}{\sqrt{(1-k^2\sin^2\phi)}} = \dfrac{\pi}{2}\left(1 + \dfrac{1^2}{2^2}k^2 + \dfrac{1^2\cdot 3^2}{2^2\cdot 4^2}k^4 + \dfrac{1^2\cdot 3^2\cdot 5^2}{2^2\cdot 4^2\cdot 6^2}k^6 + \cdots\right)$

124. $\displaystyle\int_0^{\frac{1}{2}} \dfrac{dx}{\sqrt{(1-x^3)}} = \cdot5082.$ **125.** $\displaystyle\int_0^1 \dfrac{\sqrt{x}\,dx}{\sqrt{(4-x^2)}} = \cdot3536.$

126. $\displaystyle\int_0^{\frac{\pi}{6}} \sqrt{(\sin\theta)}\,d\theta = \cdot2500.$ [Put $\sin\theta = x^2$; then expand.]

127. $\displaystyle\int_0^1 \sqrt{(4-x^2)}\sqrt{(1-x^2)}\,dx = 1\cdot520.$ [Put $x = \sin\theta$; then expand.]

128 $\displaystyle\int \dfrac{e^x}{x}\,dx = \log x + \dfrac{x}{1\cdot 1!} + \dfrac{x^2}{2\cdot 2!} + \dfrac{x^3}{3\cdot 3!} + \dfrac{x^4}{4\cdot 4!} + \cdots$

129. $\displaystyle\int \dfrac{\sin x}{x}\,dx = \dfrac{x}{1\cdot 1!} - \dfrac{x^3}{3\cdot 3!} + \dfrac{x^5}{5\cdot 5!} - \dfrac{x^7}{7\cdot 7!} + \cdots$

130. $\displaystyle\int e^{-x^2}\,dx = x - \dfrac{x^3}{3\cdot 1!} + \dfrac{x^5}{5\cdot 2!} - \dfrac{x^7}{7\cdot 3!} + \cdots$

131. Prove that the length s of the graph of $y = \sin x$, from $x = 0$ to $x = \pi$, is given by

$$s = 2\sqrt{2}\int_0^{\frac{\pi}{2}} \sqrt{(1 - \tfrac{1}{2}\sin^2 x)}\,dx = 3\cdot820.$$

132. Prove that the perimeter s of the ellipse $x = a\cos\phi$, $y = b\sin\phi$, is given by

$$s = 4a\int_0^{\frac{\pi}{2}} \sqrt{(1 - e^2\sin^2\phi)}\,d\phi = 2\pi a\left(1 - \dfrac{e^2}{4} - \dfrac{3e^4}{64} - \cdots\right),$$

where e = the eccentricity = $\sqrt{(a^2 - b^2)}/a$.

133. Prove that, if $\int f(x)dx$ can be evaluated, so can $\int f^{-1}(x)dx$, where $f^{-1}(x)$ denotes the inverse function of $f(x)$.

134. The substitution $x = \sin\theta$ apparently gives

$$\int_0^\pi \sin\theta\cos^2\theta\,d\theta = \int_0^0 x\sqrt{(1-x^2)}dx = 0 ;$$

explain this paradox.

In Exs. 135-137 prove the given results, using the given substitutions :—

135. $\int_0^\pi \frac{\sin\theta\,d\theta}{(1+\sin\theta)^3} = \frac{2}{5}.$ $\left[\text{Put }\sin\theta = \frac{1-x^2}{1+x^2}.\right]$

136. $\int_0^\pi \frac{d\theta}{(5+3\cos\theta)^3} = \frac{59\pi}{2048}.$ $\left[\text{Put }\cos\phi = \frac{3+5\cos\theta}{5+3\cos\theta}.\right]$

137. $\int_0^1 \frac{(1-x^2)dx}{(1+x^2)\sqrt{(1+3x^2+x^4)}} = \frac{\sqrt{5}}{8} + \frac{1}{2}\log\frac{1+\sqrt{5}}{2}.$ $\left[\text{Put }y = x + \frac{1}{x}.\right]$

138. If $\cos\phi = \frac{b+a\cos\theta}{a+b\cos\theta}$ prove that, when $a > b > 0$,

$$\int \frac{d\theta}{(a+b\cos\theta)^n} = \frac{1}{(a^2-b^2)^{n-\frac{1}{2}}}\int (a-b\cos\phi)^{n-1}\,d\phi.$$

139. If $a\tan\phi = b\tan\theta$, prove that

$$\int \frac{d\theta}{(a^2\cos^2\theta + b^2\sin^2\theta)^n} = \frac{1}{(ab)^{2n-1}}\int (a^2\sin^2\phi + b^2\cos^2\phi)^{n-1}\,d\phi.$$

140. If $\sin(2\theta-\phi) = k\sin\phi$, prove that

$$\int_0^\pi \frac{d\phi}{\sqrt{(1-k^2\sin^2\phi)}} = 2\int_0^{\frac{\pi}{2}} \frac{d\theta}{\sqrt{\{(1+k)^2\cos^2\theta + (1-k)^2\sin^2\theta\}}}.$$

Miscellaneous Examples IV.

1. Find the area between the parabola $y^2 = 4ax$ and the straight line $2x + y = 4a$.

2. Find the area between the parabolas $y^2 = 8ax,\ x^2 = ay$.

3. Find the area bounded by the lines $y = a,\ y = 4a$, and both branches of the curve $y(x-a)^2 = a^3$.

4. Find the area in the positive quadrant bounded by the curves $y^2 = 4x$, $x^2 + y^2 = 2x,\ x - y = 2$.

5. Find the area A bounded by the curve $y = x\sin(\pi x/a)$ and the x-axis from $x = 0$ to $x = a$. Also find the change in A caused by a small change δa in a.

6. Find the area A bounded by the curve $y = e^{ax}\sin\pi x$ and the x-axis from $x = 0$ to $x = 1$.

7. Find the area between the x-axis and each of the following curves, from $x = 0$ to $x = a$:—

$$(\text{i})\ \frac{y}{b} = \sin\frac{\pi x}{4a}; \quad (\text{ii})\ \frac{y}{b} = \tan\frac{\pi x}{4a}; \quad (\text{iii})\ \frac{y}{b} = \sec\frac{\pi x}{4a}.$$

8. Find the area bounded by the curve $y(1+x^2) = 2x$, the ordinate $x = 3$, and the x-axis from $x = 0$ to $x = 3$.

9. Find the area enclosed by the curve $y^2 = x^2(3-x)(x-2)$.

10. Prove that the area bounded by the Reciprocal Spiral $r\theta = a$ and the radius vectors of lengths $r_1,\ r_2$ is $\frac{1}{2}a(r_1 - r_2)$.

11. Prove that the area bounded by the Lituus $r^2\theta = a^2$ and the radius vectors of lengths $r_1,\ r_2$ is $a^2\log(r_1/r_2)$.

12. If $dy/dx = 3x^2\log x$, and $y = 1$ when $x = 1$, express y in terms of x.

13. If $dx/dt = k(a - x)(b - x)$, where k, a, b are constants, and if $x = 0$ when $t = 0$, express t in terms of x, both when $b \neq a$ and when $b = a$.

14. A tank, with vertical sides, contains water which flows out through a hole in the bottom at a speed proportional to the square root of the depth. If the tank is full to begin with, and if the upper half empties in one minute, how long will the lower half take to empty ?

15. If $y = \int_{-1}^{1} \dfrac{a\,dt}{\sqrt{(a^2 - 2axt + x^2)}}$, prove that $y = 2$ when x lies between a and $-a$. Draw the graph of y for all values of x.

16. The area bounded by the parabola $by = b^2 - x^2$ and the ordinates $x = a$, $x = -a$, $(a < b)$, revolves about the x-axis. Prove that, if c is the radius of either of the flat ends, the volume generated is

$$\tfrac{2}{15}\pi a(8b^2 + 4bc + 3c^2),$$

17. Find the volume common to two spheres, each of radius a, if the centre of each lies on the surface of the other.

18. A diameter of a sphere is divided in the ratio $2 : 1$ by a plane perpendicular to it. In what ratio does the plane divide (i) the area of the surface of the sphere, (ii) the volume of the sphere ?

19. Find the volume generated by the revolution of the curve $y^2 = (x - a)(b - x)$ about the x-axis; $(a < b)$.

20. Find the volume generated by the revolution of the curve whose equation is $a^4y^2 = (a^2 - x^2)^3$ about the x-axis.

21. Find the volume generated by the revolution of the curve $x^2 = y^4(1 - y^2)$ about the y-axis.

22. The area bounded by the curve $y = e^{-x^2}$ and the x-axis from $x = 0$ to $x = \infty$ revolves about the y-axis. Find the volume generated.

23. Find the volume generated when the area between the curve $y(1 + x^2) = 2x$ and the x-axis from $x = 0$ to $x = \infty$ revolves about the x-axis.

24. An arc of a circle of radius a subtends an angle 2α at the centre. Find the volume generated when the arc revolves about its chord.

25. Find the area of the surface generated when the arc of the curve $x^2y = x^3$, from the origin to any point (x, y), revolves about the x-axis.

26. Find the length of the arc of the curve $9ay^2 = 4x^3$, from the origin to any point (x, y).

27. Find the area of the surface generated when the arc of the curve $9ay^2 = 4x^3$, from the origin to the point where $x = \tfrac{1}{2}a$, revolves about the x-axis.

28. Sketch the curve $3x^2 = y(y - 1)^2$. Find the greatest breadth, the area, and the perimeter, of the loop.

29. Find the area of the ellipse $ax^2 + 2hxy + by^2 = 1$, where $h^2 < ab$, by transforming to polar co-ordinates.

30. The thickness of a disc, of radius a, at any point P is inversely proportional to $\sqrt{(4a^2 - r^2)}$, where r is the distance of P from the centre. If t is the thickness at the centre, find the average thickness.

31. A rod lies along the x-axis from $x = 0$ to $x = 8$. Find the average distance (with respect to x) of the points of the rod from the point $(0, 6)$ on the y-axis.

32. In the ellipse $l = r(1 + e \cos \theta)$, $(e < 1)$, prove that the average value of r with respect to θ is b, where $b = l/\sqrt{(1 - e^2)}$ = semi-minor axis.

33. P is any point on a circle of radius a, and C is a point at a distance c from the centre $(c < a)$. A mass M is distributed along the circumference so that the line density at P is inversely proportional to PC^2. If $PC = r$, prove that the line density at P is $(a^2 - c^2)M/2\pi ar^2$.

34. P is any point on a sphere of radius a, and C is a point at a distance c from the centre $(c < a)$. A layer of matter is distributed over the surface of the sphere so that the surface density at P is k/PC^2, where k is a constant. Find the total mass of the layer.

35. The density of a solid sphere at any point is inversely proportional to r^n, where r is the distance of the point from the centre. Find n, given that the average density is twice the density at the surface.

36. In a solid hemisphere, radius a, the density at any point is proportional to the nth power of the perpendicular distance of the point from the base. If the distance of the c.g. from the base is $\frac{1}{2}a$, find n.

37. OA, OB are the bounding radii of a quadrant of a circle, and C is a point on the arc AB. The triangle OBC revolves about OA. Find the angle BOC when the volume generated is a maximum.

38. A uniform wire has the shape of the part of the parabola $y^2 = 4x$ cut off by the line $x = 3$. Find the distance of the c.g. of the wire from the vertex.

39. Find the co-ordinates of the c.g. of the *arc* of the curve $6xy = x^4 + 3$ between $x = 1$ and $x = 3$.

40. Find the co-ordinates of the c.g. of the *area* bounded by the graph of $y = \log_e x$, the x-axis, and the ordinate $x = e$.

41. If $\left(p + \dfrac{a}{v^2}\right)(v - b) = c$ is the relation between the pressure and volume of a gas, where a, b, c are constants, find the work done by the gas while its volume changes from v_0 to v_1.

42. The sides AB, AD of a rectangular plate are of lengths a, b respectively. The thickness at any point P is proportional to the distance of P from the side AD. Find the radius of gyration about an axis through A perpendicular to the plate.

43. If $y = a + bx + cx^2 + dx^3$, prove that

$$\int_{-h}^{h} y \, dx = h(y_1 + y_2),$$

where y_1, y_2 are the values of y at $x = \pm h/\sqrt{3}$.

44. If $y = a + bx + cx^2 + dx^3$, prove that the average value of y between $x = 0$ and $x = 3h$ is $\frac{1}{8}(y_0 + 3y_1 + 3y_2 + y_3)$, where y_0, y_1, y_2, y_3 are the values of y at $x = 0$, h, $2h$, $3h$. Hence approximate to the value of the integral

$$\int_0^{\frac{\pi}{2}} \sqrt{(1 + 8 \sin^2 x)}dx.$$

45. If $y = a + bx + cx^2 + dx^3 + ex^4 + fx^5$, prove that

$$\int_0^h y \, dx = \frac{h}{20}(y_0 + y_2 + y_4 + y_6 + 5y_1 + 5y_5 + 6y_3),$$

where $y_0, y_1, y_2, \ldots y_6$ are the values of y at $x = 0, \frac{1}{6}h, \frac{1}{3}h, \ldots h$. [Weddle's Rule.]

46. Find the area of the loop of the curve $a^5y^2 = b^2x^4(x + a)$.

47. Find the area between the curve $y^2(a - x) = b^2x$ and its asymptote.

48. Find the volume generated when the curve $y^2(a + x) = a^2(a - x)$ revolves about its asymptote.

49. Find the whole length of the curve $\left(\dfrac{x}{a}\right)^{\frac{2}{3}} + \left(\dfrac{y}{b}\right)^{\frac{2}{3}} = 1$, and the area enclosed by it.

50. Find the whole length of the curve $8a^2y^2 = x^2(a^2 - x^2)$.

51. Prove that the perimeter of the limaçon $r = a \cos \theta + c$, $(c > a)$, is equal to that of an ellipse of semi-axes $c + a$, $c - a$.

52. Sketch the curve $r(1 - \theta^2) = 2a$. If s is the length of the arc from the point $(2a, 0)$ to the point (r, θ), where $0 < \theta < 1$, prove that $s = r\theta$.

53. Find the area between the curve $y^2(a - x) = x^3$ (the Cissoid) and its asymptote. When this area revolves about the asymptote, prove that the volume generated is the same as when the circle $r = a \cos \theta$ revolves about the same line.

54. Find the area between the curve $y^2(a - x) = x^2(a + x)$, (the Strophoid), and its asymptote. Also, find the area of the loop, and the volume generated when the loop revolves about the x-axis.

Show that, with the pole at the point $(- a, 0)$, the polar equation of the same curve is $r = a(\sec \theta - \tan \theta)$.

55. Find the length of the arc of the curve $y \sinh x = 2$ between the points where $x = \log_e 2$, $x = \log_e 3$. Also, find the area of the surface generated when this arc revolves about the x-axis.

56. If s is the length of a loop of the curve $(x^2 + y^2)^3 = 3x^2y - y^3$, prove that

$$s = 2 \int_0^1 \frac{dr}{\sqrt{(1 - r^6)}}.$$

ANSWERS TO THE EXAMPLES.

Examples I (Page 2).

1. $6, 0, -4, 6.$　**3.** $1, -7/4.$　**4.** $1, \frac{1}{2}, -\frac{3}{2}.$　**5.** $3 + 9h + 6h^2 + h^3.$
8. $0, 1, 0, 1/\sqrt{2}, -\frac{1}{2}, 2.$　**9.** $2, 4, 8, 1, \frac{1}{2}, \frac{1}{4}, \frac{1}{8}.$
10. $\dfrac{f(x) + f(y)}{1 - f(x)f(y)}.$　**13.** $2\cdot718.$　**17.** $1, 2, -1 ; 14.$　**18.** $3.$

Examples II (Page 4).

1. $2.$　　**2.** $-6.$　　**3.** $12.$　　**4.** $5.$　　　**5.** $-\frac{3}{2}.$
6. $\frac{1}{2}.$　　**7.** $16.$　　**8.** $3a^2.$　　**9.** $\frac{3}{5}a.$　　**10.** $n.$
11. $na^{n-1}.$　**12.** $na^{n-m}/m.$　**13.** $-3.$　　**14.** $6.$
15. $3.$　　**16.** $-21\frac{1}{3}.$　　**17.** $-\frac{1}{4}.$　　**18.** $2/(1 - x)^2.$

Examples III (Page 6).

1. $2.$　　**2.** $\frac{1}{2}.$　　**3.** $0.$　　**4.** $1.$　　　**5.** $-3.$
6. $\frac{1}{2}.$　　**7.** $10.$　　**8.** $\log 3.$

Examples VIII (Page 13).

1. $A = x^2 + \dfrac{16}{x}.$ 　　　　**2.** $y = \dfrac{x}{2}, z = \dfrac{\pi x^2}{4}, v = \dfrac{\pi x^3}{12}.$
3. $S = a^2 A/(a - x)^2.$ 　　**4.** $y = bx/(a - x).$
5. $z = 3x + x^2/4.$ 　**6.** $t = \theta/15.$ 　**7.** $r = \sqrt{(2x^2 + 4x + 4)}.$
8. $S = \sqrt{\{(49 - x^2)(x^2 - 1)\}}.$ 　**9.** $V = \pi x(36 - x^2)/3.$
10. $BC = \sqrt{(100 - 96 \cos \theta)}, 14, 2 ; S = 24 \sin \theta, 24, 0.$
11. $AC = 8 \sin \theta, BC = 8 \sin (\theta + 30°), S = 16 \sin \theta \sin (\theta + 30°).$
12. $AB = 2 \operatorname{cosec} \theta, BC = 4 \sin (\theta + 30°) \operatorname{cosec} \theta, S = 4 \sin (\theta + 30°) \operatorname{cosec} \theta.$

Examples IX (Page 15).

1. (i) 12, (ii) $12.$ 　　　　　**2.** (i) 16, (ii) $4\delta x + 2(\delta x)^2.$
3. $23\delta x + 9(\delta x)^2 + (\delta x)^3.$ 　**4.** $2\frac{1}{4}.$ 　**5.** $-3.$ 　**6.** -4π cub. ins.

Examples X (Page 18).

1. $3x^2.$　　**2.** $6x.$　　**3.** $0.$　　**4.** $1.$　　**5.** $10.$
6. $-2.$　　**7.** $10x.$　　**8.** $6x - 3x^2.$ 　**9.** $a.$　　**10.** $2ax + b.$
11. $-3/x^2.$ 　**12.** $-2/x^3.$ 　　**13.** $-3/x^4.$ 　　**14.** $-1/2x^{\frac{3}{2}}.$

15. $-1/(x+2)^2$.   **16.** $-4/(4x-3)^2$.   **17.** $-a/(ax+b)^2$.
18. $5/(1-x)^2$.   **19.** $3/2\sqrt{(3x-1)}$.   **20.** $-2x/(x^2+a^2)^2$.

Examples XI (Page 22).

1. $4x^3$.   **2.** $5x^4$.   **3.** $6x$.   **4.** 5.   **5.** -1.   **6.** x^2.
7. $3/\sqrt{x}$.   **8.** $4x$.   **9.** $-5/x^2$.   **10.** $-1/5x^2$.   **11.** $1-1/x^2$.
12. $-2/x^2 - 1/2\sqrt{x}$.   **13.** x^3.   **14.** x^{n-1}.   **15.** $2x+3/x^2$.
16. $(n-1)x^{n-2} - 1/x^2$.   **17.** $2(x+2)$.   **18.** $2x+1$.   **19.** $6x^2-5$.
20. nax^{n-1}.   **21.** $a^2 - 2ax$.   **22.** $nax^{n-1} + mbx^{m-1}$.
23. $-b/x^2$.   **24.** $\{nabx^{n-1} + (n+1)ax^n\}/c$.   **25.** $a - c/x^2$.
26. $1/(3-2y)$.   **27.** $1/2y$.   **28.** $1/3y^2$.   **29.** $y^2/(y^2-1)$.
30. y^2.   **31.** $y^2/(2y^3-1)$.
32. (i) $6u^2$,   (ii) $7/2\sqrt{u}$,   (iii) -1,   (iv) $4(2u+5)$.
33. (i) $-1/v^2$,   (ii) $2 - 3/v^2$,   (iii) $5/2v^2 - 1/\sqrt{v}$.

Examples XII (Page 25).

1. $4, 2, 0, -2, -4$.   **2.** 12.   **3.** -1.   **4** $\frac{1}{2}$.   **5.** 3.
6. $-\frac{3}{2}$.   **7.** 0.   **8.** $\frac{1}{4}$.   **9.** $-\frac{2}{3}$.   **10.** ∞.   **11.** $\frac{1}{6}$.
12. $(3, 3)$.   **13.** $(3, -13\frac{1}{2})$, $(-2, 7\frac{1}{3})$.   **14.** $(\frac{1}{2}, 1)$, $(-\frac{1}{2}, -7)$.
15. $(2, -48)$, $(-2, 48)$.   **16.** (i) $x > 3$, (ii) $x < 3$.
17. (i) $x > 2$, $x < -2$,   (ii) $-2 < x < 2$.
18. (i) $x > 1$, $x < -1$,   (ii) $-1 < x < 1$.
19. (i) $x < 1$, $x > 3$,   (ii) $1 < x < 3$.
20. (i) $-1 < x < 2$,   (ii) $x > 2$, $x < -1$.
22. $b^2 < 3ac$.   **23.** $(2, -4)$, $(\frac{2}{3}, \frac{212}{243})$.   **24.** $26° 34'$.
25. $63° 26'$, $45°$, $63° 26'$; $5° 12'$.   **26.** $(2, 4)$, $(\frac{2}{3}, 4)$.
27. $1 + \frac{1}{2}\sqrt{3}$, or $1\cdot866$.

Examples XIII (Page 27).

1. $45°$, $\tan^{-1}\frac{1}{2} = 26° 34'$.   **2.** $\tan^{-1}\frac{1}{3} = 18° 26'$, $\tan^{-1}\frac{2}{9} = 12° 32'$.
3. $90°$, $\tan^{-1} 2 = 63° 26'$.   **4.** $45°$.   **5.** $\tan^{-1} 3 = 71° 34'$.
6. $90°$, $45°$.   **7.** $90°$, $\tan^{-1}\frac{3}{4} = 36° 52'$.   **8.** $90°$, $\tan^{-1}\frac{9}{13} = 34° 42'$.
9. $0°$, $\tan^{-1}\frac{9}{5} = 60° 57'$, $\tan^{-1}\frac{5}{3} = 59° 2'$.
10. $\tan^{-1} m$, $\tan^{-1}\left(\dfrac{m}{1+2m^2}\right)$.   **11.** $\tan^{-1}\frac{9}{7} = 40° 36'$.   **12.** $90°$.

Examples XIV (Page 28).

1. $y = 2x - 1$, $x + 2y = 3$.   **2.** $y = 4$, $x = 2$.
3. $3x - 4y = 1$, $32x + 24y = 19$.   **4.** $10x - y = 22$, $x + 10y = 83$.
5. $x + y = 2$, $y = x$.   **6.** $y = a + bx$, $x + by = ab$.   **7.** $x + y = 2c$, $y = x$.
8. $6x - 4y = 5a$, $8x + 12y = 63a$.   **9.** $\tan^{-1}\frac{9}{25} = 15° 26'$.
11. $(\frac{1}{4}, -1)$, $4x + 2y + 1 = 0$; $(\frac{9}{4}, 3)$, $4x - 6y + 9 = 0$.
12. $x + 2y = 4$.   **13.** $y = 4x - 5$, $x + 4y = 14$.
14. $4y - 12x = 25$.   **15.** $y = 0$.

Examples XV (Page 29).

1. 144, 1.   **2.** 12, 4/3.   **3.** $\frac{1}{2}$, 18.   **4.** 27/64, 12.
5. 16/3, 3.   **6.** 8, 2.   **7.** $12\frac{1}{2}$, $16\frac{2}{3}$.   **8.** $6\frac{1}{3}$.   **9.** 10.

Examples XVI (Page 32).

1. $15(x^2 - 1)(x^3 - 3x)^4$.   **2.** $n(2ax + b)(ax^2 + bx + c)^{n-1}$.
3. $2/\sqrt{(4x + 5)}$.   **4.** $- 1/x^2\sqrt{(1 + x^2)}$.   **5.** $9(3x - 2)^2$.
6. $- 5(2 - x)^4$.   **7.** $12(x^2 - 2x)(x^3 - 3x^2 + 1)^3$.
8. $2/\sqrt{(4x - 1)}$.   **9.** $a/2\sqrt{(ax + b)}$.   **10.** $(3x - 1)/\sqrt{(1 - 2x + 3x^2)}$.
11. $na(ax + b)^{n-1}$.   **12.** $ax/\sqrt{(ax^2 + b)}$.
13. $(2ax + b)/2\sqrt{(ax^2 + bx + c)}$.   **14.** $1/(1 - x)^2$.
15. $- 2/(2x - 3)^2$.   **16.** $- (2ax + b)/(ax^2 + bx + c)^2$.
17. $- 3x^2/(x^3 - a^3)^2$.   **18.** $- 1/2\sqrt{x}(1 + \sqrt{x})^2$.
19. $n\left(x + \dfrac{1}{x}\right)^{n-1}\left(1 - \dfrac{1}{x^2}\right)$.   **20.** $\dfrac{4x^2 - 2}{\sqrt{(1 - x^2)}}$.   **21.** $\dfrac{x - c}{\sqrt{\{a^2 + (c - x)^2\}}}$.

Examples XVII (Page 34).

1. $2x(6x - 1)(2x - 1)^3$.   **2.** $2(6x - 1)(3x - 2)^2$.
3. $5(2x - 1)(3x + 1)^2(6x - 1)$.   **4.** $3(1 - 2x)/2\sqrt{x}$.
5. $(3x + 2)/2\sqrt{(x + 1)}$.   **6.** $(6x - 5x^2 - 2)/\sqrt{(3 - 2x)}$.
7. $x(5x + 4)/2\sqrt{(x + 1)}$.   **8.** $x(2a^2 - 3x^2)/\sqrt{(a^2 - x^2)}$.
9. $(4x^2 + 3x + 8)/\sqrt{(x^2 + 4)}$.   **10.** $n(1 + 2x)x^{n-1}(1 + x)^{n-1}$.
11. $2(1 - x)(x + 2)^2(1 - x - 3x^2)$.   **12.** $1/(1 - x)^2$.
13. $- 6/(3x - 1)^2$.   **14.** $4x/(1 - x^2)^2$.
15. $(x + 1)(x - 3)/(x + 1)^2$.   **16.** $2(3 + 2x - 2x^2)/(1 - 2x)^2$.
17. $2(1 - x^2)/(x^2 - x + 1)^2$.   **18.** $(2 - x)/2(1 - x)^{3/2}$.
19. $- a^2/x^2\sqrt{(a^2 - x^2)}$.   **20.** $\sqrt{a}/(\sqrt{a} - \sqrt{x})^2\sqrt{x}$.
21. $26(2x - 3)/(3x + 2)^3$.   **22.** $2/(1 + 2x)^{\frac{1}{2}}(1 - 2x)^{\frac{3}{2}}$.
23. $n(ad - bc)(ax + b)^{n-1}/(cx + d)^{n+1}$.

Examples XVIII (Page 36).

1. $\frac{1}{2}x^{-\frac{1}{2}}$, $\frac{5}{3}x^{\frac{1}{2}}$, $x^{-\frac{2}{3}}$, $5x^{\frac{3}{2}}$.   **2.** $- x^{-2}$, $- 4x^{-3}$, $- x^{-4}$, $-nx^{-n-1}$.
3. $-2/x^3$, $-3/x^4$, $-4/x^5$, $-n/x^{n+1}$.   **4.** $-9/4^4$, $-1/x^5$, $-1/3x^{\frac{4}{3}}$, $-1/\sqrt{(2x^3)}$.
5. $2x - 2/x^3$.   **6.** $(1 + 3x)/\sqrt{x}$.   **7.** $1 - 1/x^2$.   **8.** $x/2 + 20/x^6$.
9. $(2x + 3)/2x^3$.   **10.** $2 + 3/x^2 + 15/x^4$.   **11.** $- x/(x^2 - 2)^{3/2}$.
12. $4/(3 - 2x)^3$.   **13.** $2(x - 1)/(3x^2 - 6x)^{\frac{2}{3}}$.   **14.** $- 3(1 - 2x)^{\frac{1}{2}}$.
15. $(x + 1)/\sqrt{(x^2 + 2x)}$.   **16.** $x^2(x^2 - 3)/(x^5 - 5x^3)^{4/5}$.
17. $- 4/(2x - 3)^3$.   **18.** $- na/(ax + b)^{n+1}$.   **19.** $3/(2 - 3x)^4$.
20. $x/(1 - x^2)^{3/2}$.   **21.** $- a/2(ax + b)^{3/2}$.
22. $- (2x + 1)/2(x^2 + x + 1)^{3/2}$.   **23.** $2x/(x + 1)^3$.
24. $- \dfrac{9}{2}\left(1 + \dfrac{1}{x^3}\right)^{\frac{1}{2}}/x^4$.   **25.** $(x - a)/(2ax - x^2)^{3/2}$.
26. $3x^2(x + 1)/(3x + 1)^3$.   **27.** $a^2/(a^2 - x^2)^{3/2}$.

28. $x(x^2 + 2)/(1 - x^2)^{5/2}$. **31.** $nat^{\frac{1}{n-1}}/(n - 1)b^n$.
33. $y = 3x - 4$, $x + 3y = 28$. **34.** $5\frac{1}{8}$.
35. $45°$, $30° 58'$, $71° 34'$. **36.** $x + 2y = 4a$, $2x - y = 3a$.

Examples XIX (Page 39).

1. $3x^2$, $6x$. **2.** $2x - 3$, 2. **3.** $3x^2 - 4x$, $6x - 4$.
4. $1/2\sqrt{x}$, $- 1/4x^{\frac{3}{2}}$. **5.** $3/2\sqrt{(3x - 1)}$, $- 9/4 (3x - 1)^{3/2}$.
6. $x/\sqrt{(x^2 + a^2)}$, $a^2/(x^2 + a^2)^{3/2}$. **7.** $- 1/x^2$, $2/x^3$.
8. $- 2/(2x - 5)^2$, $8/(2x - 5)^3$. **9.** $- 2x/(x^2 - 1)^2$, $2(3x^2 + 1)/(x^2 - 1)^3$.

Examples XX (Page 43).

1. 4(max), $x = 2$. **2.** $\frac{3}{4}$ (min), $x = - \frac{1}{2}$. **3.** $- \frac{5}{4}$ (min), $x = \frac{3}{2}$.
4. 2(max), $x = 1$; $- 2$ (min), $x = - 1$. **5.** 0 (min), $x = 0$; 4 (max), $x = 2$.
6. 25 (max), $x = 2$. **7.** $\frac{1}{4}$(max), $x = 2$. **8.** 12 (min), $x = 2$.
9. 2 (min), $x = 0$; $- 6$ (max), $x = - 4$.
10. 8 (max), $x = 2$; 7 (min), $x = 3$. **11.** 4 (max), $x = 3$; 0 (min), $x = 5$.
12. $7\frac{5}{6}$ (max) $x = - 2$; $- 13$ (min), $x = 3$.
13. 128 (min), $x = 1$; 160 (max), $x = 5$.
14. $- 3$ (min), $x = - 1$; 2 (max), $x = 0$; $- 30$ (min), $x = 2$.
15. $0·631$ (max), $x = - 0·549$; $- 2·113$ (min), $x = 1·215$.
16. $(- 2, 20)$ max ; $(1, - 7)$ min. **17.** $(- 3, 2)$ min ; $(\frac{1}{3}, 20\frac{14}{27})$ max.
18. $(0, - 6)$ max ; $(1, - 7)$ min. **19.** No max or min.
20. $(a, 0)$ min ; $\{(a + 2b)/3, 4(b - a)^3/27\}$max ; if $a < b$.
21. $(- 1, - 6)$ min ; $(1, 10)$ max ; $(3, - 6)$ min.
22. $(- 1, - 2)$ max ; $(1, 2)$ min. **23.** $(3, \frac{1}{27})$ max.
24. $(2, 3)$ min. **27.** $\frac{2}{3}$, $- \frac{5}{3}$; $\frac{1}{8}$.
29. $- 1·879$, $1·532$, $0·347$. **30.** $- 1·325$.

Examples XXI (Page 44).

1. $(0, 0)$, neither. **2.** $(2, 0)$, neither. **3.** $(0, 2)$, neither ; $(-1, 1)$, min.
4. $(0, 0)$, min. **5.** $(0, 2)$, neither. **6.** $(1, 27)$, max ; $(4, 0)$ neither.
7. $(1, 1)$, neither. **8.** $(0, 20)$, max ; $(2, 4)$ min.
9. $(- 1, 0)$, neither ; $(2, 108)$, max ; $(4, 0)$, min.
10. $(- 1, 3)$, neither ; $(0, 2)$ min ; $(1, 3)$, neither.
12. $x = 0$, neither ; $x = 1$, max ; $x = 2$, neither ; $x = 3$, min.

Examples XXII (Page 45).

1. 121 ft. **2.** $u^2/2g$. **3.** $54° 44'$. **4.** $77\frac{1}{2}$ days (approx.).
7. $\sqrt{(1 + \mu^2)} - \mu$.

Examples XXIII (Page 46).

1. 625 sq. yds. **3.** 2. **5.** 200 cu. ins. **6.** 6. **7.** 12.
8. 2 cu. ft. With circular ends, $2·55$ cu. ft. **9.** $12·22$ ft.

10. 20 knots.   **11.** 12 sq. ft.   **13.** $3\frac{1}{3}$ ft. from cooler centre.
14. $1\frac{1}{5}$ mls.   **15.** 4.   **16.** $5(5x^2 - 6x + 5)/16$; **1.**
17. $\sqrt{(\frac{3}{2}\sqrt[3]{2} - 1)}$, or 0·943.   **18.** $\sqrt{2}$ ft.

Examples XXIV (Page 48).

6. $4\pi a^3/3\sqrt{3}$.   **7.** $32\pi a^3/81$.   **8.** $8\pi a^3/3$.
9. $120(3 - \sqrt{6})$ degrees $= 66° 4'$.   **10.** 12.
12. $4hk/3\sqrt{3}$, the equation of MN being $x = h$, and MN $= 2k$.

Examples XXV (Page 52).

1. 1 (max), $x = 2$; -4 (min), $x = -\frac{1}{2}$.   **2.** 4 (max), $x = \frac{1}{2}$.
3. 0 (min), $x = 0$; $\frac{3}{2}$ (max), $x = 3$.
4. 0 (max), $x = -1$; 8 (min), $x = 3$.
5. -3 (max), $x = -2$; 1 (min), $x = 0$.
6. $1/a$ (min), $x = a$; $1/b$ (max), $x = b$; if $a < b$.
7. 1 (min), $x = 6$; $-2\frac{45}{100}$ (max), $x = \frac{4}{5}$.
8. $1 - 1/\sqrt{2}$ (min), $x = 1/\sqrt{2}$; $1 + 1/\sqrt{2}$ (max), $x = -1/\sqrt{2}$.
9. 1 (max), $x = 1$; -1 (min), $x = -1$.
10. $\frac{1}{4}$ (max), $x = 1 \pm \sqrt{2}$; $-\frac{1}{4}$ (min), $x = -1 \pm \sqrt{2}$.
11. 3 (max), $x = 1$; -1 (min), $x = -1$.   **19.** 3/2.

Examples XXVI (Page 56).

1. π.   **2.** $2\pi/3$.   **3.** $2\pi/a$.   **4.** 4π.   **5.** $\pi/2$.   **6.** π/a.
7. 2π.   **8.** 2π.   **9.** π.   **10.** π.   **11.** 2π.   **12.** π.
13. 2π.   **14.** π.   **15.** π.   **16.** π.

Examples XXVII (Page 57).

1. 3.   **2.** 1.   **3.** a/b.   **4.** n.   **5.** 1.   **6.** π.
7. -2.   **8.** 1.   **9.** 8.

Examples XXVIII (Page 59).

1. $\sec^2 x$.   **2.** $\sec x \tan x$.   **3.** $-\csc x \cot x$.
4. $a \cos ax$.   **5.** $\sin 2x$.   **6.** $-a \csc^2 (ax + b)$.   **7.** 1·57.

Examples XXIX (Page 59).

1. $2 \cos 2x$.   **2.** $-3 \sin 3x$.   **3.** $-3 \cos^2 x \sin x$.   **4.** $-3x^2 \sin (x^3)$.
5. $\sin 2x$.   **6.** $3 \tan^2 x \sec^2 x$.   **7.** $4 \sec^2 4x$.   **8.** $5 \sec 5x \tan 5x$.
9. $\frac{1}{2} \sec^2 \frac{1}{2}x$.   **10.** $\frac{1}{2} \sec \frac{1}{2}x \tan \frac{1}{2}x$.   **11.** $\tan \frac{1}{2}x \sec^2 \frac{1}{2}x$.
12. $\sec^2 \frac{1}{2}x \tan \frac{1}{2}x$.   **13.** $m \sin^{m-1} x \cos x$.   **14.** $-n \cos^{n-1} x \sin x$.
15. $\sin^{m-1} x \cos^{n-1} x (m \cos^2 x - n \sin^2 x)$.   **16.** $3 \cos (3x + 1)$.
17. $b \sin (a - bx)$.   **18.** $a \sec (ax + b) \tan (ax + b)$.   **19.** $\sin (1 - x)$.
20. $-n \cos n(a - x)$.   **21.** $-a \csc^2 (ax + b)$.
22. $4 \sin (2x - 1) \cos (2x - 1)$.   **23.** $-2 \sec^2 (2 - x) \tan (2 - x)$.
24. $b \cos x/2\sqrt{(a + b \sin x)}$.   **25.** $\sin x + x \cos x$.

26. $3m \tan^2(mx + n) \sec^2(mx + n)$. **27.** $-k^2 \sin x \cos x/\sqrt{(1-k^2 \sin^2 x)}$.
28. $2x \cos x - x^2 \sin x$. **29.** $\sin x \cos x + x \cos 2x$. **30.** 0.
31. $2 \sin \theta - 3 \sin^3 \theta$. **32.** $1 + \cos 2\theta$. **33.** $\sin^2 \theta$.
34. $5 \cos 5\theta \cos \theta - \sin 5\theta \sin \theta$. **35.** $2 \sec^3 \theta - \sec \theta$.
36. $\sin (2\theta - \alpha)$. **37.** $(\theta \cos \theta - \sin \theta)/\theta^2$. **38.** $- \cos \theta/(1 + \sin \theta)^2$.
39. $\sin \alpha/\sin^2 (\theta + \alpha)$. **40.** $2x \sin (1/x) - \cos (1/x)$.
41. $-1/(1 + \sin \theta)$. **42.** $(\sin \theta - 2)/(1 + \sin \theta)^2$.

Examples XXX (Page 61).

1. 8 (max), $x = \pi/2$; 2 (min), $x = 3\pi/2$; etc.
2. 5 (max), $x = \tan^{-1} 4/3$; -5 (min), $x = \pi + \tan^{-1} 4/3$; etc.
3. 5 (min), $x = 0$; 8 (max), $x = \pi/2$; etc.
4. 3 (min), $x = 0$; 4 (max), $x = \pi/2$; etc.
5. $\sqrt{2}$ (max), $x = \pi/4$; $- \sqrt{2}$ (min), $x = 5\pi/4$; etc.
6. $\frac{8}{9}$ (max), $x = 0$; $- \frac{3}{4}$ (min), $x = 2\pi/3$; $- \frac{1}{2}$ (max), $x = \pi$; etc.
7. 4 (min), $x = \tan^{-1} 2$; etc.
8. 0 (neither), $x = 0$; $3\sqrt{3}/2$ (max), $x = 2\pi/3$; etc.
9. 0 (min), $x = 0$; $2/3\sqrt{3}$ (max), $x = \tan^{-1} \sqrt{2}$;
$\qquad\qquad\qquad - 2/3\sqrt{3}$ (min), $x = \pi - \tan^{-1}\sqrt{2}$; 0 (max.), $x = \pi$.
10. $2\sqrt{2}/3$ (max), $x = \pi/4$; $2/3$ (min), $x = \pi/2$; $2\sqrt{2}/3$ (max), $x = 3\pi/4$.
11. $3\sqrt{3}/16$ (max), $x = \pi/16$; 0 (neither), $x = \pi/2$;
$\qquad\qquad\qquad\qquad\qquad\qquad - 3\sqrt{3}/16$ (min), $x = 5\pi/6$.
12. $2\frac{1}{8}$ (max), $x = \sin^{-1} \frac{3}{4}$; 2 (min), $x = \pi/2$; $2\frac{1}{8}$ (max), $x = \pi - \sin^{-1} \frac{3}{4}$;
$\qquad - 4$ (min), $x = 3\pi/2$.
13. $14/15$ (max), $x = \pi/6$; $2\sqrt{3}/5$ (min). $x = \pi/3$; $13/15$ (max), $x = \pi/2$;
$\qquad 2\sqrt{3}/5$ (min), $x = 2\pi/3$; $14/15$ (max), $x = 5\pi/6$; etc.
14. 10 (min), $x = \tan^{-1} 2$; 15 (max), $x = \pi/2 + \tan^{-1} 2$; etc.
15. $\cos^2 \frac{1}{2}\alpha$ (max), $x = \alpha/2$; $- \sin^2 \frac{1}{2}\alpha$ (min), $x = \pi/2 + \alpha/2$; etc.
16. $2 \sin^2 \frac{1}{2}\alpha$ (min), $x = \alpha/2$; $2 \cos^2 \frac{1}{2}\alpha$ (max), $x = \pi/2 + \alpha/2$; etc.
17. $(\sec \alpha - \tan \alpha)^2$, (min), $x = \pi/4 - \alpha/2$;
$\qquad\qquad\qquad\qquad (\sec \alpha + \tan \alpha)^2$, (max), $x = - \pi/4 - \alpha/2$.
20. $-5 < a < 3$; $a = 2$.

Examples XXXI (Page 62).

1. $(2n + 1)\pi/2\omega$, where n is any integer.
2. $(\tan^{-1} a/b + n\pi)/\omega$, where n is any integer ; $\sqrt{(a^2 + b^2)}$.
3. 30 sq. ins. **5.** $V = \frac{1}{3}\pi a^3 \sin^2 \theta(1 + \cos \theta)$; $8/27$.
6. $5\sqrt{5}$. **7.** 125. **8.** $(a^{\frac{2}{3}} + c^{\frac{2}{3}})^{\frac{3}{2}}$. **9.** $\pi/2$.

Examples XXXII (Page 63).

8. $0 \cdot 739$. **9.** Three. **10.** $2 \cdot 029$. **11.** $4 \cdot 493$.

Examples XXXIII (Page 66).

1. $2/\sqrt{(1 - 4x^2)}$. **2.** $1/\sqrt{(x - x^2)}$. **3.** $a/(1 + a^2x^2)$.
4. $1/x\sqrt{(x^2 - 1)}$. **5.** $1/\sqrt{(2x - x^2)}$. **6.** $- 1/(1 + x^2)$.

ANSWERS TO THE EXAMPLES

7. $2\sin^{-1} x/\sqrt{(1-x^2)}$.   **8.** $\sin^{-1} x + x/\sqrt{(1-x^2)}$.   **9.** $1/2\sqrt{(x-x^2)}$.
10. $a/x\sqrt{(x^2-a^2)}$.   **11.** $1/\sqrt{(4+3x-x^2)}$.   **12.** $1/\sqrt{(2ax-x^2)}$.
13. $16/(4+x^2)^2$.   **14.** $2\sqrt{(a^2-x^2)}$.

Examples XXXIV (Page 69).

1. $(6-\delta t)$ ft./sec. ; 6 ft./sec.   **2.** 24 ft./sec. ; -40 ft./sec. ; 121 ft.
3. 30 m.p.h. ; $80\frac{2}{3}$ ft.
4. 24 m.p.h.   Yes, at $t=2/3$, $t=4/3$.   Max. speed $=36$ m.p.h.
5. 0·367 ins./min.   **7.** $v=12, \alpha=18$; $t=1,2$.
8. $v=6, \alpha=0$; $t=\pi/6, 3\pi/6, 5\pi/6$, etc.   **9.** $v=-3, \alpha=0$; $t=1,3$.
10. $v=-3\cdot14, \alpha=-17\cdot1$; $t=0,1,2,3$ etc.   **11.** $v=4, \alpha=-4$; $t=0,\sqrt{2}$.
12. $v=6$, $\alpha=-12$; $t=\pi/4, 5\pi/4, 9\pi/4$, etc.   **13.** 30.

Examples XXXV (Page 71).

1. 264 sq. ft./sec.   **2.** 0·477 ins./min.   **3.** 0·237 ins./sec.
5. $69\cdot1, -56\cdot5, 0$ cu. ins./sec.   **6.** $3\cdot14, 0, -4\cdot44, 6\cdot28$ sq. ins./sec.
7. $\frac{1}{4}$ rad./sec., or 14·3 deg./sec. ; $1\frac{1}{2}$ ft./sec.   **8.** 12·6, 50·3, 417, mls./min.

Examples XXXVI (Page 73).

1. 100 cu. ins./in.   **2.** $20x$ cu. ins./in.   **3.** $1\frac{1}{2}$ ft./ft.
4. $-600/x^2$ yds./in.   **5.** $-2\pi a^3/(x-a)^2$ sq. ft./ft.

Examples XXXVII (Page 74).

1. 3/5, 4/5.   **2.** 12/13, 5/13.   **3.** 3/5, $-4/5$.   **4.** 8/17, 15/17.
5. 3/5, 4/5.   **6.** $2/\sqrt{(4+\pi^2)}, \pi/\sqrt{(4+\pi^2)}$.   **7.** $1/\sqrt{(1+4x^2)}, 2x/\sqrt{(1+4x^2)}$.
8. $2x^2/(x^4+1), (x^4-1)/(x^4+1)$.   **9.** $\cos^2 x/(1+\sin^2 x), 2\sin x/(1+\sin^2 x)$.
10. $2\sqrt{x}/(x+1), (x-1)/(x+1)$.   **12.** 8, 6.   **13.** 10, 0.
14. 15, 9.   **15.** $-10, -6$.   **16.** 12, 16.

Examples XXXVIII (Page 75).

7. Except $x=\frac{1}{2}$.   **8.** Except $x=1, x=3$.
9. Except $x=\pm\pi/2, \pm3\pi/2$, etc.   **11.** $a^2<3b$.   **12.** $ad>bc$.

Examples XXXIX (Page 77).

1. (i) All values of x.   **2.** (i) $x<1$, (ii) $x>1$.
3. (i) $-1<x<1$, (ii) $x>1, x<-1$.   **4.** (2, 16).   **5.** (0, 0).
6. $(0,0),(\pm1,\mp7)$.   **7.** $(\pm1/\sqrt{3}, 3/4)$.   **8.** $(0,0),(\pm\sqrt{3}, \pm\sqrt{3}/2)$.
9. (3, 2/9).   **10.** $(0,0),(\pi,0)$, etc.   **11.** $(\pi/4,\frac{1}{2}),(3\pi/4,\frac{1}{2})$, etc.
12. $(0,0),(\tan^{-1}\sqrt{2}, 2\sqrt{6}/9)$, etc.   **13.** $(\pi/3, 9/16)$, etc.   **14.** 45°.

Examples XL (Page 79).

1. $\frac{1}{2}$.   **2.** $20\frac{5}{6}$.   **3.** ∞.   **4.** $10\frac{5}{12}$.   **5.** 1.   **6.** $125\sqrt{3}/72$.
7. $\frac{1}{2}$.   **8.** $(1+a^2)^{3/2}/2b$.   **9.** $\frac{1}{2}$.   **10.** $a/2$.   **11.** $(1+9x^4)^{3/2}/6x$.
12. $2(a+x)^{3/2}/\sqrt{a}$.   **13.** $(x+1)^2/2$.   **14.** $(1+\sin^2 x)^2/2\cos^3 x$.

15. a.　　**16.** $(x^4 + 1)^2/8x^3$.　　**18.** $a = 12$, $b = -4$, $c = 4/9$.　　**19.** $2a$.

20. $n = 1$, $\rho = \infty$; $n = 2$, $n = \frac{1}{2}$, $\rho = \frac{1}{2}$; $1 < n < 2$, $\frac{1}{2} < n < 1$, $\rho = 0$; $n > 2$, $n < \frac{1}{2}$, $\rho = \infty$.

Examples XLI (Page 81).

1. $6x\delta x$.　　**2.** $-\delta x/x^2$.　　**3.** δx.　　**4.** $\cos x \, \delta x$.　　**5.** $\sec x \tan x \, \delta x$.

6. $-\sin 2x \, \delta x$.　　　　**7.** $2\pi r \delta r$.　　**8.** $4\pi r^2 \delta r$.　　**9.** $-C\delta v/v^2$.

10. $\cdot 0003$.　　　　　　**11.** (i) $-\cdot 0006$, (ii) $-\cdot 0011$, (iii) $-\cdot 0003$.

13. $50\delta x/x$; $1\frac{1}{2}$ per cent. (approx.).　　**14.** $100 \, \delta x/3x$; $\frac{1}{2}$ per cent. (approx.).

15. $0 \cdot 42 \, \alpha$ ft.　　　**16.** $1 \cdot 7 \, \alpha \cot C$.　　**17.** $3 \cdot 5 \, \alpha \operatorname{cosec} 2\theta$.

18. $1 \cdot 285 \, \delta t$ ft.　　**19.** $2Aa^2\delta x/(a - x)^3$.　　**20.** $60 + \cdot 248\alpha$.

Examples XLII (Page 83).

1. $6x^2dx$.　　**2.** $-3dx/x^4$.　　**3.** $-dx$.　　**4.** $2ax \, dx$.　　**5.** $-dx/2\sqrt{x^3}$.

6. $-ndx/x^{n+1}$.　　　　**7.** $(1 - 1/x^2)dx$.　　**8.** $(\alpha\delta - \beta\gamma)dx/(\gamma x + \delta)^2$.

9. $2d\theta$.　　**10.** $\frac{1}{2}d\theta$.　　　　**11.** $\sec\theta\tan\theta \, d\theta$.　　**12.** $\frac{1}{2}\sec^2\frac{1}{2}\theta \, d\theta$.

13. $\sin 2\theta \, d\theta$.　　**14.** $-n\cos^{n-1}\theta\sin\theta \, d\theta$.　　**15.** $n\tan^{n-1}\theta\sec^2\theta \, d\theta$.

16. $dx/\sqrt{(1 - x^2)}$.　　**17.** $2\sin^{-1}x \, dx/\sqrt{(1 - x^2)}$.　　**18.** $dx/(1 + x^2)$.

Examples XLIII (Page 86).

7. $43° \, 26'$.　　　　　**8.** $8 \cdot 06$ ins.　　　**9.** q/A ft./sec.

10. $45 \cdot 2$ cu. ins./sec.　　**11.** $15 \cdot 1$ mins.　　**12.** $4x\cos^{-1}(a/x)$.

Examples XLIV (Page 90).

1. $x^5/5$.　　**2.** $2x^3$.　　**3.** $x^2/2$.　　**4.** x.　　**5.** $-1/3x^3$.　　**6.** $-6/x$.

7. $x^{2 \cdot 4}/2 \cdot 4$.　　**8.** $-x^{-0 \cdot 4}/0 \cdot 4$.　　**9.** $-1/2x^2$.　　**10.** $2\sqrt{x}$.　　**11.** $-5/x$.

12. $-1/(n - 1)ax^{n-1}$.　　**13.** $x^3/3 + x^2/2$.　　**14.** $x^4/4 - a^3x$.

15. $ax^3/3 + bx^2/2 + cx$.　　**16.** $x^3/3 - 2x - 1/x$.　　**17.** $-2/x + 3/2x^2$.

18. $-a/x - b/2x^2 - c/3x^3$.　　**19.** $2x^{\frac{3}{2}}/3 + 2\sqrt{x}$.　　**20.** $x + 3x^{\frac{5}{3}}/5$.

21. $2x^{\frac{3}{2}}/3 + 4x^{\frac{5}{2}}/5 + 2x^{\frac{7}{2}}/7$.　　**22.** $-a\cos\omega t/\omega$.　　**23.** $\frac{1}{3}\sin(1 + 3x)$.

24. $\cos(1 - x)$.　　**25.** $-\frac{1}{8}\cos 4x$.　　**26.** $\frac{1}{4}\sin 2x - \frac{1}{8}\sin 4x$.

27. $\frac{1}{2}\left\{\dfrac{\sin(m+n)x}{m+n} + \dfrac{\sin(m-n)x}{m-n}\right\}$.　　**28.** $\dfrac{ab}{2}\left\{t\sin\alpha - \dfrac{\cos(2\omega t - \alpha)}{2\omega}\right\}$.

Examples XLV (Page 91).

1. $\frac{1}{6}(x^2 + 4)^6$.　　**2.** $\frac{2}{3}(x^2 - 1)^{\frac{3}{2}}$.　　**3.** $\frac{3}{8}(2x - 1)^{\frac{4}{3}}$.　　**4.** $-\frac{1}{3}(a^2 - x^2)^{\frac{3}{2}}$.

5. $(ax^2 + b)^{n+1}/2(n + 1)a$.　　**6.** $(ax + b)^5/5a$.　　**7.** $(a + bx^3)^{\frac{4}{3}}/4b$.

8. $(ax^2 + bx)^{n+1}/(n + 1)$.　　**9.** $2\sqrt{(2x + 3)}$.　　**10.** $1/6(1 - 3x)^2$.

11. $-1/a(ax + b)$.　　**12.** $-1/(a^3 + x^3)$.　　**13.** $-\sqrt{(1 - x^2)}$.　　**14.** $3(ax + b)^{\frac{2}{3}}/2a$.

15. $-\dfrac{1}{12(x^6 + 1)^2}$.　　**16.** $\dfrac{2(1 + \sqrt{x})^{n+1}}{n + 1}$.　　**17.** $\dfrac{1}{n + 1}\left(\dfrac{1}{a} - \dfrac{1}{x}\right)^{n+1}$.

18. $\sqrt{(x^2 + 2x - 1)}$.　　　　　　**19.** $-1/6(3x^2 + 4x + 2)^3$.

Examples XLVI (Page 93).

1. $\sin\theta - \frac{1}{3}\sin^3\theta$. **2.** $\frac{1}{4}\sin^4\theta$. **3.** $-\frac{1}{3}\cos^3\theta$.

4. $-\cos\theta + \frac{2}{3}\cos^3\theta - \frac{1}{5}\cos^5\theta$. **5.** $\frac{1}{4}\sin^4\theta - \frac{1}{6}\sin^6\theta$. **6.** $-\frac{2}{3}\cos^3\theta$.

7. $\frac{1}{8}(3\theta - 2\sin 2\theta + \frac{1}{4}\sin 4\theta)$. **8.** $\frac{1}{16}(\theta + \frac{1}{3}\sin^3 2\theta - \frac{1}{4}\sin 4\theta)$.

9. $\frac{1}{4}(\theta + \sin 2\theta + \frac{1}{4}\sin 4\theta)$. **10.** $\sec\theta$. **11.** $2\sqrt{(\sin\theta)}$.

12. $1/\sin\theta - 1/3\sin^3\theta$. **13.** $\frac{1}{2}(3\theta - 4\cos\theta - \sin\theta\cos\theta)$.

14. $\frac{1}{4}(2 + \sin\theta)^4$. **15.** $\frac{1}{2}(5\theta - 2\cos 2\theta - \frac{3}{2}\sin 2\theta)$.

16. $\theta + \sin\theta + \frac{1}{4}\sin 2\theta + \frac{1}{3}\sin 3\theta + \frac{1}{8}\sin 4\theta$.

Examples XLVII (Page 94).

1. $(x-1)^6(6x+1)/42$. **2.** $(1-3x)/6(x-1)^3$. **3.** $-(3x^2-3x+1)/3(x-1)^3$.

4. $2(3x+2)(x-1)^{3/2}/15$. **5.** $(3x+7)(2x+3)^{3/2}/15$.

6. $2(x-4)\sqrt{(x+2)}/3$. **7.** $2(3x^2+4x+8)\sqrt{(x-1)}/15$.

8. $(12x^2 - 8x + 23)\sqrt{(2x+1)}/15$. **9.** $\sin^{-1}(x/2)$. **10.** $-\sqrt{(4-x^2)}$.

11. $\frac{1}{2}a^2\sin^{-1}(x/a) - \frac{1}{2}x\sqrt{(a^2-x^2)}$. **12.** $\sin^{-1}x$. **13.** $\sin^{-1}(ax)/a$.

14. $\frac{1}{2}\sin^{-1}(2x/3)$. **15.** $\frac{1}{2}x\sqrt{(4-x^2)} + 2\sin^{-1}(x/2)$.

16. $-\frac{1}{3}(1-x^2)^{\frac{3}{2}}$. **17.** $\frac{1}{8}\{(2x^3 - a^2x)\sqrt{(a^2-x^2)} + a^4\sin^{-1}(x/a)\}$.

Examples XLVIII (Page 95).

1. $\sin x - x\cos x$. **2.** $(2 - x^2)\cos x + 2x\sin x$.

3. $x\sin 2x + \frac{1}{2}\cos 2x$. **4.** $(x^3 - 6x)\sin x + 3(x^2 - 2)\cos x$.

5. $\frac{1}{4}(x^2 + x\sin 2x + \frac{1}{2}\cos 2x)$. **6.** $(2 + x - x^2)\sin x + (1-2x)\cos x$.

7. $-\frac{1}{2}\{(1 - 2x)\cos 2x + \sin 2x\}$. **8.** $\frac{1}{4}(-x\cos 2x + \frac{1}{2}\sin 2x)$.

9. $\frac{1}{2}\{(x^2 + 2x + \frac{1}{2})\sin 2x + (x + 1)\cos 2x\}$.

10. $\frac{1}{16}\{x(4\sin 4x + 8\sin 2x) + \cos 4x + 4\cos 2x\}$.

Examples XLIX (Page 97).

1. $y = 2x^3 + 1$. **2.** $y = 1 - \cos x$. **3.** $y = 2(1 - 1/x^3)$.

4. $y = (2x + 3)/(4x - 1)$. **5.** $y = \frac{1}{2}x^2 - \frac{1}{6}x^3$. **6.** $y = \frac{1}{12}(2x^3 - x^4 - x)$.

7. $v = t^2 - 5t + 16$; 22. **8.** $s = a(1 - \cos\pi t)/\pi$; $2a/\pi$.

9. $v = u + gt$, $s = ut + \frac{1}{2}gt^2$.

10. $v = 2(1 - \cos 2t)$, $s = 3 + 2t - \sin 2t$.

11. $v = \sqrt{(u^2 + 2gs)}$. **12.** $v = \sqrt{\{2k(a - s)/as\}}$.

13. $y = Wx^2(3l - x)/6EI$; $Wl^3/3EI$.

Examples L (Page 98).

1. 63. **2.** $\frac{2}{3}$. **3.** 144. **4.** $b - a$. **5.** 0. **6.** $4a^3/3$.

7. $\frac{9}{10}$. **8.** $\frac{1}{5}$. **9.** $14\frac{2}{3}$. **10.** 1. **11.** $\pi/4$. **12.** $16\frac{1}{3}$.

13. $2\sin\alpha$. **14.** $1\frac{1}{3}$. **15.** $\frac{2}{3}$. **16.** π. **17.** $\frac{1}{2}\pi - 1$. **18.** 3π.

19. $3\pi/8$. **20.** $\frac{1}{2}(\pi + 3\sqrt{3}/4)$. **21.** 0.

Examples LI (Page 100).

1. 16. **2.** 36. **3.** $ab/2$. **4.** $4\frac{1}{8}$. **5.** 4. **6.** $6\frac{3}{16}$.

7. $25\frac{1}{3}$. **8.** 42. **9.** $2 - \sqrt{2}$. **10.** $\pi + 2$. **11.** ab/π.

12. $(4\pi + 3\sqrt{3})/8$.   **13.** 1.   **14.** 2π.   **15.** 4π.   **16.** $2\frac{3}{8}$.
17. $\frac{3}{15}$.   **18.** $(n-1)/2(n+1)$.   **19.** $1:5$.

Examples LII (Page 104).

1. 0.   **2.** -4.   **3.** -26.   **4.** 0.   **5.** 2.   **6.** 0.
7. -3π.   **8.** $8a^3/3$.   **9.** 0.   **10.** 0.   **11.** -4π.   **12.** 0.

Examples LIII (Page 105).

1. $\frac{11}{80}$.   **2.** $4\frac{1}{3}$.   **3.** $2(8\sqrt{2}-7)/15$.   **4.** $(4\pi - 3\sqrt{3})/6$.
5. $\frac{2}{15}$.   **6.** $\pi/16$.   **7.** 1.   **8.** $\frac{1}{3}$.   **9.** $\frac{2}{5}$.   **10.** $\pi/2$.
11. $\pi/6$.   **12.** $(2\pi - 3\sqrt{3})/6$.   **13.** 12.   **14.** $\pi/4a$.
16. $a^2(\alpha - \sin\alpha\cos\alpha)$, $a^2(\pi - \alpha + \sin\alpha\cos\alpha)$.
17. $a^2\cos^{-1}(c/a) - c\sqrt{(a^2 - c^2)}$, $\pi a^2 - a^2\cos^{-1}(c/a) + c\sqrt{(a^2 - c^2)}$.
18. πab.   **19.** $\frac{8}{15}$.   **20.** $\frac{8}{35}$.   **21.** $\frac{32}{105}$.   **22.** $2a^3/3b$.

Examples LIV (Page 107).

1. 2.   **2.** Meaningless.   **3.** 6.   **4.** $1/(1-n)$, if $n < 1$.
5. Meaningless.   **6.** Meaningless.   **7.** $4a\sqrt{a}/3$.
8. Meaningless.   **9.** $1\frac{3}{5}$.   **10.** π.   **11.** $\frac{1}{2}$.   **12.** $\frac{1}{3}$.
13. $1/2a^2$.   **14.** $\pi/4$.   **15.** $\pi/2$.

Examples LV (Page 113).

1. $a(c^{n+1} - b^{n+1})/(n+1)$.   **2.** 60.   **3.** $ab/3$.   **4.** 6.
5. 144.   **6.** 20.   **7.** $83\frac{1}{3}$.   **8.** $(\pi + \sqrt{3})/3$.
9. $(3\pi - 4)/6\pi$, $= \cdot288$.   **10.** $\pi(b^2 - a^2)$.   **11.** $ah/2$ **12.** $(a+b)h/2$.

Examples LVI (Page 115).

1. $56\pi/3$.   **2.** $416\pi/3$.   **3.** 625π.   **4.** $16\pi/15$.
5. 14π.   **6.** $4\pi a^3/3$.   **7.** $\pi^2/2$.   **8.** $3\pi^2/2$.   **9.** $\pi^2 a^3/4$.
10. $4\pi ab^2/3$.   **11.** $384\pi/7$.   **12.** $256\pi/15$.   **13.** 8π.
14 2π.   **15.** $4\pi a^3/3$.   **16.** $256\pi a^3/15$.   **17.** $56\pi/15$.
18. $2\pi(3\sqrt{3} - 4\pi/3)$.   **20.** $4\pi a^3/3$.   **21.** $4\pi(b^3 - a^3)/3$.   **22.** $4\pi a^3/3$.
24. $\pi(a-c)^2(2a+c)/3$, $\pi(a+c)^2(2a-c)/3$; $c/a = \cdot3473$, a root of the
equation $x^3 - 3x + 1 = 0$.

Examples LVII (Page 116).

1. $1\frac{11}{12}$ cu. ft.   **2.** 7,400,000 cu. ft.   **3.** 104 cu. ft.
4. $16a^3/3$.   **5.** $16a^3/3\sin\alpha$.

Examples LVIII (Page 118).

1. $61/54$.   **2.** 12.   **3.** $4\frac{2}{3}$.   **4.** $7\frac{1}{3}$.   **6.** $4a\sqrt{3}$.

Examples LIX (Page 119).

1. 60π.   **2.** 60π.   **3.** $61\pi/432$.   **4.** $208\pi/9$.
5. $2\pi(3 + 2\pi/\sqrt{3})$.   **6.** $25\pi\sqrt{5}$.   **7.** 100π.   **8.** $301\pi/3$.
9. $\pi(\frac{1}{2} + 2\pi/3\sqrt{3})$.   **12.** $8\pi\sqrt{a}\{(a + h)^{\frac{3}{2}} - a^{\frac{3}{2}}\}/3$; 49π sq. ins.
13. $3\pi a^2$.   **14.** $4\pi a^2$.   **15.** $2\pi a^2(1 - \cos\alpha)$.   **16.** 10π sq. ins.

Examples LX (Page 121).

1. $2\pi a^2\rho_1$; $3\rho_1/2$.   **2.** $M/2\pi(b^2 - a^2)r$.   **3.** $\pi w a^3/4$.
4. $2\pi a^3\rho_1/3$; $\rho_1/2$.   **5.** $Q/4\pi a^2$ (on either side of the disc).
7. $6\bar{\sigma}$.   **8.** $(\sigma_0 + 2\sigma_1)/3$.

Examples LXI (Page 124).

1. $\frac{2}{3}$.   **2.** $1/(n + 1)$.   **3.** 0.   **4.** $2/\pi$.   **5.** 0.   **6.** $\frac{1}{2}$.
7. $\frac{1}{2} + 1/\pi$.   **8.** $4/15\pi$.   **9.** $\frac{1}{2}$.   **10.** $1/\omega$.   **11.** $\frac{1}{2}\sin\alpha$.
12. a, $a + 2b/\pi$.   **13.** $a + \frac{1}{3}b$.   **14.** 0, $2(a + \frac{1}{3}b)/\pi$.
15. $2a\omega/\pi$, $\pi a\omega/4$.   **16.** (i) $a^2/6$, (ii) $2a^2/15$, (iii) $a^2/6$, (iv) $na^2/(n + 1)(n + 2)$.

Examples LXII (Page 125).

1. 3π.   **2.** $5\pi/2$.   **3.** π.   **4.** $\pi + 2\frac{2}{3}$.   **5.** 7π.
6. $259\pi^2/450$.   **7.** $\frac{1}{2}\text{VI}\cos\alpha$.   **8.** $3\text{VI}/2$.   **9.** $\sqrt{(a^2 + \frac{1}{2}b^2)}$.
10. $\sqrt{(a^2 + \frac{1}{2}b^2 + \frac{1}{2}c^2)}$.   **11.** $\sqrt{(\frac{1}{2}a^2 + \frac{1}{2}b^2)}$.   **12.** $\sqrt{(a^2 + \frac{1}{3}b^2 + \frac{1}{2}c^2)}$.
13. $\sqrt{(a_0^2 + \frac{1}{2}a_1^2 + \frac{1}{2}a_2^2 + \ldots + \frac{1}{2}a_n^2)}$.   **14.** $\pi/2\sqrt{2}$.
15. $\sqrt{(1 + \frac{1}{2}b^2/a^2)}$.   **16.** $\sqrt{3}/\sqrt{2}$.

Examples LXIII (Page 127).

1. $37\cdot33$.   **2.** $1\cdot099$.   **3.** $22\cdot45$.   **4.** $3\cdot594$.   **5.** $2\cdot37$.   **6.** $2\cdot42$.

Examples LXIV (Page 130).

1. 645 ft.   **2.** $1\frac{1}{4}$ mls.   **4.** $\frac{1}{2}ma^2\omega^2$, $\frac{1}{4}ma^2\omega^2$.   **6.** Ee/r.
10. $\frac{1}{2}\text{W}l\sin\theta$; $\text{W}l$.

Examples LXV (Page 134).

1. $3a/8$.   **2.** $\bar{x} = 5$.   **3.** $2h/3$.   **4.** $7a/40$.   **5.** $3(a + c)^2/4(2a + c)$.
6. $a/2$.   **7.** $3l/4$.   **8.** $5a/12$.   **9.** $3(b^4 - a^4)/8(b^3 - a^3)$.
10. $0\cdot39$.   **11.** $h(a^2 + 2ab + 3b^2)/4(a^2 + ab + b^2)$.   **13.** $2h/3$.
14. $5/4$.   **15.** $58/35$.

Examples LXVI (Page 137).

1. $9/4$, $27/10$.   **2.** 0, $8/5$.   **3.** $\pi/2$, $\pi/8$.
4. $(\pi - 2)/2$, $\pi/8$.   **5.** $12/5$, $3/2$.   **6.** $635/217$, 0.
7. $4/3$, $31/30$.   **8.** $4a/3\pi$, $4b/3\pi$.   **9.** $8/5$, 2.

10. $A\bar{x} = 6\frac{2}{3}$, $A\bar{y} = 3\frac{1}{3}$, where $A = \dfrac{25\pi}{4} - 10 - \dfrac{25}{2}\sin^{-1}\dfrac{3}{5} = 1 \cdot 59$. Hence
$\bar{x} = 4 \cdot 20$, $\bar{y} = 2 \cdot 10$.

11. 9/20, 9/20.   **12.** 217/64, -2.   **13.** $h/3$.   **14.** $3h/5$.

15. $6\frac{1}{2}$ ins.   **17.** $\bar{x} = 4a/3\pi$.   **18.** $3a\sqrt{3}/(4\pi - 3\sqrt{3}) = \cdot705a$.

19. $3\pi a/16$.   **20.** $\pi a/4$.   **21.** $\sin\theta/\theta^2$ ft.

22. $4(a^2 + ab + b^2)/3\pi(a + b)$.   **23.** 7/5.   **24.** 1423/2745.

Examples LXVII (Page 139).

2. $6\pi a^2\sqrt{3}$, $9\pi a^3/2$.   **4.** $\pi(a + b)l$.   **5.** 32π.   **6.** 54π.

Examples LXVIII (Page 143).

1. (i) $a^2/3$, (ii) $b^2/3$, (iii) $(a^2 + b^2)/3$.   **2.** (i) $(a^2 + b^2)/2$, (ii) $(a^2 + b^2)/4$.

3. (i) $h^2/2$, (ii) $h^2/6$.   **4.** $2h^2/5$.   **5.** 6.

6. $k^2/5$, where k is the ordinate at $x = h$.   **7.** $53a^2/200$.

8. $3r^2/10$.   **9.** $3(b^5 - a^5)/10(b^3 - a^3)$.

10. $k^2/3$, where k is the ordinate at $x = h$.   **11.** $l^2\sin^2\theta/3$.

12. $(b^3\sin^2 C + c^3\sin^2 B)/3(a + b + c)$.   **13.** $(a - c)(2a + c)/3$.

14. $b^2 + 3a^2/4$.   **15.** $2a^2/3$.   **16.** $2(b^5 - a^5)/5(b^3 - a^3)$.   **17.** $2a^2/7$.

Examples LXIX (Page 145).

1. $5a^2/4$.   **2.** $7a^2/5$.   **3.** $h^2/18$.   **4.** $(2a^2 + ab + 2b^2)/6$.

5. $2a^2/3$.   **6.** $a^2/12$.   **7.** $a^2/20$.   **8.** $h^2/3 + r^2/4$.

9. (i) $3(4h^2 + r^2)/20$, (ii) $3(h^2 + 4r^2)/80$, (iii) $(2h^2 + 3r^2)/20$.

10. $83a^2/320$.   **11.** $(a^2 + b^2)/5$.

Examples LXX (Page 148).

1. $1 : 3$.   **2.** 4 ft., $9\frac{1}{3}$ ft.   **3.** 30,000 lbs. ; $93,333\frac{1}{3}$ ft.-lbs.

4. (i) $3h/4$, (ii) $h/2$.   **5.** $2\frac{10}{13}$ ft.   **6.** $3\pi a/16$.   **7.** $4c/7$.

Examples LXXI (Page 151).

1. $2/(2x + 3)$.   **2.** $a/(ax + b)$.   **3.** $x^2(1 + 3\log x)$.   **4.** $1/x$.

5. $2/x$.   **6.** $1/x\log_e 10$.   **7.** $1/x\log_e 2$.   **8.** $1/x\log x$.

9. $\cot x$.   **10.** $\cos(\log x)/x$.   **11.** $-\tan\theta$.   **12.** $\tan\theta$.

13. $\operatorname{cosec}\theta$.   **14.** $2a/(a^2 - x^2)$.   **15.** $3/(x - a) - 2/(x - b)$.

16. $1/(1 - x^2)$.   **17.** $\sec\theta$.   **18.** $-n^2x^{n-1}\log x$.

19. $1/2(1 + \sqrt{x})$.   **20.** $\tan^3\theta$.   **21.** $2(1 - x^2)/(1 + x^2 + x^4)$.

22. $\sec\theta$.   **23.** $2\tan^{-1}x$.   **24.** $\cot 2\theta$.

Examples LXXII (Page 152).

1. $-e^{-x}$.   **2.** $3e^{3x}$.   **3.** $x^{n-1}e^{ax}(ax + n)$.   **4.** $\sec^2 x e^{\tan x}$.

5. $2x(1 + x)e^{2x}$.   **6.** xe^x.   **7.** $e^x/\sqrt{(1 - e^{2x})}$.   **8.** $(2 - x^2)e^{-x}$.

9. $4/(e^x + e^{-x})^2$.   **10.** $1/(e^x + 1)$.

Examples LXXIII (Page 153).

1. $10^x \log_e 10$.   2. $2^x \log_e 2$.   3. $a^x \log a$.   4. $a^x(1 + x \log a)$.

5. $xa^{-x}(2 - x \log a)$.   6. $x^x e^{-x} \log x$.   7. $(2x^{\log x} \log x)/x$.

8. $\{x - (1 + x) \log(1 + x)\}(1 + x)^{\frac{1}{x}-1}/x^2$.   9. $(\sin x)^x(\log \sin x + x \cot x)$.

10. $(5x^2 - 24)/2\sqrt{(x + 3)}$.   11. $(2 - x)/3(1 + x)^{\frac{2}{3}}(5 + 2x)^{\frac{3}{2}}$.

12. $(x - 2)(x - 4)/(x - 1)^{\frac{5}{2}}(x - 3)^{\frac{3}{2}}$.

13. $\dfrac{(x - a)^p(x - b)^q}{(x - c)^r}\left(\dfrac{p}{x - a} + \dfrac{q}{x - b} - \dfrac{r}{x - c}\right)$.

14. (i) $n\delta x/x$, (ii) $(x - 1)^2 \delta x/(x^2 + 1)$, (iii) $(m \cot x + n \tan x)\delta x$.

18. $0 \cdot 28$.

Examples LXXIV (Page 157).

13. $0 \cdot 173648$.   14. $0 \cdot 515038$.   15. $2 \cdot 041393$.

Examples LXXV (Page 161).

1. $0 \cdot 43$.   4. $0 \cdot 0006$.   5. $0 \cdot 0003$.

8. 0 (min), $x = 0$; $4/e^2$ (max), $x = 2$.   9. $1/e$ (max), $x = 1$.

10. 0 (min), $x = 0$; n^n/e^n (max), $x = n$; $(n > 1)$.

11. $-27/e^3$ (min), $x = -3$; at $x = 0$ is a point of inflexion.

12. $-1/e$ (min), $x = 1/e$.   13. $1/e$ (max), $x = e$.

14. $1/2e$ (max), $x = 1/\sqrt{e}$.   15. $1/27$ (max), $x = \log 3$.

16. $(\pm 1/\sqrt{2}, 1/\sqrt{e})$.   17. $1, -e^{-\pi}, e^{-2\pi}, -e^{-3\pi}, \ldots$ 18. $(\cdot 328, \cdot 432)$.

Examples LXXVI (Page 163).

1. $e^{2x}/2$.   2. $-e^{-x}$.   3. $10^x/\log_e 10$.   4. $2^{3x}/3 \log_e 2$.

5. $e^{x^2}/2$.   6. $e^{\sin x}$.   7. $e^{\tan x}$.   8. $2 \log(3x - 4)$

9. $(\log x)^3/3$.   10. $\frac{1}{2}ax^2 + bx + c \log x$.   11. $-\log(a - bx)/b$.

12. $(\log x)^{n+1}/(n + 1)$, if $n \neq -1$; $\log(\log x)$, if $n = -1$.

13. $-\cos(\log x)$.   14. $\log(\sin x)$.   15. $\log(\tan x)$.   16. $\log(ax^2 + bx + c)$.

17. $\frac{1}{2}\log(x^2 - a^2)$.   18. $\log(e^x + e^{-x})$.   19. $\log(\tan^{-1} x)$.

Examples LXXVII (Page 163).

1. $x^2(2 \log x - 1)/4$.   2. $x^3(3 \log x - 1)/9$.

3. $-(\log x + 1)/x$.   4. $(x - 1)e^x$.   5. $(x^2 - 2x + 2)e^x$.

6. $(a^3x^3 - 3a^2x^2 + 6ax - 6)e^{ax}/a^4$.   7. $e^x(\cos x + \sin x)/2$.

8. $-e^{-x}(\sin 2x + 2 \cos 2x)/5$.   9. $e^{ax}(a \cos bx + b \sin bx)/(a^2 + b^2)$.

10. $x^{n+1}\{(n + 1) \log x - 1\}/(n + 1)^2$, if $n \neq -1$; $(\log x)^2/2$, if $n = -1$.

Examples LXXVIII (Page 163).

1. $\log a$.   2. $\frac{1}{2}\log 3$.   3. $\frac{1}{2}\log 5$.   4. 1.   5. 1.   6. 1.

7. $-1/4$.   8. $-1/(n + 1)^2$, $(n > -1)$.   9. $1/(n - 1)^2$, $(n > 1)$.

10. $9/\log 10$.   11. $1/\log a$, $(a > 1)$.   12. $\left(1 + e^{-\frac{\pi}{2}}\right)/2$.

13. $1 - \sqrt{2} + \log(1 + \sqrt{2})$.　**14.** $7\log 3 - 4$.　**15.** ab.　**16.** $\pi ab^2/2$.

17. $(1 + e^{-\pi})/2$.　**18.** $\pi(1 - e^{-2\pi})/8$.　**20.** $\log 2$; $v_0/\log 4$.

21. $A = 100$, $k = \log 10$; total pressure $= 2\pi A(1 - e^{-k} - ke^{-k})/k^2$.

23. $y = 3e^{2x}$.　**24.** $y = 6e^{x-3}$.　**25.** $T = T_0 e^{\mu\theta}$.

26. $y = \dfrac{b}{a}(e^{ax} - 1)$.　**27.** $i = \dfrac{E}{R}\left(1 - e^{-\frac{Rt}{L}}\right)$.　**28.** $\theta = \theta_1 + (\theta_0 - \theta_1)e^{-kt}$.

Examples LXXIX (Page 166).

1. $\tan 3\theta/3$.　**2.** $\tan^2\theta/2$.　**3.** $\sec^3\theta/3$.　**4.** $\tan\theta + \tan^3\theta/3$.

5. $\tan^{n+1}\theta/(n+1)$.　**6.** $\sec^5\theta/5 - \sec^3\theta/3$.　**7.** $\tan\theta + 2\tan^3\theta/3 + \tan^5\theta/5$.

8. $\sec^n\theta/n$.　**9.** $2\sec\frac{1}{2}\theta$.　**10.** $-\cot\theta - \theta$.　**11.** $-\cot^3\theta/3 + \cot\theta + \theta$.

12. $-\cot\theta - \cot^3\theta/3$.　**13.** $x\sin^{-1}x + \sqrt{(1 - x^2)}$.

14. $\{x\sqrt{(1 - x^2)} - (1 - 2x^2)\sin^{-1}x\}/4$.　**15.** $\{(x^2 + 1)\tan^{-1}x - x\}/2$.

16. $(\sin^{-1}x)^2/2$.　**17.** $(\tan^{-1}x)^2/2$.　**18.** $\tan\theta + \sec\theta$.

19. $\log(a + b\sin x)/b$.　**20.** $\frac{1}{2}\tan^{-1}(\frac{1}{2}\tan\theta)$.　**21.** $(1 + \log x)^2/2$.

22 $\pi/2$.　**23.** $\pi/3\sqrt{3}$.　**24.** $\log 3$.　**25.** $\pi/8$.　**26.** $\pi/2a$.

27. $\log 2$.　**28.** 1.　**29.** $4/3$.　**30.** $(\pi - \log 4)/4$.

Examples LXXX (Page 166).

1. $x\{(\log x)^4 - 4(\log x)^3 + 12(\log x)^2 - 24\log x + 24\}$.

2. $x^{m+1}\{(m + 1)^3(\log x)^3 - 3(m + 1)^2(\log x)^2 + 6(m + 1)\log x$
$$- 6\}/(m + 1)^4.$$

Examples LXXXI (Page 168).

1. $2x - \log(x + 2)$.　**2.** $x - \log(x + 1)$.　**3.** $-\frac{1}{2}x + \frac{5}{4}\log(1 - 2x)$.

4. $\dfrac{\alpha x}{\gamma} + \dfrac{\beta\gamma - \alpha\delta}{\gamma^2}\log(\gamma x + \delta)$.　**5.** $\dfrac{x^3}{3} + \dfrac{x^2}{2} + x + \log(x - 1)$.

6. $\frac{1}{12}\log\{(3x - 2)/(3x + 2)\}$.　**7.** $3\log(x + 2) - 2\log(x + 3)$.

8. $\log x - \frac{1}{2}\log(2x + 3)$.　**9.** $\frac{1}{2}x + \log(x - 3) - \frac{3}{4}\log(2x + 1)$.

10. $x + 2\log(x - 2) - 2\log(x - 3)$.　**11.** $\frac{1}{2}\log(x^2 + 1) - \frac{1}{2}\log(x^2 + 2)$.

12. $3x + 2\log x + \log(x + 1) - 3\log(x - 1)$.　**13.** $\log(\sin x) - \log(1 + \sin x)$.

14. $\frac{1}{2}\log(x - 1) - \log(x - 2) + \frac{3}{2}\log(x - 3)$.　**15.** $\dfrac{1}{\alpha\delta - \beta\gamma}\log\dfrac{\alpha x + \beta}{\gamma x + \delta}$.

16. $-\dfrac{\Sigma a(b - c)\log(x - a)}{(b - c)(c - a)(a - b)}$.　**17.** $\log(4/3)$.　**18.** $\frac{3}{2}\log 6$.

19. $\log 6$.　**20.** $\log 3 - \frac{3}{2}\log 2$.

Examples LXXXII (Page 170).

1. $\frac{1}{2}\tan^{-1}(\frac{1}{2}x)$.　**2.** $\frac{1}{2}\log(x^2 + 4)$.　**3.** $x - 2\tan^{-1}(\frac{1}{2}x)$.

4. $\log(x^2 + 4) + \frac{3}{2}\tan^{-1}(\frac{1}{2}x)$.　**5.** $\frac{1}{3}\tan^{-1}(\frac{1}{3}x) - \frac{3}{2}\log(x^2 + 9)$.

6. $\dfrac{1}{2\sqrt{3}}\log\dfrac{x - \sqrt{3}}{x + \sqrt{3}}$.　**7.** $\frac{1}{2}\tan^{-1}\dfrac{x + 2}{2}$.

8. $\frac{1}{2}\log(x^2 + 4x + 8) - \tan^{-1}\dfrac{x + 2}{2}$.　**9.** $x - 2\log(x^2 + 4x + 8)$.

10. $\frac{1}{2}x^2 + 2x + \log(x^2 - 2x + 2) - 2\tan^{-1}(x - 1)$.

11. $\frac{1}{6}\log(9x^2 + 6x + 5) + \frac{1}{6}\tan^{-1}\frac{3x+1}{2}$.   12. $\frac{1}{\sqrt{11}}\tan^{-1}\frac{3x+2}{\sqrt{11}}$.

13. $\frac{1}{2\sqrt{7}}\log\frac{x+2-\sqrt{7}}{x+2+\sqrt{7}}$.   14. $\frac{1}{2}\log(3x^2 + 2x + 1) - \sqrt{2}\tan^{-1}\frac{3x+1}{\sqrt{2}}$.

15. $\{(3+\sqrt{41})\log(4x+3+\sqrt{41}) - (3-\sqrt{41})\log(4x+3-\sqrt{41})\}/4\sqrt{41}$.

16. $\frac{1}{2}\log 3 + \frac{\pi\sqrt{3}}{18}$.   17. $\frac{1}{\sqrt{5}}\log\frac{3+\sqrt{5}}{2}$.   18. $\frac{\pi}{12}$.   19. $\frac{\pi}{8}$.

20. $\frac{1}{2}\log 2 - \frac{\pi}{8}$.   21. $\frac{1}{2} - \frac{1}{8}\log\frac{17}{5} + \frac{1}{8}\tan^{-1}\frac{6}{7}$.   22. $\frac{\pi^2}{32}$.   23. $\frac{1}{4}\log\frac{5}{3}$.

24. $\pi/3\sqrt{3}$.   25. $\frac{1}{2}\pi - 2 + \log 2$.   26. $\frac{1}{6}(\frac{1}{2}\pi - 1 + \log 2)$.   27. $\frac{1}{6}$.

Examples LXXXIII (Page 173).

1. $-\frac{a}{x-a} + \log(x-a)$.   2. $-\frac{2}{x+1} + \log\frac{x+1}{x}$.   3. $\frac{1}{x-2} + \log\frac{x-3}{x-2}$.

4. $\frac{x^2 - 2ax}{x-a} + 2a\log(x-a)$.   5. $\frac{2x-1}{x(1-x)} + 2\log\frac{x}{1-x}$.

6. $\frac{2x-1}{2x^2} - 2\log\frac{x}{x+1}$.   7. $\frac{x^3 + 3ax^2 - 9a^2x + 3a^3}{2(x-a)} + 3a^2\log(x-a)$.

8. $\frac{2x}{1-x^2} + \log\frac{1-x}{1+x}$.   9. $-\frac{1}{x-1} + \frac{1}{3}\log\frac{x+2}{x-1}$.

10. $\frac{4x+7}{2(x+2)^2} + 2\log\frac{x+1}{x+2}$.   11. $\frac{8x^2 + 3x - 3}{x^2(x+1)} + 9\log\frac{x}{x+1}$.

12. $\log 2 - \frac{1}{2}$.   13. $\frac{3}{4} - \log 2$.   14. $\frac{1}{4}(1 - \log 2)$.

15. $\frac{1}{2}\log(x^2 + 4) - \log(1-x) - \tan^{-1}\frac{x}{2}$.   16. $\frac{1}{20}\log\frac{x-2}{x+2} - \frac{1}{5}\tan^{-1}x$.

17. $\frac{1}{2}x^2 - \frac{1}{2}a^2\log(x^2 + a^2)$.

18. $\frac{1}{2}\log x - \frac{1}{4}\log(x^2 - 2x + 2) + \frac{1}{2}\tan^{-1}(x-1)$.

19. $\frac{1}{3}\tan^{-1}x - \frac{1}{6}\tan^{-1}\frac{x}{2}$.   20. $\frac{1}{6}\log\frac{(x-1)^2}{x^2+x+1} - \frac{1}{\sqrt{3}}\tan^{-1}\frac{2x+1}{\sqrt{3}}$.

21. $x - \frac{1}{2}\log(x+1) - \frac{1}{4}\log(x^2+1) - \frac{1}{2}\tan^{-1}x$.

22. $-1/2x^2 - \log x + \frac{1}{2}\log(x^2+1)$.   23. $\pi/8$.

24. $\frac{1}{2(x^2+1)} + \frac{1}{10}\log\frac{(x-2)^2}{x^2+1} - \frac{2}{5}\tan^{-1}x$.   25. $\frac{x^3+3x}{x^2+1} - 2\tan^{-1}x$.

26. $\frac{1}{4\sqrt{2}}\log\frac{x^2+x\sqrt{2}+1}{x^2-x\sqrt{2}+1} + \frac{1}{2\sqrt{2}}\tan^{-1}\frac{x\sqrt{2}}{1-x^2}$.   27. $\frac{\pi}{2}$.   28. $\frac{1}{\sqrt{3}}\tan^{-1}\frac{x\sqrt{3}}{1-x^2}$.

29. $1/3(x^3+1) + \frac{1}{3}\log(x^3+1)$.   30. $\pi/4 - 1/3$.   31. $(\pi+1)/8$.

32. $(-\pi + \log 3 + 2\tan^{-1}2)/4$.   33. $\pi/3\sqrt{3} + \log 8$.   34. $2 + 5\log 3$.

Examples LXXXIV (Page 176).

1. $\frac{1}{2}\log(\sin 2\theta)$.   2. $2\log(\sec\frac{1}{2}\theta + \tan\frac{1}{2}\theta)$.   3. $1/a \cdot \log\sec(ax+b)$.

4. $\frac{1}{3}\log\tan\frac{3}{2}\theta$.   5. $1/n \cdot \log(\sec n\theta + \tan n\theta)$.   6. $\log(1 + \sin\theta)$.

7. $\sin\theta - \frac{1}{3}\sin^3\theta$.   8. $\frac{1}{4}(\frac{3}{2}\theta + \sin 2\theta + \frac{1}{8}\sin 4\theta)$.

9. $\sin\theta - \frac{2}{3}\sin^3\theta + \frac{1}{5}\sin^5\theta$.   10. $\frac{1}{2}\tan^2\theta - \log(\sec\theta)$.

11. $\theta - \tan\theta + \frac{1}{3}\tan^3\theta$.   12. $\frac{1}{4}(\log 4 - 1)$.   13. $-\cos\theta/2\sin^2\theta + \frac{1}{2}\log\tan\frac{1}{2}\theta$.

14. $-\cot\theta - \frac{1}{3}\cot^3\theta$.   15. $-1/\sqrt{2} + \log(1 + \sqrt{2})$.   16. $\log(\sin\theta) - \frac{1}{2}\sin^2\theta$.

17. $\log(\sec\theta + \tan\theta) - \sin\theta - \frac{1}{3}\sin^3\theta$.   **18.** $1/\sqrt{2} - \frac{1}{2}\log(1 + \sqrt{2})$.

19. $\frac{1}{2}\tan^2\theta$.   **20.** $\tan^{n+1}\theta/(n+1)$.   **21.** $\tan\theta - \cot\theta$.   **22.** $\frac{1}{3}\tan^3\theta + \frac{1}{5}\tan^5\theta$.

23. $\tan^{n+1}\theta/(n+1) + \tan^{n+3}\theta/(n+3)$.   **24.** $\frac{2}{3}\sqrt{(\tan^3\theta)} - 2\sqrt{(\cot\theta)}$.

Examples LXXXV (Page 178).

1. $\pi/4$.   **2.** $3\pi/16$.   **3.** $3\pi/128$.   **4.** 0.   **5.** $35\pi/128$.

6. 0.   **7.** (i) $1/60$, (ii) $3\pi/16$.   **8.** (i) $3\pi/128$, (ii) $\pi/16$.

9. (i) $4/3\pi$, (ii) $3/8$, (iii) $(2n)!/2^{2n}(n!)^2$, (iv) $2^{2n+1}(n!)^2/\pi(2n+1)!$

Examples LXXXVI (Page 179).

1. $\log\tan\theta$.   **2.** $\dfrac{1}{\sqrt{2}}\tan^{-1}\dfrac{\tan\theta}{\sqrt{2}}$.   **3.** $\dfrac{1}{4}\log\dfrac{2+\tan\theta}{2-\tan\theta}$.   **4.** $\dfrac{1}{4}\tan^{-1}\dfrac{\tan 2\theta}{2}$.

5. $\dfrac{1}{5}\log\dfrac{1+2\tan\theta}{2-\tan\theta}$.   **6.** $\dfrac{\pi}{3\sqrt{3}}$.   **7.** $-\dfrac{\cos\theta}{b(a\cos\theta + b\sin\theta)}$.   **8.** $\dfrac{\pi}{2}$.

9. $\dfrac{1}{b}\log\dfrac{a\cos\theta + b\sin\theta}{\cos\theta}$.   **10.** $\dfrac{2\pi}{ab}$.   **11.** $\dfrac{1}{8}\log\dfrac{2+\tan\theta}{2-3\tan\theta}$.

Examples LXXXVII (Page 180).

1. $\log\tan\frac{1}{2}\theta$.   **2.** $\dfrac{1}{4}\log\dfrac{2+\tan\frac{1}{2}\theta}{2-\tan\frac{1}{2}\theta}$.   **3.** 2.   **4.** $\log\dfrac{1+\tan\frac{1}{2}\theta}{1-\tan\frac{1}{2}\theta}$.

5. $\frac{1}{2}\tan^{-1}\left(2\tan\dfrac{\theta}{2}\right)$.   **6.** $\dfrac{1}{\sqrt{2}}\log(3+2\sqrt{2})$.   **7.** $\dfrac{1}{5}\log\dfrac{1+2\tan\frac{1}{2}\theta}{2-\tan\frac{1}{2}\theta}$.

8. $\log\dfrac{3-\tan\frac{1}{2}\theta}{1-\tan\frac{1}{2}\theta}$.   **9.** $\log(1+\tan\frac{1}{2}\theta)$.   **10.** $\dfrac{-1}{2(3+2\tan\frac{1}{2}\theta)}$.

11. $\pi/\sqrt{3}$.   **12.** $\frac{1}{3}\sqrt{3}\log(2+\sqrt{3})$.   **13.** $5\pi/64$.

14. $\dfrac{2}{\sqrt{(a^2-b^2)}}\tan^{-1}\left\{\left(\dfrac{a-b}{a+b}\right)^{\frac{1}{2}}\tan\dfrac{\theta}{2}\right\}$, $(a > b > 0)$;

$\dfrac{1}{\sqrt{(b^2-a^2)}}\log\dfrac{\sqrt{(a+b)} + \sqrt{(b-a)}\tan\frac{1}{2}\theta}{\sqrt{(a+b)} - \sqrt{(b-a)}\tan\frac{1}{2}\theta}$, $(b > a > 0)$.

16. $\{3\theta - 4\log(4\cos\theta + 3\sin\theta)\}/25$.   **17.** $\frac{1}{2}\theta + \frac{1}{2}\log(\cos\theta + \sin\theta)$.

18. $\log(\cos\theta + \sin\theta)$.

19. $2\theta - \log(\cos\theta + 2\sin\theta + 3) - 4\tan^{-1}(1+\tan\frac{1}{2}\theta)$.

20. $\frac{1}{2}(\pi - 1) - 2\log 3 + 3\log 2$.

Examples LXXXVIII (Page 181).

1. $-x + 2\sqrt{x}(3+x)/3 - 2\log(1+\sqrt{x})$.

2. $-\frac{4}{3}\log(2+\sqrt{x}) - \frac{2}{3}\log(1-\sqrt{x})$.   **3.** $\frac{1}{2}\log(5/3)$.   **4.** $3 - 4\log 2$.

5. $\log\{x + \sqrt{(x-1)}\} - \dfrac{2}{\sqrt{3}}\tan^{-1}\dfrac{1+2\sqrt{(x-1)}}{\sqrt{3}}$.   **6.** $\pi - 2\tan^{-1}\sqrt{(1+x)}$.

7. $2 + \log(3/2)$.   **8.** $1 + \pi/2$.   **9.** $\dfrac{2}{\sqrt{(a+c)}}\tan^{-1}\dfrac{\sqrt{(x-a)}}{\sqrt{(a+c)}}$, $(a + c > 0)$.

10. $\frac{1}{2}\log 3 + \pi/2\sqrt{3}$.   **11.** $2\{(x+a)^{\frac{3}{2}} + (x+b)^{\frac{3}{2}}\}/3(a-b)$.

12. $(6\sqrt{3} - 5)/3$.   **13.** $4 - 2\sqrt{2} - \log 3 + \log(3+2\sqrt{2})$.

14. $5(x+1)^{\frac{4}{5}}(4x-5)/36$.   **15.** $6(x-1)^{\frac{1}{2}}\{(x-1)^{\frac{2}{3}}/7 - (x-1)^{\frac{1}{3}}/5 + 1/3\}$.

16. $6\log 2 - 3$.   **17.** $9/10$.   **18.** $3(\pi - 2 - 2\log 2)/4$.

Examples LXXXIX (Page 183).

1. $\log \{x + \sqrt{(x^2+3)}\}$.   2. $\sin^{-1}(x/\sqrt{3})$.   3. $\log \{x-3 + \sqrt{(x^2-6x+12)}\}$.
4. $\frac{1}{2}\sqrt{2}\,\sin^{-1}(x\sqrt{2}/\sqrt{3})$.   5. $\frac{1}{3}\sqrt{3}\,\log\{x + \sqrt{(x^2 - \frac{1}{3})}\}$.
6. $\frac{1}{2}\log(2x - 1)$.   7. $\log\{x - b + \sqrt{(x^2 - 2bx)}\}$.   8. $\sin^{-1}(2x - 1)$.
9. $\frac{1}{3}\sqrt{3}\,\log\{x + \frac{2}{3} + \sqrt{(x^2 + \frac{4}{3}x + \frac{5}{3})}\}$.   10. $\pi/2$.   11. $\log 3$.   12. $\log 3$.
13. $\log(2 + \sqrt{3})$.   14. $\log 2$.   15. $\sqrt{2}\tan^{-1}\sqrt{2}$.   16. $-2\sqrt{(1-x^2)} + \sin^{-1}x$.
17. $3\sqrt{(x^2 + 5)} - \log\{x + \sqrt{(x^2 + 5)}\}$.   18. $\sin^{-1}x - \sqrt{(1 - x^2)}$.
19. $\sqrt{(x^2 - ax)} + \frac{1}{2}a\log\{x - \frac{1}{2}a + \sqrt{(x^2 - ax)}\}$.
20. $4\sqrt{(x^2 + x - 1)} - 3\log\{x + \frac{1}{2} + \sqrt{(x^2 + x - 1)}\}$.
21. $\frac{2}{3}\sqrt{(3x^2 - 6x + 4)} + 5/\sqrt{3} \cdot \log\{x - 1 + \sqrt{(x^2 - 2x + \frac{4}{3})}\}$.
22. $\sqrt{(x^2 + c)} + a\log\{x + \sqrt{(x^2 + c)}\}$.   23. $-\sqrt{(6x - x^2)} + 4\sin^{-1}\frac{1}{3}(x - 3)$.
24. $-\frac{1}{2}\sqrt{(2 - 3x - 2x^2)} - 3\sqrt{2}/8 \cdot \sin^{-1}\frac{1}{5}(4x + 3)$.

Examples XC (Page 184).

1. $\frac{1}{2}x\sqrt{(a^2 - x^2)} + \frac{1}{2}a^2\sin^{-1}(x/a)$.   2. $\frac{1}{2}x\sqrt{(x^2 + a^2)} + \frac{1}{2}a^2\log\{x + \sqrt{(x^2 + a^2)}\}$.
3. $\frac{1}{2}x\sqrt{(x^2 - a^2)} - \frac{1}{2}a^2\log\{x + \sqrt{(x^2 - a^2)}\}$.   4. $\frac{1}{4}\sqrt{2} + \frac{1}{2}\log(1 + \sqrt{2})$.
5. $\sqrt{3} - \frac{1}{2}\log(2 + \sqrt{3})$.   6. $10 - \frac{9}{2}\log 3$.
7. $\frac{1}{2}(x - 3)\sqrt{(x^2 - 6x + 6)} - \frac{3}{2}\log\{x - 3 + \sqrt{(x^2 - 6x + 6)}\}$.
8. $\frac{1}{2}(x - 1)\sqrt{(7 + 6x - 3x^2)} + 5/\sqrt{3} \cdot \sin^{-1}\{(x - 1)\sqrt{(3/10)}\}$.
9. $\frac{1}{2}(x - 1)\sqrt{(x^2 + 2x + 3)}$.
10. $\frac{1}{2}(x + 6)\sqrt{(x^2 - 4x + 8)} + 2\log\{x - 2 + \sqrt{(x^2 - 4x + 8)}\}$.
11. $1 - \pi/4$.   12. $\sqrt{3} + \sqrt{2}\log(3\sqrt{3} + 2\sqrt{6} - 3\sqrt{2} - 4)$.

Examples XCI (Page 185).

1. $\sec^{-1}x$.   2. $\frac{1}{2}\log x - \frac{1}{2}\log\{2 + \sqrt{(4 - x^2)}\}$.
3. $\log x - \log\{3x + 2 + 2\sqrt{(2x^2 + 3x + 1)}\}$.
4. $1/a \cdot \sec^{-1}(x/a)$.   5. $\log\{x + \sqrt{(x^2 - 9)}\} + \frac{1}{3}\sin^{-1}(3/x)$.
6. $\frac{1}{4}\sqrt{(4x^2 + 1)} + \log x - \log\{1 + \sqrt{(1 + 4x^2)}\}$.   7. $\sqrt{(2x^2 - 1)}/x$.
8. $\sqrt{(x^2 + 1)} + \log x - \log\{1 + \sqrt{(x^2 + 1)}\}$.   9. $\log\{x + \sqrt{(x^2 - 1)}\} - \sec^{-1}x$.
10. $\log(1 + \sqrt{2})$.   11. 1.   12. $\pi/6 - \sqrt{3}/8$.   13. 1.
14. $\frac{1}{3}\sqrt{3}\log(2 + \sqrt{3})$.   15. $\pi/18$.   16. $\frac{1}{2}\log 3$.

Examples XCII (Page 186).

1. $\frac{1}{2}\sin^{-1}x - \frac{1}{2}x\sqrt{(1 - x^2)}$.   2. $\sec^{-1}x$.   3. $\frac{1}{2}\sec^{-1}x - \sqrt{(x^2 - 1)}/2x^2$.
4. $x/a^2\sqrt{(a^2 - x^2)}$.   5. $x/a^2\sqrt{(x^2 + a^2)}$.   6. $-x/a^2\sqrt{(x^2 - a^2)}$.
7. $\frac{1}{2}x\sqrt{(4 - x^2)} + 2\sin^{-1}(x/2)$.   8. $\frac{1}{2}x\sqrt{(x^2 + 1)} + \frac{1}{2}\log\{x + \sqrt{(x^2 + 1)}\}$.
9. $\frac{1}{8}(5x - 2x^3)\sqrt{(1 - x^2)} + \frac{3}{8}\sin^{-1}x$.   10. $\sqrt{3} - \pi/3$.   11. $5\pi a^3/16$.
12. $a^2(1 - \pi/4)$.   13. $5\pi/256$.   14. $5\pi a^4/8$.   15. $\frac{2}{3}(\sqrt{3} - 1)$.
16. $\sqrt{3}/2$.   17. $\pi\sqrt{2}/4$.   18. $\frac{1}{4}\log(9/5)$.   19. π.
20. $\pi(a + b)/2$.   21. $\pi(b - a)^2/8$.   22. $\pi(b - a)^3(5a + 3b)/128$.

Examples XCIII (Page 187).

1. $\log(b/a)$.   2. $\frac{1}{2}\log 2$.   3. $1 - a + a\log a$.   4. $\log(1 + \sqrt{2})$.
5. $\frac{1}{4}$.   6. 2.   7. $\pi/4$.   8. $\frac{1}{2}\log 7$.   9. $\frac{1}{2}\log 3$.   10. $\frac{1}{4}\log 3$.

10*

11. $\pi/2$. **12.** πa^2. **13.** 2. **14.** 2π. **15.** $5\pi a^2/4$. **16.** $2a^2(1 - \pi/4)$.
17. $3\pi^2/8$. **18.** $21\pi^2/8$. **19.** 2π. **20.** $\pi^2 a b^2/2$. **21.** $3 + \frac{1}{2}\log 2$.
22. $2 - \pi/4$. **23.** $\log(1 + \sqrt{2})$. **24.** $(156 + 25\log 5)/100$.
25. $3(1 + \log 3 - \log 2)$. **26.** $\sqrt{5} - \sqrt{2} + \frac{1}{2}\log\{(6 + 4\sqrt{2})/(3+\sqrt{5})\}$.
27. $2\pi\{\sqrt{2} + \log(1 + \sqrt{2})\}$. **28.** $4\pi\sqrt{2}$.
29. $3\pi\{\sqrt{10} + \log(\sqrt{10}-1)-5/4\}$. **30.** $\pi\{27-16\log 2 -4\,(\log 2)^2\}/16$.
31. $\pi(820 - 81\log 3)/2592$. **32.** $\pi(4 + 3\log 3)$.

33. (i) $2\pi b^2 + 2\pi ab\,\dfrac{\sin^{-1}e}{e}$, (ii) $2\pi a^2 + \dfrac{\pi b^2}{e}\log\dfrac{1 + e}{1 - e}$,

where $e =$ eccentricity $= \sqrt{(a^2 - b^2)}/a$.

Examples XCIV (Page 189).

1. $4x/y$. **2.** $(9x^2 + 2y^2)/2(1 - 2xy)$. **3.** $-(2x + 3y)/(3x + y)$.
4. $-(x - 2)/(y - 3)$. **5.** $2\cos(2x + 3y)/\{1 - 3\cos(2x + 3y)\}$.
6. $e^y/(1 - xe^y)$. **7.** $-y/x$. **8.** $-2\tan y/x$. **9.** $-my/nx$.
10. $m/n \tan x \tan y$. **11.** $-(6x + 7y)/2y$. **12.** $1, -1, -\frac{1}{2}; -1, -3, 4$.
15. $\alpha, \sin\alpha, \sin 2\alpha$. **17.** $\frac{4}{3}$; $4x-3y = 10$. **18.** 11; $y = 11x - 31$.
19. $-\frac{1}{5}$; $x + 6y = 18$. **20.** 2; $y = 2x - a$. **21.** $\frac{3}{2}$; $3x - 2y = 2$.
22. -4; $4x + y = 18$. **23.** $7x-6y=10$, $26x-21y + 40 = 0$. **24.** $45°$.
25. $76x-48y=153$. **26.** $(2\frac{6}{7}, -2\frac{5}{7})$. **27.** $3\frac{33}{34}$. **28.** $12\frac{1}{2}$.
29. $2\sqrt{2}$. **30.** $\frac{1}{2}a$. **31.** $(1 + m^2)^{\frac{3}{2}}/2(a + bm + cm^2)$. **32.** $a\sqrt{2}$.
33. $bc/2a$, $b(b - c)/2a$, $c(c - b)/2a$. **34.** $2(x + y)^{\frac{3}{2}}/a^{\frac{1}{2}}$.
35. $(3a^2 - 2x^2)^2/8a^2x$. **37.** $3\sqrt{2}/8$; $(2\frac{5}{8}, 2\frac{5}{8})$.
38. $(\pm a\sqrt{2}/\sqrt{3}, \pm a/\sqrt{2})$. **39** $\sqrt{\{(2\sqrt{7} - 5)/3\}}$.

Examples XCV (Page 192).

2. 333 yds./min. **3.** $-ux/y$, u/y. $-a^2u^2/y^3$. **4.** 4 ft./sec.
5. $2\sqrt{3}$ rad./sec. **6.** $8\omega/3$, $44\omega/49$, $8\omega/13$. **9.** 5 ins.

Examples XCVI (Page 194).

1. 6, 4. **7.** $(3 - 2\sqrt{2})/4$. sq. mls.

Examples XCVII (Page 195).

1. y, x. **2.** $2xy^3$, $3x^2y^2$. **3.** $a\cos(ax + by)$, $b\cos(ax + by)$.
4. $-y/x^2, 1/x$. **5.** $-y/x^2 \cdot \sec^2 y/x$, $1/x \cdot \sec^2 y/x$. **6.** $-y/(x^2+y^2)$, $x/(x^2+y^2)$
7. $-y/(x - y)^2$, $x/(x - y)^2$. **8.** $4xy^2/(x^2 + y^2)^2$, $-4x^2y/(x^2 + y^2)^2$.
9. $-2nx/(x^2 + y^2)^{n+1}$, $-2ny/(x^2 + y^2)^{n+1}$.
10. $e^{-ax}\{b\sin(pt - bx) - a\cos(pt - bx)\}$, $-pe^{-ax}\sin(pt - bx)$.
11. $-x/r^3$, $-y/r^3$, $-z/r^3$. **16.** $-3/2$.

Examples XCVIII (Page 198).

1. $x\,dy + y\,dx$. **2.** $a\,dx + b\,dy$. **3.** $(3x^2 + 2y^2)dx + 4xy\,dy$.
4. $dr\cos\theta - r\sin\theta\,d\theta$. **5.** $(a\,dx + b\,dy)e^{ax+by}$.
6. $\{\log(3x + y) + 3x/(3x + y)\}dx + x\,dy/(3x + y)$. **7.** $(x\,dy - y\,dx)/x^2$.
8. $-(x\,dy + y\,dx)/x^2y^2$. **9.** $-(r\sin\theta\,d\theta + dr\cos\theta)/r^2$.
10. $(x^2\,dy + y^2\,dx)/(x + y)^2$. **13.** $r\theta\,\delta r + \frac{1}{2}r^2\,\delta\theta$. **15.** 6 per cent.

ANSWERS TO THE EXAMPLES

299

Examples XCIX (Page 200).

1. $-(ax + hy + g)/(hx + by + f)$. 2. $2y(y - x)/x(4y - x)$.
3. $x(3y^2 - x^2)/y(3x^2 - y^2)$. 4. $-\sin(x + y)/\{1 + \sin(x + y)\}$.
5. $(\sin x + \cos y)/x \sin y$. 6. $y(y - x \log y)/x(x - y \log x)$. 7. $1/y$.
In Exs. 8-13 the equations of the *tangents* are :—
8. $y\mathrm{Y} = 2a(\mathrm{X} + x)$. 9. $2ay\mathrm{Y} = x^2(3\mathrm{X} - x)$.
10. $(x^2 - ay)\mathrm{X} + (y^2 - ax)\mathrm{Y} = axy$. 11. $my\mathrm{X} + nx\mathrm{Y} = (m + n)xy$.
12. $ax\mathrm{X} + by\mathrm{Y} = 1$. 13. $\mathrm{X}x^{n-1} + \mathrm{Y}y^{n-1} = a^n$. 24. 10.

Examples C (Page 203).

1. 2 ; $y = 2x + 6$. 2. $(3t^2 - 1)/2t$; $y^2 = x^2(1 - x)$.
3. $3t/2$; $(y - 2)^2 = (x - 1)^3$. 4. $4t - 2$; $y = x^2 - 4x + 3$.
5. $b/a \sin \theta$; $x^2/a^2 - y^2/b^2 = 1$. 6. $-\tan \theta$; $x^{\frac{2}{3}} + y^{\frac{2}{3}} = a^{\frac{2}{3}}$.

7. $t(2 - t^3)/(1 - 2t^3)$; $x^3 + y^3 = 3xy$. 8. $\frac{1}{2}(t - 1/t)$; $y = \frac{1}{2}c(e^{\frac{x}{c}} + e^{-\frac{x}{c}})$.
9. $x + 3y = 12, y = 3x - 16$. 10. $2x + y = 7, 2y - x = 4$.
11. $x + y = \frac{3}{2}, x - y = \frac{1}{2}$. 12. $5y - 4x = 4a, 15x + 12y = 26a$.
13. $9\frac{37}{240}$. 14. $562\frac{1}{2}$. 15. $\frac{1}{2}(1 + t^2)^2$. 16. $e^u(e^u + e^{-u})^2$.
17. $\sec \theta (1 + \sin^2 \theta)^2$.

Examples CI (Page 205).

1. $y = x/t + at, y + tx = 2at + at^3$.
2. $x \cos \phi/a + y \sin \phi/b = 1$, $ax \sin \phi - by \cos \phi = (a^2 - b^2) \sin \phi \cos \phi$.
3. $x \sec \theta/a - y \tan \theta/b = 1$, $ax \tan \theta + by \sec \theta = (a^2 + b^2) \sec \theta \tan \theta$.
4. $x \sin \theta + y \cos \theta = a \sin \theta \cos \theta$, $x \cos \theta - y \sin \theta = a \cos 2\theta$.
5. $-(t^2 + 2)/t$. 7. $y = \pm\sqrt{2}(x - 8/27)$. 8. -2λ.
9. $3a^2\sqrt{3}/2$. 11. $ay = x^2 + a^2$. 12. $x = m^2 - 1, y = m(m^2 - 1)$.

Examples CII (Page 209).

1. (i) $36a^2$, (ii) $c^2 \log 10$, (iii) $\frac{1}{2}\pi ab$, (iv) $3a^2$, (v) $3\pi a^2/8$, (vi) $\pi a^2/2$,
   (vii) $ab\{\sqrt{3} - \frac{1}{2} \log (2 + \sqrt{3})\}$.
2. (i) $162\pi a^3$, (ii) $9\pi c^3/10$, (iii) $4\pi ab^2/3$, (iv) $\pi a^3(15 + 16 \log 2)/4$,
   (v) $32\pi a^3/35$, (vi) $4\pi a^3/3$, (vii) $4\pi ab^2/3$.
3. (i) 4, (ii) $2(4 + \log 3)$, (iii) 3π, (iv) $2(2\sqrt{2} - 1)$.
4. (i) 11π, (ii) $4\pi\{28 - 9 \log 3 - (\log 3)^2\}$, (iii) $\pi(3\pi^2 - 16)$,
   (iv) $\frac{1}{2}\pi\{7\sqrt{2} + 3 \log (1 + \sqrt{2})\}$.
5. (i) $4a/3$, (ii) $5a/6$. 6. (i) $6a$, (ii) $3\pi a^2/8$, (iii) $32\pi a^3/105$, (iv) $12\pi a^2/5$.

Examples CIII (Page 211).

1. $\frac{1}{2}ab(\beta - \alpha)$. 2. $\frac{1}{2}ab \log (\sec \alpha + \tan \alpha)$. 3. $\frac{1}{3}a^2(t_2^3 - t_1^3)$.
4. $\frac{1}{6}a^2(\beta^3 - \alpha^3)$. 5. $\pi(\alpha\delta - \beta\gamma)$. 6. $\pi a^2(n + 1)(n + 2)/n^2$.

Examples CV (Page 217).

In Exs. 1-6, the values of ϕ are :—
1. $\pi/4$. 2. α. 3. $\pi - 2\theta, (0 < \theta < \pi/2)$. 4. $\pi/2 + \theta, (-\pi/2 < \theta < \pi/2)$.

5. $\theta/2$.　　　　**6.** $\pi/2 - n\theta$, $(-\pi/2n < \theta < \pi/2n)$.
11. 10, $7\frac{1}{2}$, 8, $4\frac{1}{2}$.　　　　**12** $r \sec \alpha$, $r \operatorname{cosec} \alpha$, $r \tan \alpha$, $r \cot \alpha$.
19. $60°$.　　　**20.** $\tan^{-1} \frac{1}{2}$.　　　**21.** $60°$.　　　**22.** $2 \tan^{-1} \frac{3}{4}$.

Examples CVI (Page 219).

1. $a^2(\alpha + \sin \alpha \cos \alpha)$.　　**2.** $a^2(\tan \frac{1}{2}\alpha + \frac{1}{3} \tan^3 \frac{1}{2}\alpha)$.　　**3.** $\frac{1}{4}a^2 \log \tan \alpha$.
4. $\frac{1}{4}ab \log \{(b + a \tan \alpha)/(b - a \tan \alpha)\}$.　　**5.** $3l^2(20 - 9 \log 3)/128$.
6. $3\pi a^2/2$.　　**7.** $\pi(\frac{1}{2}a^2 + c^2)$.　　　**8.** πab.　　　**9.** $\pi l^2/(1-e^2)^{\frac{3}{2}}$.
10. $\frac{1}{2}a^2$.　　　**11.** $5\pi a^2/4$.　　　**13.** $(2\pi + 3\sqrt{3}) : (4\pi - 3\sqrt{3})$.
15 $(\frac{1}{2}a^2+c^2)(\pi-\cos^{-1} c/a)+\frac{3}{5}c\sqrt{(a^2-c^2)}$, $(\frac{1}{2}a^2+c^2) \cos^{-1} c/a-\frac{3}{5}c\sqrt{(a^2-c^2)}$.
16. $\frac{2}{3}\pi a^3 (1 - \cos \alpha)$.　　**17.** $8\pi a^3/3$.　　**18.** $\frac{1}{2}\pi a^3(\pi^2 - 8)$.　　**19.** $\frac{2}{3}\pi a^3(\sec^4 \frac{1}{2}\alpha - 1)$.
20. $\dfrac{2a \sin \alpha}{3\alpha}$, 0.　　**21.** $\dfrac{a}{3}\dfrac{3\alpha + 2 \sin 2\alpha + \sin \alpha \cos \alpha \cos 2\alpha}{\alpha + \sin \alpha \cos \alpha}$, $\dfrac{2a}{3}\dfrac{1 - \cos^4 \alpha}{\alpha + \sin \alpha \cos \alpha}$.
22. $3a/\pi$, $a(-2 + 3/\pi^2)$.　　　**23.** $5a/6$.　　　**24.** $(r_2 - r_1) \sec \alpha$.
25. $a\sqrt{(1 + \beta^2)}/\beta$, $(\beta > 0)$.　　　　**26.** $3\pi a/2$.
27. $\dfrac{\pi a \cdot n!}{\{(n-1)(n-3) \ldots 4 \cdot 2\}^2}$, $(n \text{ odd})$; $\dfrac{2a \cdot n!}{\{(n-1)(n-3) \ldots 3 \cdot 1\}^2}$, $(n \text{ even})$.
28. $a\{\sec \frac{1}{2}\alpha \tan \frac{1}{2}\alpha + \log (\sec \frac{1}{2}\alpha + \tan \frac{1}{2}\alpha)\}$.　　**29.** $15/8 + \log 4$.
30. $a[\sqrt{5}-2+\sqrt{3} \log \{(2+\sqrt{3})(\sqrt{5}-\sqrt{3})/\sqrt{2}\}]$.　　**31.** $5 + 12 \log (3/2)$.
32. $2\pi a^2 (\cos \alpha - \cos \beta)$.　　**33.** $4\pi^2 a^2$.　　**34.** πa^2.　　**35.** $32\pi a^2/5$.
36. $2\pi a^2(1 + e^{-2\beta\pi})\sqrt{(1 + \beta^2)}/(1 + 4\beta^2)$.　　**37.** $8\pi a^2 (\sec^3 \frac{1}{2}\alpha - 1)/3$.
38. $4\pi a^2 \{\cos \alpha - (\frac{1}{2}\pi - \alpha) \sin \alpha\}$.　　**39.** $4a/5$.　　　**40.** $50a/63$.

Examples CVII (Page 223).

1. $r^3 = 2ap$; a.　　　　　　**2.** $r^3 = 2ap^2$; $\sqrt{(8ar)}/3$.
3. $p = ar/\sqrt{(a^2 + r^2)}$; $r(a^2 + r^2)^{\frac{3}{2}}/a^3$.　　**4.** $p = r \sin \alpha$; $r \operatorname{cosec} \alpha$.
5. $p^2 = ar$; $\sqrt{(4r^3/a)}$.
6. $p = 2a^2r/\sqrt{(4a^4 + r^4)}$; $r(4a^4 + r^4)^{\frac{3}{2}}/2a^2(4a^4 - r^4)$.
7. $pr = a^2$; r^3/a^2.　　　　**8.** $pa^n = r^{n+1}$; $a^n/(n + 1)r^{n-1}$.
9. $2p^2 = lr$; $\sqrt{(8r^3/l)}$.　　**10.** $p^2(a^2 + b^2 - r^2) = a^2b^2$; $(a^2 + b^2 - r^2)^{\frac{3}{2}}/ab$.
11. $\dfrac{b^2}{ap^2} = \dfrac{2}{r} - \dfrac{1}{a}$, $(e < 1)$; $\dfrac{b^2}{ap^2} = \dfrac{2}{r} + \dfrac{1}{a}$, $(e > 1)$; $\rho = (rr')^{\frac{3}{2}}/ab$; in the usual notation.
12. $p^2(r^2 - a^2 + b^2) = a^2b^2$; $(r^2 - a^2 + b^2)^{\frac{3}{2}}/ab$.　　**15.** $250/21$.

Examples CVIII (Page 225).

2. 1·5431, 1·1752.　　　　**5.** $(x - y\epsilon^a)(x - ye^{-a})$; $x = e^a$, e^{-a}.

Examples CIX (Page 227).

19. (i) $c = \pm\sqrt{(a^2 - b^2)}$, according as $a >$ or < 0 ; $h = \tanh^{-1} (b/a)$,
(ii) $c = \pm\sqrt{(b^2 - a^2)}$, according as $b >$ or < 0 ; $h = \tanh^{-1} (a/b)$.

Examples CX (Page 229).

1. $\operatorname{sech}^2 x$.   **2.** $-\operatorname{sech} x \tanh x$.   **3.** $2 \cosh^2 x$.   **4.** $\sinh 2x$.
5. $2 \tanh x \operatorname{sech}^2 x$.   **6.** $\tanh x$.   **7.** $n \cosh nx$.   **8.** $-n \sinh n(a-x)$.
9. $2 \operatorname{cosech} 2x$.   **10.** $n \cosh^{n-1} x \sinh x$.   **11.** $\cos x \sinh x - \sin x \cosh x$.
12. $\frac{1}{2} \operatorname{sech} x$.   **14.** $1/3\sqrt{3}$.   **15.** $1/2b \cdot \log\{(a+b)/(a-b)\}$.

Examples CXI (Page 231).

1. $\log_e 2, \log_e 3$.   **3.** (i) $\log_e 2$, (ii) $\log_e 3$, (iii) $\frac{1}{2}\log_e 3$.   **4.** $1/\sqrt{(x^2+4)}$.
5. $1/\sqrt{(x^2-2x+5)}$.   **6.** $5/(x+1)\sqrt{(3x^2-14x+8)}$.   **7.** $3/(9-x^2)$.
8. $1/x\sqrt{(2x^2-2x+1)}$.   **9.** $1/(1-x^2)$.

Examples CXII (Page 232).

1. $\frac{1}{2}(\sinh x \cosh x - x)$.   **2.** $\tanh x$.   **3.** $x - \tanh x$.
4. $\frac{1}{3}\cosh^3 x - \cosh x$.   **5.** $\log(\cosh x) - \frac{1}{2}\tanh^2 x$.
6. $\frac{1}{2}\operatorname{sech} x \tanh x + \tan^{-1}(e^x)$.   **7.** $x \cosh x - \sinh x$.
8. $(a \sinh ax \cos bx + b \cosh ax \sin bx)/(a^2 + b^2)$.
9. $x \sinh^{-1} x - \sqrt{(x^2+1)}$.   **10.** $x \tanh^{-1} x + \frac{1}{2}\log(1-x^2)$.
11. $\frac{1}{2}\{x - (1-x^2)\tanh^{-1} x\}$.   **12.** $\{x - \log(a+e^x)\}/a$.
13. $\frac{1}{2}\{x + \log(e^x+2)\}$.   **14.** $x - 1/(e^x-1) - \log(e^x-1)$.
15. $1 \cdot 1752$.   **16.** $1 \cdot 4067$.   **17.** $0 \cdot 6321$.   **18.** 1.   **19.** $\pi/2$.   **20.** $1/3$.
21. $\log 3$.   **22.** $\pi/2$.   **23.** $\sinh nb/n$.   **24.** $\sinh a\pi/(1+a^2)$.

Examples CXIII (Page 234).

1. $\sinh^{-1} x$.   **2.** $\cosh^{-1} x$.   **3.** $\frac{1}{2}x\sqrt{(x^2+1)} - \frac{1}{2}\sinh^{-1} x$.
4. $\sinh^{-1}(x/\sqrt{3})$.   **5.** $\frac{1}{4}\sqrt{(4x^2-1)} + \frac{1}{2}\cosh^{-1} 2x$.   **6.** $\cosh^{-1}(2x-1)$.
7. $\frac{1}{2}x\sqrt{(x^2+4)} + 2\sinh^{-1}(x/2)$.   **8.** $\frac{1}{2}x\sqrt{(x^2-4)} - 2\cosh^{-1}(x/2)$.
9. $\frac{1}{2}(x-3)\sqrt{(x^2-6x+5)} - 2\cosh^{-1}(x-3)/2$.   **10.** $\cosh^{-1} x - \sqrt{(x^2-1)}/x$.
11. $-\sqrt{(x^2+1)}/x$.   **12.** $(1+2x^2)\sqrt{(x^2-1)}/3x^3$.
13. $\frac{1}{2}\tan^{-1} 2x/\sqrt{(x^2+5)}$.   **14.** $\frac{1}{4}\log\{2x+\sqrt{(x^2-1)}\}/\{2x-\sqrt{(x^2-1)}\}$.

Examples CXV (Page 237).

1. $4+3i$.   **2.** $-2+7i$.   **3.** $5+12i$.   **4.** $2(1+i)$.   **5.** $128(1-i)$.
6. $1+8i$.   **7.** 56.   **8.** $29-8i$.   **9.** (i) $(2,-1)$; (ii) $(3,-2),(-3,2)$.
10. $\pm(2-i)$.   **11.** (i) $\pm(3+i)/\sqrt{2}$, (ii) $\pm(5-3i)$, (iii) $\pm(1+i)/\sqrt{2}$.
12. (i) $(-1 \pm i\sqrt{3})/2$, (ii) $a \pm ib$, (iii) $i, 1-i$; (iv) $2+3i, -2+i$.

Examples CXVI (Page 240).

1. (i) $2e^{\frac{\pi i}{6}}$, (ii) $\sqrt{2}e^{-\frac{\pi i}{4}}$, (iii) $e^{\frac{\pi i}{2}}$, (iv) $5e^{\pi i}$, (v) $3e^{-\frac{\pi i}{2}}$, (vi) $5e^{0 \cdot 927i}$.
4. (i) $-2i$, $\sqrt{3}+i$, $-\sqrt{3}+i$; (ii) $3i$, $3(\sqrt{3}-i)/2$, $-3(\sqrt{3}+i)/2$;
(iii) $-1+i$, $1 \cdot 366 + \cdot 366i$, $-\cdot 366 - 1 \cdot 366i$;
(iv) $1 \cdot 67 + \cdot 364i$, $-1 \cdot 15 + 1 \cdot 27i$, $-0 \cdot 520 - 1 \cdot 63i$.
5. (i) $1, -1, i, -i$; (ii) $1+i, 1-i, -1+i, -1-i$.

6. (i) $\pi i/2$,   (ii) πi,   (iii) $\frac{1}{2}\log 2 + \frac{1}{4}\pi i$, $= \cdot 347 + \cdot 785i$,

(iv) $\frac{1}{2}\log 10 + i\tan^{-1}\frac{1}{3}$, $= 1\cdot 151 + \cdot 322i$.

8. (i) $8\{\cos(\log 2) + i\sin(\log 2)\}$, $= 6\cdot 154 + 5\cdot 112i$;

(ii) $2\cos(\log 3)$, $= 0\cdot 9097$.

Examples CXVII (Page 242).

1. (i) $(3 - i)/10$;   (ii) $(-3 - 4i)/25$;   (iii) $\cdot 2597 + \cdot 4776i$;

(iv) $(1 - r\cos\theta + ir\sin\theta)/(1 - 2r\cos\theta + r^2)$.

2. (i) $-4e^{x}\cos x$;   (ii) $2^{\frac{n}{2}}e^{x}\cos(x + n\pi/4)$.

3. (i) $(e^{2\pi} - 1)/2$;   (ii) $\pi e^{2\pi}$;   (iii) $\frac{1}{2}$;   (iv) $a/(a^2 + b^2)$;   (v) $b/(a^2 + b^2)$.

4. (i) $\cos x\cosh y - i\sin x\sinh y$;

(ii) $\dfrac{2(\cos x\cosh y + i\sin x\sinh y)}{\cos 2x + \cosh 2y}$;   (iii) $\dfrac{\sin 2x - i\sinh 2y}{\cosh 2y - \cos 2x}$.

5. (i) $\sinh x\cos y + i\cosh x\sin y$;   (ii) $\cosh x\cos y + i\sinh x\sin y$;

(iii) $\dfrac{\sinh 2x + i\sin 2y}{\cosh 2x + \cos 2y}$.

8. (i) $0\cdot 666 + 1\cdot 061i$;   (ii) $-0\cdot 570 + 1\cdot 98i$.

10. (i) $1\cdot 017 + 0\cdot 402i$;   (ii) $-1\cdot 410 + 0\cdot 229i$.

Examples CXVIII (Page 246).

1. $y = \frac{1}{4}x^4 + A$.   **2.** $y^2 = 1/(A - 2x)$.   **3.** $y = \frac{1}{2}ax^2 + A$.   **4.** $y = Ae^{ax}$.

5. $y = \frac{1}{3}x^3 - x + A$.   **6.** $y = (C + e^{2x})/(C - e^{2x})$.   **7.** $y = \frac{1}{3}x^3 - \frac{1}{2}x^2 - 2x + A$.

8. $y = (2 + Ce^{3x})/(1 - Ce^{3x})$.   **9.** $y = (A - \cos nx)/n$.

10. $\tan(\frac{1}{2}ny) = Ce^{nx}$.   **11.** $y = A + \tan x$.   **12.** $y + \sin y\cos y = 2x + C$.

13. $y = A + \sec x$.   **14.** $\cos y + \log\tan\frac{1}{2}y = x + A$.

15. $y = \sqrt{(x^2 - 1)} - \sec^{-1}x + A$.   **16.** $y^2 = x^2 + 2Ax + A^2 + 1$.

17. $y = x + A$.   **18.** $y = \frac{1}{3}x^3 + A$.   **19.** $y^2 = 2(x - A)$.   **20.** $y = Cx^2$.

21. $y = (x - A)^2$.   **22.** $9(y - A)^2 = 4x^3$.   **23.** $x^2 + y^2 = C$.

24. $(x - a)^2 + (y - b)^2 = C$.   **25.** $xy = C$.   **26.** $y = cx + 2$.

27. $y = 1/(2 - x)$.   **28.** $y = 2e^{-x}$.   **29.** $y = 3(1 - e^{-x})$.

30. $y = 1 - \cos x$.

Examples CXIX (Page 249).

1. $y = Ax/(x - A)$.   **2.** $(y + b)^2 = C(x + a)^3$.   **3.** $y = A\{x + \sqrt{(x^2 + c)}\}$.

4. $y = (1 + Cx)/(1 + x)$.   **5.** $y = 4/(x - A)^2$.   **6.** $y^2 = a^2 - Ce^{-x/a}$.

7. $y = e^{Ax}$.   **8.** $y^2(\log y - \frac{1}{2}) = A + \tan^2 x$.   **9.** $2y = 1 - (1 + Ax)^2/x^2$.

10. $\log\tan\frac{1}{2}y = A + e^{-x}$.   **11.** $A\sec y = (1 - e^{x})^2$

12. $2y^2 + 4\log y = A + 2x - 5\log(3 + 2x)$.   **13.** $y = (e^{x} + A)/(1 - Ae^{x})$.

14. $1/y = \log\{x + 2\sqrt{(x - 1)}\} + 2/\{1 + \sqrt{(x - 1)}\} + A$.

15. $xy = C$.   **16.** $x^2y^3 = C$.

17. $ax^2 + 2hxy + by^2 + 2gx + 2fy = C$.

18. $y = x^4 + Ax$.   **19.** $y = x(1 - Ax)/(x + A)$.   **20.** $y = Ax$.

21. $r^2\cos\theta = C$.   **22.** $x = 1/y(A - y^2)$.   **23.** $x = 4y/(A - y^4)$.

24. $xy + \log(x/y) = C$.   **25.** $y^2 = x^2(A - e^{x})$.   **26.** $y = xe^{x}/(Ax - 2)$.

27. $y = Ae^{-2x} + 4$.   **28.** $y = Ae^{2x} - 2e^{-x}$.   **29.** $y = x + A/x^3$.

30. $y = Ae^{-x} + 2\sin 2x + \cos 2x$.   **31.** $y = (A + 2\sin^{-1}x)/\sqrt{(1 - x^2)}$.

32. $y = A\sin x - \cos x$.   **33.** $y = x^{m+1}/(m + n + 1) + A/x^n$.

34. $y = \{A - \log(x+1)\}(x+1)^2/x^2 + x + 2 + 2x^{-1} + \frac{1}{2}x^{-2}$.

35. $y = (x + C)\cot x - \frac{1}{2}$.   **36.** $y = A\cos^n x + \cos x/(n-1)$.

37. $y^2 = 2x^2(\log x + C)$.   **38.** $x^2 + y^2 = Cy$.   **39.** $x^2 + 2xy - y^2 = C$.

40. $x^2 - y^2 = Ax$.   **41.** $y = x\sin^{-1}(x/a)$.   **42.** $\log(y - x) = C + x/(y-x)$.

43. $4x = y(\log y - A)^2$.   **46.** $y = 2(3x + 1)/(2x - 1)$.

47. $y = (4 - x^2)/(x^2 - 1)$.   **48.** $4y = 1 - 2x^{-1} + 3e^{-2/x}$.

49. $y = \cos x + A\cos^2 x$.

Examples CXX (Page 252).

1. $y^2 + y'^2 = 1$.   **2.** $xy' = y\log y$.

3. $(xy' - y)^2 = p^2(1 + y'^2)$.   **4.** $y' = (1 + y^2)/(1 + x^2)$.

5. $y'' = 0$.   **6.** $y'' = 2$.   **7.** $xy'' = y'$.

8. $x^2y'' - 4xy' + 6y = 0$.   **9.** $yy'' = 2y'^2$.

10. $x^2y'' + 8xy' + 12y = 0$.   **11.** $xyy'' = 2y'(xy' - y)$.

12. $y'' + 2y'^3 = 0$.   **13.** $xy'' + y' = 0$.

14. $(x\log x)^2y'' + \{(\log x)^2 - 2\log x\}xy' + 2y = 0$.

15. $y'' = n^2 y$.   **16.** $y'' = n^2 y$.   **17.** $xy'' + 2y' - n^2 xy = 0$.

18. $y'' - 4y' + 4y = 0$.   **19.** $y'' + 2y' + 2y = 0$.

Examples CXXI (Page 254).

1. $y = \frac{1}{10}x^5 + Ax^2 + Bx + C$.   **2.** $y = A(\log x)^2 + B\log x + C$.

3. $y = x\log x + Ax^2 + Bx + C$.   **4.** $y = A + B\log\{(1 + x)/(1 - x)\}$.

5. $y = A + B\log x$.   **6.** $y = (\sin^{-1} x)^2 + A\sin^{-1} x + B$.

7. $A^2(y^2 - A^2) = (x - B)^2$.   **8.** $(1 - y)^2 = Ax + B$.

9. $y = (2 + Ae^{cx})/c$.   **10.** $\tan\frac{1}{2}\theta = e^{a(\phi - \phi_0)}$.

11. $y = g/n^2 + A\cos nt + B\sin nt$.   **12.** $y = 5\cos x$.

13. $y = 3\cos 2x + 2\sin 2x$.   **14.** $y = 4/(x + 1)$.

15. $x = y\log y + y - 1$.   **16.** $y = 1 + \log(1 + x^2)$.

17. $y = \dfrac{n}{1 - n^2} + \frac{1}{2}\left(\dfrac{x^{1+n}}{1 + n} - \dfrac{x^{1-n}}{1 - n}\right)$, if $n \neq \pm 1$;

      $y = \frac{1}{4}(x^2 - 1) - \frac{1}{2}\log x$, if $n = 1$.

18. $nt = \log\tan\frac{1}{4}(\pi + \theta)$.

Examples CXXII (Page 260).

1. $y = Ae^{-2x} + Be^{-3x}$.   **2.** $y = Ae^{3x} + Be^{\frac{2}{3}x}$.

3. $y = e^{-3x}(A\cos 2x + B\sin 2x)$.   **4.** $y = e^{-\frac{1}{2}x}(A\cos x\sqrt{3}/2 + B\sin x\sqrt{3}/2)$.

5. $y = (Ax + B)e^{3x}$.   **6.** $y = (Ax + B)e^{-nx}$.

7. $y = Ae^{-ax} + b/a$.   **8.** $y = Ae^{4x} + \frac{2}{5}(3\sin 3x - 4\cos 3x)$.

9. $y = Ae^x + Be^{-3x} + 2e^{2x}$.   **10.** $y = Ae^x + Be^{-3x} + \frac{1}{2}xe^x$.

11. $y = e^{2x}(A\cos x + B\sin x) + 2(\cos x + \sin x)$.

12. $y = Ae^x + Be^{-x} - 2 - 5x$.

13. $y = (Ax + B)e^x - \frac{2}{5}(3\cos 2x + 4\sin 2x)$.

14. $y = Ae^x + Be^{-x} + 2\cosh 2x$.   **15.** $y = Ae^{-x} + Be^{-2x} + 2x - 1$

16. $y = Ae^x + Be^{-x} + 3x\sinh x$.

17. $y = A + e^{-x}(A\cos x + B\sin x) + x^3 - 3x^2 + 3x$.

18. $y = A\cos nx + B\sin nx + \cos px/(n^2 - p^2)$, $(p \neq n)$;

      $y = A\cos nx + A\sin nx + x\sin nx/2n$, $(p = n)$.

19. $y = A\cosh nx + B\sinh nx$.   **20.** $y = A\cos nx + B\sin nx$.

21. $y = A + Be^{nx}$.

22. $y = A \cos kx + B \sin kx + C \cosh kx + D \sinh kx$.

23. $y = e^x(A \cos x + B \sin x) + e^{-x}(C \cos x + D \sin x)$.

24. $y = A + Bx + Ce^{kx} + De^{-kx}$.

25. $y = Ae^{kx} + e^{-\frac{1}{2}kx}(B \cos x\sqrt{3}/2 + C \sin x\sqrt{3}/2)$.

26. $y = A + B \cos x + C \sin x$.   **27.** $y = A + Bx + Ce^{ax}$.

28. $y = Ae^x + Be^{2x} + Ce^{3x}$.   **29.** $y = Ae^x + (Bx + C)e^{-x}$.

30. $y = Ae^x + Be^{-x} + Ce^{2x} + De^{-2x}$.

31. $y = A \cos x + B \sin x + C \cos 2x + D \sin 2x$.

32. $y = Ae^{2x} + e^{-x}(B \cos x + D \sin x)$.

33. $y = (Ax + B)e^x + Ce^{-2x}$.   **34.** $y = A + Be^{3x} + Ce^{-x}$.

35. $y = (Ax + B)e^x + (Cx + D)e^{-x}$.

36. $y = e^{\frac{1}{2}x}(A \cos x\sqrt{3}/2 + B \sin x\sqrt{3}/2) + e^{-\frac{1}{2}x}(C \cos x\sqrt{3}/2 + D \sin x\sqrt{3}/2)$.

37. $y = e^{-x}$.   **38.** $y = 1 - e^{-x}$.   **39.** $y = \sin x + \cos x - e^{-x}$.

40. $y = 5 \cos x$.   **41.** $y = 3 \cos 2x + 4 \sin 2x$.

42. $x = \sin t$, $y = 1 - \cos t$.

43. $x = 2e^{-t} \sin t$, $y = e^{-t}(\cos t + \sin t)$.

44. $x = 2(e^{-t} - e^{-2t})$, $y = 2e^{-t} - e^{-2t}$.   **45.** $\theta = 1 - (1 + t)e^{-t}$.

46. (i) $y = Ax^2 + B/x - 2x$;

(ii) $y = Ax^n + B/x^n$, $(n \neq 0)$; $y = A \log x + B$, $(n = 0)$;

(iii) $y = \sqrt{x}\{A \cos (\sqrt{3} \log x)/2 + B \sin (\sqrt{3} \log x)/2\}$;

(iv) $y = x^2(A \log x + B) + \frac{1}{5}\{3 \cos (\log x) - 4 \sin (\log x)\}$;

(v) $y = A(x - 1)^2 + B/(x - 1)^2 + \frac{5}{2} - 4x + \frac{3}{2}(x - 1)^2 \log (x - 1)$.

47. $y = A \cos (n \cos^{-1} x) + B \sin (n \cos^{-1} x)$.

48. $y = Ax + B\sqrt{(1 - x^2)} + \frac{1}{3}(2 - x^2)$.

49. $xy = A \cos nx + B \sin nx$.

50. $xy = \frac{1}{4}(x + 1)^4 + \frac{1}{3}A(x + 1)^3 + B$.

Examples CXXIII (Page 262).

1. $y = Ax^n$.   **2.** $y^2 = kx^2 + A$.   **3.** $xy = C$.

4. $y^2 = a^2 + Ae^{-x/a}$.   **5.** $2a(x - A) = a^2 \log y - \frac{1}{2}y^2$.

6. $(x + y)^3(x - y) = C$.   **7.** $r = Ae^{\theta \cot \alpha}$.

8. $r = A(1 - \cos \theta)$.   **9.** $x^2 - y^2 = A$.

10. $x^2 + y^2 = 2By$, $x^2 + y^2 = 2Ax$.

11. $x^2 + y^2 - c^2 = 2By$, $x^2 + y^2 + c^2 = 2Ax$.

13. $\sqrt{(8u^3/9k)}$.   **15.** $4 \cdot 6a$; $V\{t - (1 - e^{-at})/a\}$.

18. $\pi/ \log (1 + \sqrt{2})$, = $\cdot 891$.   **20.** $20\sqrt{2}$, $= 28 \cdot 3$ ft./sec.

21. (i) $x = a \cos t\sqrt{\mu}$;   (ii) $x = (u/\sqrt{\mu}) \sin t\sqrt{\mu}$.

22. $x = (u/n)e^{-\frac{1}{2}kt} \sin nt$.

28. (i) $y = Bx(l - x)(l^2 + lx - x^2)$,   (ii) $y = Bx^2(l - x)^2$,

(iii) $y = Bx^2(6l^2 - 4lx + x^2)$, where $B = w/24$ EI.

29. $P = \pi^2 EI/l^2$, or generally $n^2\pi^2 EI/l^2$.

30. $\omega^2 = \pi^4 EIg/wl^4$, or generally $n^4\pi^4 EIg/wl^4$.

31. 8570 lb.   **32.** $(1 + \sqrt{2})T$.   **34.** $\theta = \theta_0 + (a/h)(1 - e^{-ht/b})$.

37. (i) $x = \frac{E_0}{R}(1 - e^{-Rt/L})$,   (ii) $x = Ae^{-Rt/L} + \frac{E_0 \cos (pt - \epsilon)}{\sqrt{(R^2 + p^2L^2)}}$,

where $\epsilon = \tan^{-1} (pL/R)$.

38. $q = EC\{1 - \cos t/\sqrt{(LC)}\}$.

40. (i) $v = Ve^{-nx}, i = mVe^{-nx}$, where $n = \sqrt{(RG)}, m = \sqrt{(G/R)}$;

(ii) $v = V \sinh n(l - x)/\sinh nl, i = mV \cosh n(l - x)/\sinh nl$;

(iii) $v = V \cosh n(l - x)/\cosh nl, i = mV \sinh n(l - x)/\cosh nl$.

Miscellaneous Examples I (Page 267).

1. $3x^2 + 1$.　**2.** $1/(2 - x)^2$.　**3.** $3/2\sqrt{(3x + 2)}$.　**4.** $3 \sec^2 3x$.　**5.** $1/(1+x^2)$.

6. $a/(ax + b)$.　**7.** $- 4 \sin 4x$.　**8.** $x^2(3 \sin x + x \cos x)$.　**9.** $e^{-x}(1 - x)$.

10. $\sqrt[x]{x}(1 - \log x)/x^2$.　**11.** $a^{\sqrt{x}} \log a/2\sqrt{x}$.　**12.** $\cos x \log x + \sin x/x$.

13. $(\sin x)^{\tan x}(1 + \sec^2 x \log \sin x)$.　**14.** $a \sin x/\sqrt{(1 - a^2 \cos^2 x)}$.

15. $\cos^{-1} x - x/\sqrt{(1 - x^2)}$.　**16** $\cos x/2\sqrt{(\sin x - \sin^2 x)}$.

17. $\sin x \cos x(1 + \cos^2 x)^{-\frac{3}{2}}$.　**18.** $1/(1 - x^2)^{\frac{3}{2}}$.

19. $\sec x$.　**20.** $\mathrm{sech}\, 2x$.　**21.** $2ax/(x + a)^3$.

22. $- 1/x^2\sqrt{(1 - x^2)}$.　**23.** $1/(1 + \sin x)$.　**24.** $(2x - 3a)x^{\frac{1}{2}}/2(x - a)^{\frac{3}{2}}$.

25. $- 2a/x^2 . \sin a/x \cos a/x$.　**26.** $2x/(x^4 - 1)$.　**27.** $1/(6x^2 + 4x + 1)^{\frac{3}{2}}$.

28. $2/\sqrt{(a^2 + x^2)}$.　**29.** $- \frac{1}{2}$.　**30.** $\sqrt{(b^2 - a^2)}/(b + a \cos x)$.

31. $3 + 2 \log x$.　**32.** $2e^x \cos x$.　**33.** $- 2 \cos x/(1 + \cos^2 x)^{\frac{3}{2}}$.

34. $3/4(1 + x + x^2)^{\frac{3}{2}}$.　**35.** $(2 + \sin x)/(1 - \sin x)^2$.　**36.** $4/(x-5)^3-2/(x-3)^3$.

37. $(y^3 + 6x^2y - 5x^3)/(x^3 + 6xy^2 - 5y^3)$.　**38.** $(x - y)/x(1 + \log xy)$.

39. $y^2/x(1 - y \log x)$.　**56.** $(0, 0)$ min ; $(2a/3, 4a/27)$ max ; $(a > 0)$.

57. $(1, 3)$ max ; $(3, - 25)$ min ; $(0, 2)$ inflex.

58. $(0, 1)$ max ; $(\pi/3, - 1/8)$ min ; $(\pi/2, 0)$ max ; etc.

59. $(0, 1)$ max ; $(\pi/4, 1/\sqrt{2})$ min ; $(\pi/2, 1)$ max ; $(\pi, - 1)$ min ;
　　　　　　　　$(5\pi/4, - 1/\sqrt{2})$ max ; $(3\pi/2, - 1)$ min ; etc.

60. $(3, 1)$ max ; $(7, 9)$ min.　**61.** $(0, - 1)$ min ; $(2\frac{2}{5}, - 25)$ max.

62. $x = 0, \pm \pi/2, \pm \pi$, etc. (inflexions).

63. $x = 1/e^{\frac{1}{2}}$ (min) ; $x = 1/e^{\frac{3}{2}}$ (infl.).

64. $x = 0$ (min), $x = \pm 1$ (max) ; $x = \pm \sqrt{(5 \pm \sqrt{17})}/2$ (infl.).

65. $x = 1$ (min), $x = 2$ (infl.).

66. $x = 1$ (infl.).　**67.** $x = 0$ (infl.), $x = 2\pi/3$ (max), etc.

Miscellaneous Examples II (Page 268).

1. $y = 3x - 17, y = 3x + 41/27$; $500/81, 500/27$.

2. $4/3$.　**3.** $7x + y = 32, 3x + y = 24, y = 13x - 72$.

4. $x^3 - 3x + 5$; $(1, 3)$ min, $(- 1, 7)$ max.　**5.** $a = - 2, b = 8$.

6. $A = 1, B = \frac{1}{2}, C = 2$.　**7.** $4\frac{1324}{3125}$.　**8.** $2^{\frac{3}{2}}/3^{\frac{3}{4}}$.　**9.** 1.　**10.** $\frac{1}{2}a$.

12. $(\pm\sqrt{3}, 2)$.　**14.** $18° 48'$.　**15.** $64° 5'$.　**17.** Max.　**22.** $\sqrt[3]{(30\sqrt{2}/\pi)}, = 2.38$.

23. $a^2(\sqrt{2} - 1)$.　**24.** $\sqrt{3} : 1$.　**25.** 15.6 knots.　**26.** $11 - \sqrt{13}$.

29. $(3, 8), 24, 24\sqrt{5}$.　**30.** $5\sqrt{3}$ cu. ft./min.　**33.** $k^2 = 2a^2/3$.

40. (i) $- 1.325$, (ii) $.5672$, (iii) $.7391$, (iv) 4.493, (v) 2.365, (vi) 4.730.

46. $45 + 9(\alpha - \beta)/10\pi$.　**47.** $3a\sqrt{2}/5^{\frac{5}{4}}$.　**51.** $a = 1, b = 0, c = - 3, d = 2$.

52. $(- 1, - 2/3)$.　**54.** $- 1/t^2, - t^4$.

Miscellaneous Examples III (Page 273).

1. $\frac{1}{3}$.　**2.** $2\frac{2}{3}$.　**3.** $\frac{1}{4}$.　**4.** $x + \frac{4}{3} \log (x - 2) - \frac{1}{3} \log (x + 1)$.

5. $(x^2 + x - 1)/(x + 1) - 2 \log (x + 1)$.　**6.** $\frac{1}{2}x^2 - \frac{1}{2} \log (x^2 + 1) + \tan^{-1} x$.

7. $1/2a^2 . \log \{x^2/(a^2 - x^2)\}$.　**8.** $\frac{1}{4} \log (x^4 + 1)$.

9. $- 1/x - \log x + \frac{1}{2} \log (x^2 + x + 1) - 1/\sqrt{3} . \tan^{-1} (2x + 1)/\sqrt{3}$.

10. $\pi/3\sqrt{3}$. **11.** $\log 6$. **12.** $\log 2 - \frac{1}{2}$. **13.** $1 + \frac{1}{2}\pi$. **14.** $\frac{1}{2}(x - \sin x \cos x)$.

15. $-\cos x + \frac{1}{3}\cos^3 x$. **16.** $\frac{1}{4}(\frac{3}{2}x - \sin 2x + \frac{1}{8}\sin 4x)$. **17.** $\log \sec x$.

18. $\tan x - x$. **19.** $\frac{1}{2}\tan^2 x - \log \sec x$. **20.** $\log (\sec x + \tan x)$.

21. $\tan x$. **22.** $\frac{1}{2}\sec x \tan x + \frac{1}{2}\log (\sec x + \tan x)$. **23.** $\frac{1}{8}\sin 4\theta + \frac{1}{4}\sin 2\theta$.

24. $\frac{1}{3}\sec^3 \theta$. **25.** $\log \sin \theta - \frac{1}{2}\sin^2 \theta$. **26.** $\tan \theta + \sin \theta$. **27.** $-\tan^{-1}(\cos \theta$.

28. $\theta - \tan \frac{1}{2}\theta$. **29.** $\sin^{-1}x/\sqrt{(1 - x^2)}$. **30.** $\pi/\sqrt{\{(a^2 + c^2)(b^2 + c^2)\}}$.

31. $(3\pi + \frac{1}{3}8)/32$. **32.** $(3\pi - 8)/12$. **33.** $4/3$. **34.** $\frac{1}{2}\log 2 - \frac{1}{4})$

35. $35\pi/256$. **36.** $1/24$. **37.** $8/45$. **38.** $\pi/8$. **39.** $7/15$. **40.** $\pi/16$.

41. $\frac{2}{3}\tan^{-1}\frac{1}{3}$. **42.** $\frac{1}{4}\pi + \frac{1}{2}\sqrt{2}\log (1 + \sqrt{2})$. **43.** $\frac{1}{3}\log 2$. **44.** $\log (81/64)$.

45. $\frac{1}{3}$. **46.** $\frac{1}{2}\{\log (2 + \sqrt{3})\}^2$. **47.** $\sin x - x \cos x$.

48. $(a^2x^2 \sin ax + 2 ax \cos ax - 2 \sin ax)/a^3$. **49.** $\frac{1}{4}x^4\{(\log x)^2 - \frac{1}{2}\log x + \frac{1}{8}\}$.

50. $\pi^2 - 4$. **51.** $\frac{1}{2}\pi - 1$. **52.** $\frac{3}{4}(1 + \log 4/9)$. **53.** $\pi^2/4$. **54.** $\pi - 2$.

55. $\frac{1}{8}(\pi - \log 4)$. **56.** $-1/(n + 1)^2$, $(n > -1)$. **57.** $\frac{1}{2}\log 2$.

58. $\pi/6\sqrt{3} + \frac{1}{2}\log \frac{3}{4}$. **59.** 0. **60.** $a/(1 + a^2)$. **61.** $\frac{5}{10}$. **62.** $\log 2$.

63. $x \log \{x + \sqrt{(x^2 + c)}\} - \sqrt{(x^2 + c)}$. **64.** $\frac{1}{2}x^2 \sec^2 x - x \tan x + \log(\sec x)$.

65. $x \log \{a + \sqrt{(x^2 + a^2)}\} + a \log \{x + \sqrt{(x^2 + a^2)}\} - x$.

66. $x^x e^{-x}$. **67.** $-\sqrt{(1 - x^2)}$. **68.** $\log x - \log \{1 + \sqrt{(1 - x^2)}\}$.

69. $\sqrt{(1 - x^2)} + \log x - \log \{1 + \sqrt{(1 - x^2)}\}$.

70. $\frac{1}{2}x\sqrt{(x^2 + c)} - \frac{1}{2}c \log \{x + \sqrt{(x^2 + c)}\}$. **71.** $-\sqrt{(x^2 + c)}/cx$.

72. $\log \{x + \sqrt{(x^2 + c)}\} - \sqrt{(x^2 + c)}/x$. **73.** $\sqrt{(ax^4 + c)}/2a$.

74. $\frac{2}{3}\sin^{-1}(x/a)^{\frac{3}{2}}$. **75.** $\log \{x + \sqrt{(x^2 - a^2)}\} + \sin^{-1}a/x$.

76. $\frac{2}{5}(x + c)^{\frac{5}{2}}$. **77.** $x + 2\sqrt{(e^x + 1)} - 2 \log \{1 + \sqrt{(e^x + 1)}\}$.

78. $\frac{1}{5}(x^2 + c)^{\frac{5}{2}}$. **79.** $\frac{1}{2}(x - 2)\sqrt{(2 + 4x - x^2)} + 3 \sin^{-1}(x - 2)/\sqrt{6}$.

80. $\frac{1}{24}(8x^2 + 2x + 5)\sqrt{(x^2 + x + 1)} - \frac{3}{16}\log \{x + \frac{1}{2} + \sqrt{(x^2 + x + 1)}\}$.

81. $\log \{x + \frac{1}{2} + \sqrt{(x^2 + x + 2)}\}$.

82. $\frac{1}{3}\sqrt{(3x^2 + 2x + 1)} - \frac{1}{9}\sqrt{3}\log \{x + \frac{1}{3} + \sqrt{(x^2 + \frac{2}{3}x + \frac{1}{3})}\}$.

83. $2\sqrt{(2x^2 + 3x - 7)}$.

84. $(\frac{1}{2}x - 3)\sqrt{(x^2 + 4x + 2)} + 5 \log \{x + 2 + \sqrt{(x^2 + 4x + 2)}\}$.

85. $6 \log 2 - 4$. **86.** $2\pi/\sqrt{3} - 3$. **87.** $\frac{3}{2} + \sqrt{3} - \log (2 + \sqrt{3})$.

88. $2\{\log (1 + \sqrt{2}) - \log 2\}$. **89.** $\frac{1}{4}(x^2 - 2a^2)\sqrt{(a^4 - x^4)} - \frac{1}{4}a^4 \sin^{-1}x^2/a^2$.

90. $4\sqrt{(x - 1)} - 2\sqrt{(x - 4)} - 4\{\tan^{-1}\sqrt{(x - 1)} - \tan^{-1}\frac{1}{2}(x - 4)\}$.

91. $(4\pi - 3\sqrt{3})/24$. **92.** $(3\sqrt{3} - \pi)/3$. **93.** $\pi/10$. **94.** 57. **95.** 1.

96. $\pi/\sqrt{2}$. **97.** $1\frac{2}{3}$. **98.** $\log 2$. **99.** $2 - \log 3 - \pi/3\sqrt{3}$. **100.** $\frac{2}{3}$.

101. $\frac{1}{4}\log 3$. **102.** $\tan^{-1}a/c$. **103.** $\frac{1}{2}\log (2 + \sqrt{3})$.

104. $\dfrac{1}{\sqrt{(a^2 + c^2)}} \log \dfrac{a + \sqrt{(a^2 + c^2)}}{c}$. **105.** 28π.

106. $28\frac{1}{2} + \dfrac{1}{4\sqrt{2}}\log (3 + 2\sqrt{2})$.

107. See List of Integrals. **108.** (i) $2\pi/3$, (ii) $\pi^2/32$, (iii) $\pi^2/4$.

In Exs. 110-118, I_n denotes the given integral :—

110. $(2n + 1)I_n = x(ax^2 + c)^n + 2nc I_{n-1}$.

111. $2(n - 1)cI_n = x/(ax^2 + c)^{n-1} + (2n - 3)I_{n-1}$.

112. $2I_n = (n - 1)I_{n-2}$. **113.** $(n^2 + 1)I_n = -1 + n(n - 1)I_{n-2}$.

114. $I_n = \pi^n - n(n - 1)I_{n-2}$. **115.** $(n - 1)I_n = (n - 2)I_{n-2}$.

116. $(2n + 1)aI_n = 2x^n\sqrt{(ax + b)} - 2nbI_{n-1}$.

117. $2(n - 1)bI_n = -2\sqrt{(ax + b)}/x^{n-1} - (2n - 3)aI_{n-1}$.

118. $naI_n = x^{n-1}\sqrt{(ax^2 + 2bx + c)} - (2n - 1)bI_{n-1} - (n - 1)cI_{n-2}$.

119. $2 \cdot n!/(m+1)(m+3)(m+5) \ldots (m+2n+1)$.
120. $A = \frac{1}{4}$, $B = -\frac{3}{8}$, $C = \frac{3}{8}$; $\{-\sqrt{2} + 3 \log(1 + \sqrt{2})\}/8$.

Miscellaneous Examples IV (Page 277).

1. $9a^2$. 　　**2.** $8a^2/3$. 　　**3.** $4a^2$. 　　**4.** $4(4 + 3\sqrt{3})/3 - \pi/2$.
5. a^2/π, $2a\delta a/\pi$. 　　**6.** $\pi(e^a + 1)/(a^2 + \pi^2)$.
7. (i) $2ab(2 - \sqrt{2})/\pi$; (ii) $2ab \log 2/\pi$; (iii) $4ab \log(1 + \sqrt{2})/\pi$.
8. $\log_e 10$. 　　**9.** $5\pi/8$. 　　**12.** $y = \frac{1}{3}\{x^3(3 \log x - 1) + 4\}$.
13. $t = \dfrac{1}{k(b-a)} \log \dfrac{a(b-x)}{b(a-x)}$; $t = \dfrac{x}{ka(a-x)}$. 　　**14.** $(1 + \sqrt{2})$ mins.
17. $5\pi a^3/12$. 　　**18.** (i) $2 : 1$, (ii) $20 : 7$. 　　**19.** $\pi(b - a)^3/6$.
20. $32\pi a^3/35$. 　　**21.** $4\pi/35$. 　　**22.** π. 　　**23.** π^3.
24. $4\pi a^3 (\sin \alpha + \frac{1}{2} \sin \alpha \cos^2 \alpha - \frac{3}{2}\alpha \cos \alpha)/3$.
25. $\pi\{(a^4 + 9x^4)^{\frac{3}{2}} - a^6\}/27a^4$. 　　**26.** $2\{(a + x)^{\frac{3}{2}} - a^{\frac{3}{2}}\}/3\sqrt{a}$.
27. $\frac{1}{12}\pi a^2 \log(2 + \sqrt{3})$. 　　**28.** $4/9$, $8/15\sqrt{3}$, $4/\sqrt{3}$. 　　**29.** $\pi/\sqrt{(ab - h^2)}$.
30. $4(2 - \sqrt{3})t$. 　　**31.** $(20 + 9 \log 3)/4$. 　　**34.** $2\pi ak/c \cdot \log\{(a + c)/(a - c)\}$.
35. $\frac{3}{2}$. 　　**36.** $\sqrt{3} - 1$. 　　**37.** $60°$.
38. $\{7\sqrt{3} - \frac{1}{4} \log(7 + 4\sqrt{3})\}/\{4\sqrt{3} + \log(7 + 4\sqrt{3})\}$.
39. $(60 + \log 27)/28$, $52/21$. 　　**40.** $(e^2 + 1)/4$, $(e - 2)/2$.
41. $c \log\{(v_1 - b)/(v_0 - b)\} + a/v_1 - a/v_0$. 　　**42.** $\sqrt{(\frac{1}{2}a^2 + \frac{1}{3}b^2)}$.
44. $3\cdot364$. 　　**46.** $32 ab/105$. 　　**47.** πab. 　　**48.** $2\pi^2 a^3$.
49. $4(a^2 + ab + b^2)/(a + b)$, $3\pi ab/8$. 　　**50.** $\pi a\sqrt{2}$. 　　**53.** $3\pi a^2/4$.
54. $\frac{1}{2}a^2(4 + \pi)$, $\frac{1}{2}a^2(4 - \pi)$, $\frac{1}{3}\pi a^3(3 \log 4 - 4)$.
55. $5/6 + \log 3 - \log 2$, $185\pi/36$.

LIST OF DIFFERENTIAL COEFFICIENTS.

$y.$	$\dfrac{dy}{dx}.$	$y.$	$\dfrac{dy}{dx}.$
x^n	nx^{n-1}		
e^x	e^x		
a^x	$a^x \log a$		
$\log x$	$\dfrac{1}{x}$		
$\log_a x$	$\dfrac{1}{x \log a}$		
$\sin x$	$\cos x$	$\sinh x$	$\cosh x$
$\cos x$	$-\sin x$	$\cosh x$	$\sinh x$
$\tan x$	$\sec^2 x$	$\tanh x$	$\operatorname{sech}^2 x$
$\cot x$	$-\operatorname{cosec}^2 x$	$\coth x$	$-\operatorname{cosech}^2 x$
$\sec x$	$\sec x \tan x$	$\operatorname{sech} x$	$-\operatorname{sech} x \tanh x.$
$\operatorname{cosec} x$	$-\operatorname{cosec} x \cot x$	$\operatorname{cosech} x$	$-\operatorname{cosech} x \coth x$
$\sin^{-1} x$	$\dfrac{1}{\sqrt{(1-x^2)}}$	$\sinh^{-1} x$	$\dfrac{1}{\sqrt{(x^2+1)}}$
$\cos^{-1} x$	$-\dfrac{1}{\sqrt{(1-x^2)}}$	$\cosh^{-1} x$	$\dfrac{1}{\sqrt{(x^2-1)}}$
$\tan^{-1} x$	$\dfrac{1}{1+x^2}$	$\tanh^{-1} x$	$\dfrac{1}{1-x^2}$
$\cot^{-1} x$	$-\dfrac{1}{1+x^2}$	$\coth^{-1} x$	$-\dfrac{1}{x^2-1}$
$\sec^{-1} x$	$\dfrac{1}{x\sqrt{(x^2-1)}}$	$\operatorname{sech}^{-1} x$	$-\dfrac{1}{x\sqrt{(1-x^2)}}$
$\operatorname{cosec}^{-1} x$	$-\dfrac{1}{x\sqrt{(x^2-1)}}$	$\operatorname{cosech}^{-1} x$	$-\dfrac{1}{x\sqrt{(x^2+1)}}$

$$\int x^n \, dx = \frac{x^{n+1}}{n+1}, \ (n \neq -1).$$

$$\int \frac{dx}{x} = \log x, \qquad\qquad \int \frac{dx}{ax+b} = \frac{1}{a} \log (ax+b).$$

$$\int e^x \, dx = e^x, \qquad\qquad \int a^x \, dx = \frac{a^x}{\log a}.$$

$$\int \cos x \, dx = \sin x. \qquad\quad \int \tan x \, dx = \log (\sec x).$$

$$\int \sin x \, dx = -\cos x. \qquad \int \cot x \, dx = \log (\sin x).$$

$$\int \operatorname{cosec} x \, dx = \int \frac{dx}{\sin x} = \log \left(\tan \frac{x}{2} \right).$$

$$\int \sec x \, dx = \int \frac{dx}{\cos x} = \log \tan \left(\frac{\pi}{4} + \frac{x}{2} \right) = \log (\sec x + \tan x).$$

$$\int \cos^2 x \, dx = \tfrac{1}{2}(x + \sin x \cos x).$$

$$\int \sin^2 x \, dx = \tfrac{1}{2}(x - \sin x \cos x).$$

$$\int \sec^2 x \, dx = \tan x. \qquad\quad \int \tan^2 x \, dx = \tan x - x.$$

$$\int \operatorname{cosec}^2 x \, dx = -\cot x. \qquad \int \cot^2 x \, dx = -\cot x - x.$$

$$\int \cosh x \, dx = \sinh x. \qquad\quad \int \tanh x \, dx = \log (\cosh x).$$

$$\int \sinh x \, dx = \cosh x. \qquad\quad \int \coth x \, dx = \log (\sinh x).$$

$$\int \frac{dx}{\sinh x} = \log \left(\tanh \frac{x}{2} \right). \qquad \int \frac{dx}{\cosh x} = 2 \tan^{-1} (e^x).$$

$$\int \cosh^2 x \, dx = \tfrac{1}{2}(\sinh x \cosh x + x).$$

$$\int \sinh^2 x \, dx = \tfrac{1}{2}(\sinh x \cosh x - x).$$

$$\int \operatorname{sech}^2 x \, dx = \tanh x. \qquad\quad \int \tanh^2 x \, dx = x - \tanh x.$$

$$\int \operatorname{cosech}^2 x \, dx = -\coth x. \qquad \int \coth^2 x \, dx = x - \coth x.$$

$$\int \frac{dx}{a^2 + x^2} = \frac{1}{a} \tan^{-1} \frac{x}{a}, \text{ or } -\frac{1}{a} \cot^{-1} \frac{x}{a}.$$

$$\int \frac{dx}{a^2 - x^2} = \frac{1}{2a} \log \frac{a+x}{a-x} = \frac{1}{a} \tanh^{-1} \frac{x}{a}, \ (x^2 < a^2).$$

$$\int \frac{dx}{x^2 - a^2} = \frac{1}{2a} \log \frac{x-a}{x+a} = -\frac{1}{a} \coth^{-1} \frac{x}{a}, \ (x^2 > a^2).$$

$$\int \frac{dx}{x^2 + px + q} = \frac{2}{\sqrt{(4q - p^2)}} \tan^{-1} \frac{2x + p}{\sqrt{(4q - p^2)}}, \ (p^2 < 4q);$$

$$= \frac{1}{\sqrt{(p^2 - 4q)}} \log \frac{2x + p - \sqrt{(p^2 - 4q)}}{2x + p + \sqrt{(p^2 - 4q)}}, \ (p^2 > 4q).$$

$$\int \frac{dx}{\sqrt{(a^2 - x^2)}} = \sin^{-1} \frac{x}{a}, \text{ or } - \cos^{-1} \frac{x}{a}.$$

$$\int \frac{dx}{\sqrt{(x^2 + a^2)}} = \sinh^{-1} \frac{x}{a}, \text{ or } \log \{x + \sqrt{(x^2 + a^2)}\}.$$

$$\int \frac{dx}{\sqrt{(x^2 - a^2)}} = \cosh^{-1} \frac{x}{a}, \text{ or } \log \{x + \sqrt{(x^2 - a^2)}\}.$$

$$\int \frac{dx}{\sqrt{(x^2 + c)}} = \log \{x + \sqrt{(x^2 + c)}\}.$$

$$\int \frac{dx}{\sqrt{(x^2 + px + q)}} = \log \{x + \tfrac{1}{2}p + \sqrt{(x^2 + px + q)}\}.$$

$$\int \frac{dx}{\sqrt{(q + px - x^2)}} = \sin^{-1} \frac{2x - p}{\sqrt{(4q + p^2)}}.$$

$$\int \sqrt{(ax^2 + c)}\,dx = \tfrac{1}{2}x\sqrt{(ax^2 + c)} + \tfrac{1}{2}c \int \frac{dx}{\sqrt{(ax^2 + c)}}.$$

$$\int \frac{dx}{(x^2 + 1)\sqrt{(ax^2 + c)}} = \frac{1}{2\sqrt{(a - c)}} \log \frac{x\sqrt{(a - c)} + \sqrt{(ax^2 + c)}}{x\sqrt{(a - c)} - \sqrt{(ax^2 + c)}}, \ (a > c);$$

$$= - \frac{1}{\sqrt{(c - a)}} \tan^{-1} \frac{\sqrt{(ax^2 + c)}}{x\sqrt{(c - a)}}, \ (a < c).$$

$$\int \frac{x^n}{y}\,dx = (Ax^{n-1} + Bx^{n-2} + \ldots + L)y + \int \frac{M\,dx}{y},$$

where $y = \sqrt{(ax^2 + 2bx + c)}$. The constants A, B, ... M can be found by differentiating, multiplying throughout by y, and equating coefficients of like powers of x. The numerator, x^n, of the integrand on the left may be replaced by any polynomial of the nth degree in x. [Cf. Misc. Exs. III., No. 120.]

$$\int e^{ax} \cos bx \, dx = \frac{e^{ax}(a \cos bx + b \sin bx)}{a^2 + b^2}.$$

$$\int e^{ax} \sin bx \, dx = \frac{e^{ax}(a \sin bx - b \cos bx)}{a^2 + b^2}.$$

INDEX.

The numbers refer to the pages.